# FLOWERING VINES
# OF THE WORLD

# FLOWERING VINES
# OF THE WORLD

## An Encyclopedia of Climbing Plants

*by*

EDWIN A. MENNINGER, D.Sc.

and 50 Collaborators

HEARTHSIDE PRESS INCORPORATED

Publishers • New York

To the memory of a great plantsman
GEORGE  W.  MERCK
who had a special love for things
that grow in the forest,
this book is affectionately dedicated
by his friend,
the author

# TABLE OF CONTENTS

# THE COLLABORATORS

This encyclopedic panorama of the world of vines has been made possible by the gracious cooperation of scholars throughout the world. More than twoscore of them have given of their time, energy, and skill to present to the dirt gardener a glimpse of the climbing plants which contribute to the beauty of gardens everywhere. The Author expresses his gratitude to these collaborators and acknowledges the honor they have done him by their contributions to this volume. (Their names are shown between type ornaments ❦ in the text pages that follow.)

*Dr. Herbert G. Baker* ................................................................ PLUMBAGINACEAE
Director of Botanical Garden, University of California, Berkeley

*Harry Blossfeld* .............................................................. BIGNONIACEAE
Director, Municipal Nursery Expansion Project, São Paulo, Brazil

*Dr. T. K. Bose* ................................................................ DILLENIACEAE
Royal Agri-Horticultural Society of India, Calcutta

*Margaret E. Coon* ................................................................ ROSACEAE
Former Editor of *American Rose Magazine* and *American Rose Annual,*
Columbus, Ohio

*Ladislaus Cutak* ............................................................ CACTI (Cactaceae)
Missouri Botanical Garden, St. Louis

*Ralph D. Dickey* ............................................... JASMINUM (Oleaceae)
Ornamental Horticulturist, University of Florida, Gainesville

*Dr. Armando Dugand* ......................................................... BIGNONIACEAE
Barranquilla, Colombia

*Dr. John Dwyer* .............................................................. LEGUMINOSAE
Missouri Botanical Garden, St. Louis

*Douglas Elliott* .................................................. CLIANTHUS (Leguminosae)
Plantsman-Photographer, New Plymouth, New Zealand

*Dr. David Fairburn* ........................................................... ORCHIDACEAE
Director, McKee Jungle Gardens, Vero Beach, Florida

*J. Fisk* ................................................. CLEMATIS (Ranunculaceae)
Fisk's Clematis Nursery, Westleton, Suffolk, England

*Dr. John M. Fogg, Jr.* ...................................................... MAGNOLIACEAE
The Morris Arboretum, Philadelphia

*Eric V. Golby* ................................................. BOUGAINVILLEA (Nyctaginaceae)
Nurseryman, Bradenton, Florida

*Peter S. Green* ................................................................ SOLANACEAE
Royal Botanic Gardens, Kew, England

*Dr. Francis Hallé* ....................................................... MARCGRAVIACEAE
Ecole des Sciences, Brazzaville, Congo

*Wyndham Hayward* ....................................... GLORIOSA (Liliaceae)
Plantsman, Winter Park, Florida

*Dr. R. E. Holttum* ............................................ BOUGAINVILLEA (Nyctaginaceae)
Royal Botanic Gardens, Kew, England

*Dr. Richard A. Howard* ................................................................ POLYGONACEAE
Director, Arnold Arboretum, Cambridge, Massachusetts

*Dr. Howard S. Irwin* ..................................................................... LEGUMINOSAE
Head Curator, New York Botanical Garden

*Dr. Marshall Johnston* ............................................ BERCHEMIA (Rhamnaceae)
University of Texas, Austin

*Dr. Job Kuijt* ....................................................................................... PARASITES
Plant Science, University of British Columbia, Vancouver, Canada

*Dr. David B. Lellinger* ............................................................................. FERNS
Associate Curator, Ferns, Smithsonian Institution, Washington, D.C.

*Ernest E. Lord* ............................................................................. LEGUMINOSAE
Plantsman-Author, Melbourne, Australia

*T. R. N. Lothian* ................................................................................. LILIACEAE
Director, Botanic Garden, Adelaide, S. Australia

*Dr. J. K. Maheshwari* ................................................................. LEGUMINOSAE
Assistant Director, National Botanic Gardens, Lucknow, India

*Dr. Elizabeth McClintock* ........................................................ MALPIGHIACEAE
California Academy of Sciences, San Francisco

*Dr. F. A. McClure* ................................................................................ BAMBOO
Research Associate in Botany, Smithsonian Institution, Washington, D.C.

*Dr. Sidney McDaniel* ......................................................................... ERICACEAE
State College, Mississippi

*Dr. Harold N. Moldenke* ............................... VERBENACEAE, SYMPHOREMACEAE
Paterson State College, Paterson, New Jersey

*Dr. Harold E. Moore, Jr.* ..................................................................... GESNERIACEAE
Director, Bailey Hortorium, Cornell University, Ithaca, New York

*Dr. Lorin Nevling, Jr.* .................................................................. SAXIFRAGACEAE
Arnold Arboretum, Cambridge, Massachusetts

*Dr. Dan H. Nicolson* .............................................................................. ARACEAE
Associate Curator, Botany, Smithsonian Institution, Washington, D.C.

*Dr. Eliane Norman* ............................................................................ LOGANIACEAE
Rutgers State University, New Brunswick, New Jersey

*Dr. Duncan M. Porter* ................................................................. ZYGOPHYLLACEAE
Stanford University, Stanford, California

*Dr. Donald G. Rhodes* ............................................................. MENISPERMACEAE
Louisiana Polytechnic Institute, Ruston, Louisiana

*Dr. Robert J. Rodin* ................................................................................ GNETUM
California State Polytechnic College, San Luis Obispo, California

*Dr. Russell J. Seibert* ........................................................................ BIGNONIACEAE
Director, Longwood Gardens, Kennett Square, Pennsylvania

*Dr. H. Sleumer* ............................................................................. FLACOURTIACEAE
Senior Curator, Rijksherbarium, Leiden, Holland

Thomas R. Soderstrom ............................................................ GRASSES
Curator, Grasses, Smithsonian Institution, Washington, D.C.

Jaroslav Soukup, S.D.B. ............................................. TROPAEOLACEAE
P.O. Box 999, Lima, Peru

Dr. Mona Lisa Steiner .......................... STRONGYLODON (Leguminosae)
Vienna III, Austria

Dr. Julian A. Steyermark .................................................... RUBIACEAE
Instituto Botánico, Ministerio de Agricultura y Cria, Caracas, Venezuela

Dr. Benjamin C. Stone ........................................................ RUTACEAE
University of Malaya, Kuala Lumpur, Malaya

Dr. V. T. Stoutemyer ........................................................ SOLANACEAE
University of California, Los Angeles, California

Dr. John W. Thieret ................................................ SCROPHULARIACEAE
University of Southwestern Louisiana, Lafayette, Louisiana

Dr. Stephen S. Tillett .................................................. PASSIFLORACEAE
Centro Experimental de Estudios Superiores, Barquisimeto, Lara, Venezuela

Dr. C. G. G. J. van Steenis ........................ AGALMYLA (Gesneriaceae)
Director, Rijksherbarium, Leiden, Holland

Dr. Bernard Verdcourt .............................. MORNING-GLORIES (Convolvulaceae)
Royal Botanic Gardens, Kew, England

Dr. Edgar T. Wherry .................................................... POLEMONIACEAE
University of Pennsylvania, Philadelphia, Pennsylvania

Dr. John Wurdack .................................................. MELASTOMATACEAE
Smithsonian Institution, Washington, D.C.

(For other acknowledgments and photo credits, please turn to page 393)

ERRATA

*Color plates*

1. Genus is *Adhatoda*

5. Species is *Kalbreyeri*

87. Species is *galpinii*

166 and 167. Captions are transposed.

183. Picture is upside down.

191. Species variety is *albiflora*

194. Species is *philippensis*

# FLOWERING VINES
# OF THE WORLD

# An Introduction to the World of Vines

The tropical forests of the world are rich in climbing plants, some gigantic, some of medium size, some small; an astounding variety of twisting, twining green forms shaped largely by their surroundings. A tiny fraction of this vining exuberance has worked its way into the Temperate Zones, but the greater the distance from the equator, the fewer become the climbers, the less their vigor, the smaller their stature, the weaker their stems.

The North Temperate Zone has perhaps a score of outstanding flowering vines, notably Chinese and Japanese. Those usually found in American or English gardens are clematis, honeysuckle, and roses. South of the equator Schimper* (98) found the finest examples of epiphytes and lianas in the wet forests of Chile and New Zealand but few of them in cultivation. Oakman (87) selected six most frequently seen in Australia but lamented: "Not one of them is commonly grown as a garden climber." In South Africa Dyer (31) reported "relatively few [of our climbers] are in cultivation."

Contrast this paucity with a hot spot like Burma where Hundley (60) found 870 different vines, half of them floriferous. Not counted in this tally were the climbing ferns, climbing aroids, climbing palms, and climbing parasites. Such uncontrolled enthusiasm for escalating results from high temperatures, adequate water supply, and intense competition offered by other forms of plant life in the battle for light from the sun and a place for roots to grow.

Gardeners in the tropics and subtropics do cultivate a vast number of ornamental climbers, some because they have pretty leaves or striking fruits, but most for the wide variety of beautiful flowers. Yet viniculture is not without its problems, because, in any landscaping plan, climbers must be kept under control. Of all plant forms, they are perhaps most difficult to hold within bounds and to imprison where their lines and color are wanted. If growing conditions are favorable, vines tend to become rampant and overwhelming; if unfavorable they give any garden a bedraggled air.

Every gardener approaches all vines cautiously, pruning shears in one hand and an axe in the other, for each wildling must be tamed. It must not interfere

---

*Throughout the text, figures in parentheses after a quotation or the name of an author or a book refer to the List of Publications that precedes the Index.

with or smother other plants, it must produce copious flowers low down where they can be seen, and stems and foliage must be reduced so as not to dwarf the surroundings. If these objectives cannot be attained, the axe comes into play. Any grower would rather coax new young vines than fight with old ones.

Florists and their nonprofessional imitators in private glasshouses everywhere have given new dignity to many small plants and groundlings. They have put them in hanging baskets and tubs and encouraged them to develop long runners, especially if that improves the flower display. Many shrubs are thus forced to become scandent willy-nilly as they reach for the sunlight. This artificial elongation gives a vining effect. These techniques, in copying nature, have increased the number of tropical "trailers" or "climbers" that must be included if this book is to be complete.

Having gone this far, this book must consider man-made vines out-of-doors as well as in, for espaliers are nothing more than a symmetrical adaptation of a particular plant to a niche where a 3-dimensional form will not fit. Some plants, naturally scandent or not, lend themselves particularly well to utilization as espaliers, growing as a vine would grow, flat against a wall, or on a flat frame beside a garden walk. The fruiting pear trees, espaliered on brick walls at beautiful Mount Vernon on the Potomac, would not be there at all in that narrow garden if each tree required the normal 100 square feet of ground space.

Originally this book was projected as a study solely of vines in the tropics and subtropics; surely enough of them originate there to fill several books and satisfy everybody. But difficulties grew out of the inability of the plants themselves to recognize climatic lines. *Clematis* may be thought of as a Temperate-Zone plant, but various kinds are found all over Africa, and more cultivated forms are found in Mexico City than in Cleveland, Ohio. Honeysuckle (*Lonicera* species) is no respecter of Jack Frost and his threats; it grows anywhere. More clambering roses are to be found in Kenya than in Kansas City, Missouri. *Wisteria* may be a cold-country plant, but it thrives also in California, Florida, and other warm areas all over the globe. Hence the bars were down, and this became a worldwide picture of the flowering climbers.

Dwellers in the Temperate Zones may feel that their vines get insufficient attention in this book and that too much emphasis is placed on tropicals. They need to bear in mind, however, that ten times, yea, fifty times as many vines grow in tropical countries as in the cooler regions of the world, and it should be no surprise to find Temperate-Zone plants far outnumbered and outshone. Burma is a country the size of Texas, but instead of endless plains, parched climate, and no trees, it is a region of high mountains, dense forests, ample rainfall, and very high temperatures all the year; plants grow madly and in great profusion. Yet Burma represents only a fractional part of the world's tropical areas where such plant concentrations exist.

While the gardener can recognize a few familiar names among climbing plants alone in this same little Burma, he discovers hundreds of unfamiliar species. He learns that there are 9 kinds of *Combretum,* 15 kinds of honeysuckle (*Lonicera*), 6 species of *Senecio,* 24 species of *Jasminum,* 10 kinds of *Hoya,* 14 kinds of *Argyreia,* 60 kinds of morning-glories (*Ipomoea* and others), and 12 species of

*Thunbergia.* Turning to the family of *Allamanda* (Apocynaceae), he discovers that literally hundreds of climbing plants have been described in genera which are unknown to him: *Winchia, Alyxia, Pottsia, Ecdysanthera, Parameria, Urceola, Ichnocarpus, Nouettea, Pagiantha,* and *Amalocalyx,* for example. Similarly, in the milkweed family (Asclepiadaceae), hundreds of species have been described in these unfamiliar genera: *Myriopteron, Toxocarpus, Genianthus, Oxystelma, Adelostemma, Cynanchum, Sarcolobus, Tylophora, Lygisma, Telosma,* and *Leptadenia.* This plethora of climbing plants continues through a hundred families. By contrast, poor dear Texas has fewer than a dozen native ornamental flowering vines.

With tropical vines becoming increasingly available, the gardener's problem the world around is to learn how to transfer as many as possible to the Temperate Zone and bring them into cultivation, even if only in the glasshouse.

The word "vine" in England (and usually in the Bible) refers exclusively to the grape; in this book it is used synonymously with the word "climber." As the reader will soon discover, many plants escalate into the wild blue yonder without vining tendencies and without climbing ability. It is a twisty, curly, creeping, scrambling plant world, from which emerge thousands of different kinds of spectacular flowers.

The reader of this book can easily imitate a vine and become badly twisted himself.

He must contend with *Littonia* and *Fittonia, Manotes* and *Monotes, Nitraria* and *Mitraria, Bossiaea* and *Bosea, Rhynchosia* and *Rhynchodia,* until he discovers these are quite different and unrelated plants, despite the similarity of names.

Then he starts getting acquainted with all the anagrams like *Podranea* and *Pandorea, Zacateza* and *Tacazzea,* etc. It is not difficult for a reader to become thoroughly confused.

# I

## *How Vines Are Constructed*

The process of vining—elongation of the stem or stems—is fundamentally an adaptation to environment. The plants grow that way to survive. Out-of-doors, if they are husky and vigorous in their skyward extension, they are called climbers. If they are small, weak, and delicate, they are often classed as groundcovers or mat-forming herbs. Yet who shall say exactly where the dividing line is between these two kinds of plants? The difficulty of deciding when a vine is not a vine, or which herbs or shrubs can be vines under duress, becomes apparent in the descriptions of some of the plants included here.

Vines are of many kinds. They may be evergreen or deciduous. Some are annuals, most are perennials. This distinction often disappears because in gardens and glasshouses a lot of perennial vines get too large for the space allotted them; so they are grown as annuals with new seed being sown each year and the whole plant removed after flowering. Some climbers produce useful, edible, or pretty fruits. Many foliage vines with handsome leaves are effective in gardens as tree-climbers, or as screens over outbuildings or waste areas. Many of these, in abbreviated form, are used as house plants. But the vast majority of cultivated vines are grown for their annual display of flowers. It is of them and for them that this book has been written.

Not all blooming periods are annual. Many vines flower several times a year, at intervals which the plants themselves may regulate, or that may be the result of controlled conditions of moisture, light, and other factors. The glasshouse owner has the knack and the facilities for finding the right combination of these conditions to get best results or to produce the peak of bloom at a special, prefixed time, as for a flower show. But, generally speaking, out-of-doors the Christmas-vine (*Porana paniculata*) blooms in December, herald's trumpet or the Easter-lily vine (*Beaumontia grandiflora*) unfolds its white trumpets in the spring. Many other vines similarly find a seasonal place on the calendar. But this is less true in tropical lands where seasons are not clearly marked; for example, in the Philippines, Steiner (106) says *Beaumontia* flowers all year and *Porana* from November to April.

As a matter of convenience, different kinds of vines are loosely called by special names:

*Lianas* are woody perennials with ropelike stems generally climbing into the crowns of trees and there producing the flowers and fruits. Examples are *Landolphia, Combretum, Calycobolus*. The visible parts of these plants to the observer on the ground look like ropes stretching from ground to treetops; these may be enormous on a 500-foot vine, and they are usually leafless. A few lianas flower

19

and fruit on these old woody stems. Examples: *Pararistolochia, Tiliacora,* and the primitive genus *Gnetum.*

Relatively few woody climbers are found in gardens because they tend to become too big and too unwieldy. They are tolerated only insofar as they can be trained on tree or trellis, or confined to a rock wall where they can be enjoyed without interfering with other plants.

*Scramblers* are woody or tough herbaceous plants spreading over neighboring vegetation and often forming tangles. They may have prickly stems, like rambler roses, or spines like blackberries, or thorny branches sticking out stiffly at right angles to the main stems, like *Bougainvillea.* The stems lack the strong upward-growing tendency of climbers but usually are highly successful in throwing a blanket over nearby vegetation, thus depriving it of light and reducing its vigor.

*Straggling* and *trailing* are adjectives used to describe the apparently aimless spreading habit of some weak-stemmed species, particularly herbaceous ones, though many big vines will also spread over the ground in this fashion until they meet a suitable support and begin to climb. Examples: *Ipomoea, Senecio.*

*Creeping plants* lie prostrate on the ground, usually rooting at the nodes, but they will climb over obstacles in their path. Examples: many grasses; also *Commelina.* In other books big climbers are sometimes called "creepers," but in this volume that word is reserved for groundlings.

To understand vines and their behavior, it is essential to study their make-up and structural peculiarities as a group; whether great or small, they have many common features.

Vines are weak-stemmed plants whose long, slender, fast-growing shoots rely on other plants or objects for support. Unwilling to be bound to one spot by the circumstance of birth, they send forth their stems, usually single but often multiple, with instructions to get to the top by any means they can, even if this involves leaning on, crushing, or even killing neighbors in the process. This habit of growth enables the plants to get better light with a maximum economy of supporting tissues, and the rapid growth enables them to produce leaves, flowers, and fruit in advantageous positions in a short time.

Vines are a subsidiary form evolved by woody plants to permit them to make use of tree trunks and so to reach the light with less expenditure for their own trunk building. In their blindness, climbers often climb on themselves, tendrils hook around tendrils, branches twine around the stems of the same plant. Most of these stems have developed some kind of structural modification— thorns, tendrils, hooks, or the like—to help them maintain their place on whatever support they have, because they must keep their leaves exposed to the sun.

Woody climbers are often plentiful in secondary forests where the original timber has been cleared. Their dense growth on the edge of the jungle gives the impenetrable tangle that renders access difficult. One reason for their abundance is that many of them produce edible fruits. Seeds are readily dispersed by birds and mammals, and with adequate sunlight the growth becomes very dense. In the high forest, where few vines can grow on the ground because of inadequate sunlight, this tangle is carried up into the canopy and provides runways between the trees for many arboreal animals.

When a climber gets to the treetop, it can go no higher, so it spreads itself over the crown of the tree and may produce as many leaves, flowers, and fruits as the tree. The vine continues to grow sideways, interlacing the tree branches. Its increasing girth and weight may pull down on the superstructure so that the long stem, usually quite leafless, piles up in coils on the forest floor. Absence of any visible means of support for the vine from below merely indicates that the tree which once held it up has rotted away. Although non-parasitic climbers utilize the tissues of other plants over which they grow, and to this extent appear to be parasites, there is no direct nutritional relationship between them and their hosts. When woody vines spread their canopies over the tops of trees, they do interfere with the trees' normal growth. If they have twined about the trunks and branches, they may by constriction upset the downward translocation of food in the tree tissues and may even kill them. The masses of vines on forest trees may be so great that they break off limbs or even force a whole tree down to the ground (59).

In this way vines are a factor in tropical forestry practice. Sometimes the tree canopy is so woven together by hundreds of climbers that trees will not fall when cut, and must be felled in groups.

In the Temperate Zone, vines are not so vigorous, hence not a great factor in forest economy, but in the tropics they are dramatically important in forest development. Their ascending stems, with Mother Root all but forgotten in the earth, fight and jostle their way upwards, multiplying in size and vigor. Some climbers become enormous, both in length that may exceed 500 feet, and in thickness and viciousness. Botanically, most of them are dicots like the grape, honeysuckle, and watermelon. However, a considerable number of vines are monocots such as the lilies, bromeliads, and palms. Ordinarily these are much smaller in stature because their stems contain little cambium (wood-forming tissue). Exceptions are the rattans (climbing palms) with the most gigantic stems of all.

Woody climbers generally require a long growing period before they will flower. When they are brought into the garden, therefore, they are apt to be ungainly, requiring too much room in which to grow. The ideal setting is a long arbor or pergola. As this is impossible in most gardens, it remains for man to curb the natural inclinations of the vine and discover or breed dwarf forms that will flower in a convenient space. This problem confronts every grower who attempts to check the vigor of vines from the tropics, where most of them originate. Many fine leguminous climbers need 50 to 100 feet of growth before they come into full flower. The genus *Entada* comprises one group of enormous climbers. In 18 months one of these vines will grow 100 feet and develop a stem bigger than a man's wrist, just getting ready to flower. In the tropical forest, nature puts no curbs on these rampant growers, but cultivation in the garden requires a disciplining hand.

A study of the anatomy of climbers reveals how differently they are constructed from that other great group of woody plants, the trees. The fibers that make up the bulk of the tree's trunk, and enable it to stand erect, are missing in the vine. Instead of small canals for water and food conduction, guarded by

21

tough fibers, the vine's woody cylinder is an accumulation of strands separated by photosynthetic storage tissues surrounding wide and long canals. A cross section of some vines shows these canals to be like strands of rope. They are so prominent the outside covering appears to be merely incidental.

These peculiarities make, on the one hand, for suppleness, and on the other, assurance of an adequate water supply through a very slender pipeline for the vast expanse of leaves far above.

Suppleness is of enormous importance to the vines. No matter how they twist above, or how they coil and squirm on the forest floor below, there must be no kinks in the water supply lines. Flexibility enables them to live a roughhouse life in competition with other plants. The tissues are laminated with and around the water canals to withstand compression or expansion without interference with food supply. The suppleness is important, too, because the support that the vine climbs is apt to be rigid and unyielding; if anything flexes, it must be the vine.

When a climber becomes woody, its very existence depends on the absence of kinks in its lifeline. This objective is achieved by *Bignonia capreolata* (a pretty climber of the southeastern United States) by developing its stem not as a smooth unit, but as four wedge-shaped parts meeting in the middle. A cross section of the stem looks like a pie cut into four wedges. This gives the climber its common name of cross-vine. In some species of *Bauhinia*, cambium is formed at various centers, resulting in a series of twisted separate strands, as in a rope.

Other *Bauhinia* species develop flat stems that are varied by humps on one side and hollows on the other, alternating along the stem. To this bumpy form in Burma forests the natives give the name of "monkey staircase." Some species of *Vitis* (related to the grape) have flat stems that may be 6 inches wide and only one-half inch thick (55). Such devices will at least keep the stems from kinking.

# II

## *The Theory of Vines*

The study of vines as a plant form can be somewhat mystifying. From an evolutionary viewpoint the vine is a structure somewhere between earthbound herbs and shrubs and the sky-searching trees. Vines are a part of both these realms. It is impossible to draw a line to separate vines from the other groups of plants.

Except for size, there is no difference between the creeping herb in the rockery and the gigantic liana in the forest jungle. Both have the same "oomph," the same desire to go places, preferably upward, but if no support is available they grow just as well horizontally until they come to a support. Consequently, in the compilation of an encyclopedia of climbing plants, the author cannot exclude any that has long extending stems which, with suitable opportunity, will surge upward.

Various factors in a plant's environment control how it grows. These are not necessarily the same in all places. In fact, a variation in temperature, humidity, or soil constituency, including soil acidity or the presence of certain compounds in the soil, usually results in a considerable difference in the manner of growth. The environment seems to have a great deal more to do with the proclivity of a vine than we can imagine. It includes not only climate, rainfall, drought duration, enzymic conditions in the growing medium, but a great many other factors not ordinarily taken into consideration.

Many such plants are described in this book as climbers despite this or that reader's insistence that they are only ground covers, herbs, or other minor plant forms that have been "forced," "trained," or otherwise compelled to grow unnaturally.

The growth habit of many tropical plants, for want of understanding, is described as scandent. Under one set of conditions the plants may be herbs or small shrubs; under other circumstances they may become robust bushes; again, they may decide to vine and go climbing to the treetops. The observer describes what he sees, and in many instances this increases the mystery surrounding scandent plants.

An astonishing example of this is *Podranea brycei* in South Africa. Brown (17) first described it as a subshrub, 1½ to 2 feet, and he said nothing about its being a climber. Chittenden (22) classified it as a shrub or undershrub. Sprague (102) referred to it as "a scandent undershrub about 1½ feet high." Hall (49) said it was a climbing shrub with "long, flexible, arching stems to 6 to 8 feet in a season." Eliovson (32) named it an evergreen, showy climber that "sends out long waving branches that turn woody and thicken with age." Jex-Blake (67) declared it is a "terribly strong grower and wonderful to cover a screen or terrace quickly. . . . It must be given lots of room." And to crown the dispute, Hutchinson (63) called it "a small Bignoniaceous tree up to 15 feet high."

These authorities are all writing about the same plant, and an amateur cannot help becoming confused when the botanists so flatly contradict one another.

Who is going to decide whether this species of *Podranea* is a vine? Similar confusion attends thousands of plants, and the individual gardener must determine exactly what form each plant is going to take in *his* garden. One grower insists that *Phlox subulata* is a mat-forming herb that runs all over the place but is not a climber in any sense of the word. Another grower disputes this because the same plant in his garden climbs over all sorts of obstacles. Another grower insists that this encyclopedic work on vines cannot afford to ignore any plant that could be called a vine even if it is necessary to stretch the imagination. He suggests that the book classify the disputed plants by some of their individual characteristics. He writes: "If, like *Phlox* and *Campanula,* they have no permanent wood, they are in one class. If, like *Thymus* and *Dryas,* they are procumbent trailers with woody growth and evergreen, they are in another class. *Daphne* and *Hypericum* are weak shrubs, and constitute another class. They must all be included in a comprehensive work on climbers."

But this book would never end if any such classification were attempted. The difficulty of deciding what is a vine and what is not a vine is not confined to small plants. It extends to shrubs and to trees, and examples of uncertainty may be found on all sides.

English gardens exhibit non-vines in vinelike forms primarily because the humid climate produces, on many plants, more extended stems than develop in other lands. The so-called wall shrubs are extensively utilized in England also because of the economy of ground space which they occupy. They grow in only two dimensions—height and width—so that they take almost no ground area away from any other form of plant life. Using the patterns set by ordinary climbers, the English gardener plants shrubs close to the building, fastens them to· supports there, and keeps them pruned to grow in a single plane. Bean (16) describes more than 100 shrubs and trees that in normal form occupy a lot of ground area but in English gardens are grown in the vine manner. A few of these will be found in this book because they are on the borderline between trees or shrubs and the vines which they may become under conducive circumstances.

The fact that there is no sharp dividing line between herbs and shrubs on the one hand and vines on the other, merely adds to the mystery of the twining, twisting plants that are grown in the vine manner. *Iochroma* in California is a low shrub, but in England it becomes a climber to 15 feet, definitely a vine. Who shall decide in which classification it belongs? Similar examples could be cited by the score.

Hutchinson (63) says that in tropical Africa *Mussaenda erythrophylla* is a "shrub, vine or tree." In Florida it is cultivated sparingly as a shrub, but if the sunlight is inadequate the plant becomes scandent and quickly climbs 30 feet or more to the top of the overhanging foliage.

*Kopsia fruticosa* is a shrub in Malaya and Florida, but Steiner (106) reports

24

that in the Philippines it is a climber. *Acacia auriculiformis* in Florida and Australia is a 30-foot tree, but Hundley (60) lists it as a climber in Burma. *Swainsona galegifolia* in its native Australia, according to Harris (51), "grows about 1 foot in height," and no mention is made of vining; Bailey (5) reports that in the United States it is 3 to 4 feet high, "branches long, flexuous or half-climbing." Britton (12) describes *Chamaefistula antillana* from Puerto Rico as a vine; in Florida gardens is a 15-foot bushy tree, not viney. Irvine (65) in Nigeria found *Euclinia longiflora* as a "scrambling shrub or tree"; Hallé (50) says it is "common in Ivory Coast but never as a vine"; Chittenden (22) designates it a "climbing shrub or small tree." Miquel (82) originally described *Callichlamys riparia* as a shrub or tree of moderate height, branches not at all climbing. But Macmillan (78) reports it as a "woody climber with beautiful yellow flowers." *Portlandia* in Jamaica is a 4-foot bush; in the Singapore Botanic Garden it is a climber that overtops a 15-foot telephone post.

*Metrosideros robusta* in New Zealand (Photograph 4) begins life as a vine, climbing a big pine tree (*Dacrydium* species). In time as it grows bigger and bigger, it engulfs the pine tree and eventually kills it, going on to become itself a giant tree. Its pretty flowers are only incidental. (See Chapter X.)

*Bougainvillea "arborescens,"* so called, is a street tree in Rio de Janeiro (Photograph 3, also Color Plate 144). Yet no trees of *Bougainvillea* are described in botanical literature. Is this therefore a vine?

The Turk's-cap or sleeping hibiscus (*Malvaviscus arboreus*), according to Bailey (5), is a "little shrub." But at Edenlawn Plantation, Jensen Beach, Florida, this plant has taken off into the Australian pines (*Casuarina* species) which overhang it and has climbed 30 feet to display its red flowers in the canopy.

Bailey (5) says that the firethorn (*Pyracantha coccinea*) is a "shrub to 6 feet, rarely to 20 feet." In Melbourne, Australia, this plant covers the side of a four-story hotel with a curtain of red berries at fruiting time (Photograph 345).

When is a vine not a vine?

Because vines have evolved from all manner of flowering plants, there are many curious transitions between vines and herbs, shrubs and trees. Several vines start as shrubs or small trees and then throw up long, sprawling branches that scramble and climb (*Premna, Leea*). The opposite is much less common. In the mountains about Rio de Janeiro grows *Ceiba rivieri,* allied to the kapok tree. It is a viney thing for years, growing tight up against some tree for support and throwing its arms (roots) around the host without strangling, just to keep upright. When it reaches the sunlight in the canopy, it becomes a tree (Photograph 1). *Freycinetia* does exactly the same thing (Photograph 2). *Securidaca sellowiana* in Brazil is a vine which at maturity also becomes a tree.

*Luehea divaricata* in its juvenile stage has exceedingly long, sprawling branches that suggest a career as a climber, but given a few years it becomes a 100-foot timber tree. This curious habit fooled one experienced plantsman, for Hume (59) called it a vine "not sufficiently tested." *Brownea macrophylla* is a tree in the forest of northern South America. Bailey (3) calls this a "half climbing shrub." This means that the plant weaves its limbs through the crotches of branches of adjacent trees and uses them as supports.

1. CEIBA RIVIERI    2. FREYCINETIA SP. (MALAYA)

3. BOUGAINVILLEA "ARBORESCENS"    4. METROSIDEROS ROBUSTA

Botanists and plant physiologists have offered no explanation whatever for the curious fact that 90 percent of all climbing plants are concentrated in just 10 families. The closely allied Connaraceae and Leguminosae, being well advanced with sympetalous flowers, are completely isolated from the other 8 families, which may all be related. Climbers might be viewed as plants modified in all stages of evolution into trees, and woody climbers in the families Apocynaceae, Menispermaceae, and Bignoniaceae might be regarded as a development toward soft-wooded trees, just a step ahead of their associates in the Acanthaceae, Asclepiadaceae, Passifloraceae, Cucurbitaceae, and Convolvulaceae, which have almost no woody forms. An analysis of the relationship on this hypothesis might establish a reason to link some of these together. The Leguminosae seem to be far distant and, by contrast, seem rich in both relatively primitive and well advanced climbing forms. What is the bridge that connects these families?

Any gardener who has grown *Tabebuia argentea,* a Paraguayan tree of the Bignoniaceae, has puzzled over the fact that the tree never grows erect. The reason is that for years it seems undecided whether to be a tree or a vine. Most mature specimens, even 30 feet high, have twisted tops as if ready to climb. Is this symbolic of the evolutionary link between the ground runners and the trees? This Paraguayan ornamental, *Tabebuia argentea,* is often planted in Florida as a street tree because of its beautiful flowers. Nurserymen growing it from seed find the seedlings twisted, curly, even decumbent. If these can be induced to throw water sprouts, the original twisty growth is immediately cut off, for the water sprouts are erect, vigorous, and never twisting!

Some woody climbers are more shrublike in habit, developing an abundance of leafy stems. In open situations many of them appear as shrubs, but if deprived of light by too much leafage overhead, their branches begin lengthening and finding ways to climb. Plants with this habit are ordinarily referred to as scandent shrubs. Examples: *Allamanda, Cryptostegia, Mussaenda.* Other plants in this category, if growing in full sun, can sprawl out into giant shrubs 20 feet across with no evidence of their climbing capabilities. Examples: *Hiptage madablota* and *Nicodemia madagascariensis.*

*Dalbergia variabilis,* of the pea or bean family, is a curious borderline plant. In the open it is a shrub with pendent twigs. In the forest it becomes a huge liana with short lateral shoots that are sensitive to contact and become climbing instruments.

# III

## *The Mechanics of How Vines Climb*

Vines differ from all other plants in an impulsion to elongate without proportionate lateral growth. To facilitate an understanding of how they adjust their extra lengths to fit into the landscape, attention centers first on the mechanics of climbing. This book is concerned primarily with flowering vines, but in this chapter other climbers are included to illustrate the thirty different ways that escalation is accomplished in the plant world. These methods may conveniently be separated into five groups.

These groups may overlap. Again, a climber may encounter difficulties in its career that cause it to switch climbing methods, quitting the old and continuing its upward movements by an entirely different procedure.

Furthermore, some vines, when growing horizontally (as in a pasture), will not flower. However, when a runner strikes an obstacle such as fence-post, shrub, or tree, and can climb, flowers will appear. A good example of this is the cross-vine (*Bignonia capreolata*).

As to vining methods, Boston-ivy (*Parthenocissus tricuspidata*) is supposed to climb with tendrils, but if planted by a chicken-wire fence it escalates by weaving, and no tendrils are in evidence. Flame-vine (*Pyrostegia*) also customarily climbs by tendrils, but if established on a wire fence, a search reveals none. Many other vines that are supposed to climb by tendrils, if planted by a wall, will develop adhesive discs. *Ercilla volubilis,* a Chilean vine, is one example. While grape-vines (*Vitis* species) ordinarily make use of tendrils, these may end in discoid suckers. Willis (118) explains: "The tendril may be negatively phototropic and thus force its way into the crevices of the support; in these crevices the tips of the tendrils form large balls of tissue, the outer parts of which become mucilaginous and cement the tendril to its support."

Many smooth vines, like *Quisqualis,* when old and heavy, will develop big hooks to cling to their support, without these having been in evidence in the earlier stages of growth.

This switch from one method of climbing to another is a faculty possessed by hundreds of vines. With them, environment seems to play a bigger part in the selection of method than does the nature or habit of the plant. Such switches are, however, the exception rather than the rule, and normal climbing methods are separated into the following five categories.

### 1. THE LEANERS

First come the vines that have neither the desire to grow vertically nor the mechanical devices needed to pull themselves erect; nor have they the backbone

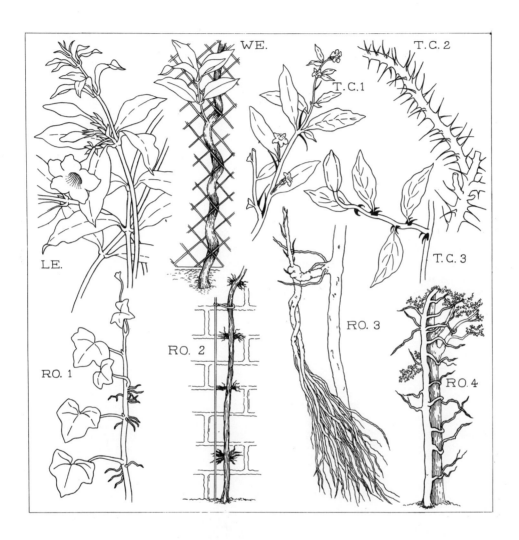

Le—Leaner.                *Allamanda cathartica*

We—Weaver.               *Trachelospermum jasminoides*

Tc—Thorn clingers.       1) *Lycium halimifolium* 2) *Euphorbia milii* 3) *Capparis erythrocarpos*

Ro—Rooters.              1) *Hedera helix* 2) *Campsis radicans* 3) *Solandra* 4) *Ceiba rivieri*

required to stay up. They have no ability to cling to anything, so the gardener must arrange some support for them if they are to get off the ground. A lot of them, like *Allamanda* or the cape-honeysuckle (*Tecomaria capensis*), if tied to a post, will rise a little, then flop again until hitched at a new level. By some authors this process is called arching because, from each tie, the plant throws new stems that curve upward and outward, with flowers on each one. In nature these leaners grow through or over other plants and flop onto them. In the garden a trellis or similar device may carry the heavy stems to levels where their greenery and blossoms are wanted. These "climbers" go through life helplessly. If their support fails, they fail, too.

## 2. THE THORN CLINGERS

Most climbers are equipped, in one way or another, to help themselves in their skyward drive, affixing themselves to any existing support, be it tree, wall, post, wire, or another vine. The weakest clingers, almost as helpless as the leaners, come equipped with thorns on the stems. While these prove of no help whatever in the process of climbing, they play an important part in holding the vine fast to its support, once such underpinning has been established. Thus their passive assistance does help to keep the leaves exposed to best light conditions. These are the "thorn clingers," and the relative effectiveness of their mode of aerial suspension quickly separates them into 4 groups, each having one of the following types of thorns:

### Prickles on Stems

Weakest of all are those with superficial modifications such as prickles on the stems that grasp other foliage. Most brambles (*Rubus* sp.) are in this category, and other examples are *Lantana camara, Lycium halimifolium,* and *Schrankia leptocarpa.*

### Substantial Thorns

Somewhat stronger and more effective are the plants with substantial thorns that are not specialized for climbing but which prove of definite passive value by preventing backsliding. *Bougainvillea* will grow 50 feet in the air with the proper screen or tree to which to anchor its thorny limbs. Rambler roses (*Rosa wichuraiana*), growing by a picket fence, will get enough reverse grip on the palings to rise far above the supporting frame. The Christ-thorn (*Euphorbia milii*) is grown ordinarily as a shrub in warm gardens, but give it wire or a fence to hook itself onto, and it attempts to turn vine.

### Recurved Spines

Somewhat more successful are the plants with recurved stipular spines which are not only sharp but hook-shaped, designed to hold fast to anything they touch. The leafy cactus *Pereskia aculeata,* the Cherokee rose (*Rosa laevigata*), and one of the capers in tropical Africa (*Capparis erythrocarpos*) are all effectively armed in

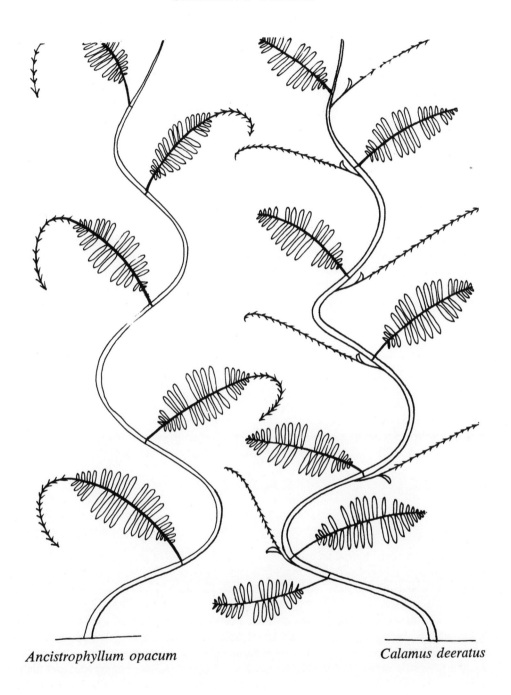

Ancistrophyllum opacum                    Calamus deeratus

this way. Once they gain a foothold, they are difficult to dislodge. "Vines" in this category have their thorns from the beginning; other climbers develop similar hooks late in life, when their sheer weight threatens to pull them down; these are described later.

## Armed Whips

Most successful of the thorn climbers are the plants whose leaves end in vicious armed whips. Thrashing around in the forest, they are bound to catch hold of something. The biggest and most destructive vines of the eastern tropical forests are the climbing palms, known as rattans. *Calamus,* with 300 species, is the chief example. With long whips of thorns at the ends of the leaves or with spiny leaf stalks and spiny sheaths, they are most intractable, if not positively dangerous. They have never been brought into true cultivation, though they are the source of supply of the split rattan used in manufacturing.

The American genus of climbing palms called *Desmoncus,* with 25 species, is similarly armed; each pair of thorns is a pair of leaflets. James E. Smith, palm seed collector of Pompano Beach, Florida, measured the stalk of a *Desmoncus* vine in Costa Rica; its length exceeded 3,000 feet! Incidentally, this palm has beautiful flowers, but the climber itself is much too big to find a place in this book. The Indian vine *Willughbeia zeylanica* uses long, whiplike, leafless shoots to make its way upward.

### 3. THE WEAVERS

Much more effective in their determination to rise are the plants which weave back and forth, knitting themselves fast to their supports. If a wire trellis is available, they literally weave themselves in and out as they extend upward. They lean first toward the dark side as new growth appears, then switch back to the light as this growth matures and becomes woody. Conspicuous examples in any warm-climate garden are the Confederate jasmine (*Trachelospermum jasminoides*), and the "Port St. Johns creeper" (*Podranea ricasoliana*). These vines have plenty of upward impulsion but are entirely dependent on a fixed support to stay erect.

### 4. THE GRASPERS

Most vines fall under this general heading, with structural modifications that enable them to grasp a support and hold on. They do this by four different methods, which provide a key for separating them: the twiners, with tips on the growing stems that twist around and around a vertical support; the stickers, that adhere by vaccum or glue to the support that will keep them erect; the clingers, which use tendrils of many kinds to hold them fast; and the hookers, which develop hooks at just the right places, to catch and hold a convenient support. Sometimes these categories overlap a bit, and vines may shift from one method to another if so doing results in escalation where the first method failed. The grape and the Virginia creeper (*Parthenocissus quinquefolia*), like its relative, Boston-ivy, as described at the beginning of this chapter, both normally develop tendrils that merely encircle and cling to some handy wire. If they are up against a flat wall,

Tw—Twiners.

1) *Celastrus.* 2) *Ipomoea.* 3) leaf petiole, *Clematis.*
4) branch, *Bauhinia galpinii.*

St—Stickers.

1) branchlets, *Phaedranthus buccinatorius.* 2) Vanilla.
3) tripartite tendrils, *Bignonia capreolata.*

Cl—Clingers.

*Porana paniculata*

Te—Tendrils.

1) tendril, leaf opposed, *Vitis angulata.* 2) leaf opposed, *Ampelocissus.* 3) terminal leaflet replaced by tendril, *Pyrostegia ignea.*

however, they develop cushions on the tips of their tendrils. These become adhesive discs that glue themselves to the stone. The vines then cease to be clingers and become stickers.

## The Twiners

Twiners are old friends in the vegetable plot, where garden peas and pole beans quickly demonstrate the art of encircling the nearest upright support. Most stem-twiners are herbaceous, although *Stephanotis, Celastrus, Lonicera, Thunbergia fragrans,* and others, may be woody. All the twiners use their growing tips (young internodes) to encircle any upright obstacle and guide the vine upward. Commonest examples are the morning-glories (*Ipomoea* species), flycatchers like *Ceropegia* and *Cynanchum,* a few ferns like *Lygodium,* some lilies like *Ruscus,* some in the potato or nightshade group (*Solanum* species), all climbing jasmines (*Jasminum* species), and many in the bean family like *Wisteria* and *Camoensia.* Other twiners are found among Apocynaceae, Aristolochiaceae, Malpighiaceae, and Menisper- maceae, also in the genera *Dipladenia* (which has some hookers too), *Polygonum, Schizandra, Freycinetia, Gnetum,* and *Hoya.*

Some vines are equipped in their climbing parts with tissues which are touch-

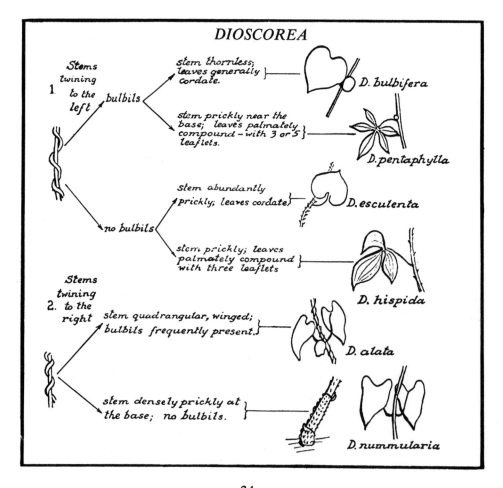

sensitive, but others are not. The sprout from a sweet-pea (*Lathyrus odoratus*) will shoot straight up through a foot of soil, then start waving its tip around in a continuous circle (circumnutation). If in this circling it strikes a horizontal obstacle, it will retreat and resume circling. But if it strikes a vertical wire or stick, it will twine around and around and go up and up. A reaction between gravity and the auxins (growing material) in the vine tip is somehow involved here; if the support is a stick that falls over or is inverted, the last-formed coils of the vine unwind and start over.

A silly argument often arises over vines in this twining group, whether they twist to the right north of the equator and to the left "down under." The equator is not involved; neither is the earth's rotation. At least 95 percent of twisting vines go in a direction characteristic of the species, and this is constant in New York or New Zealand. The true yams (*Dioscorea* species) are of many kinds; some twist left and some go right; the direction is one of the characteristics by which botanists determine the species.

The remaining vines are indifferent about which way they are going to twist; they may go either right or left as opportunity offers. The European-bittersweet (*Solanum dulcamara*) is an example. After all, the vine has only two choices.

Another kind of twining is included here, although the principles involved are somewhat different. On many vines the young green buds lengthen rapidly and expose sensitive surfaces. If these touch anything, friction causes the young flexible stem to curl around the cause of the friction. This is exactly what happens when the stem of a leaf of a clematis vine touches a wire or twig. The petiole (stem) acts like a tendril, coils around the obstacle, and becomes one of the vine's anchors. Other vines with sensitive leaf petioles that behave similarly are *Dalbergia, Fumaria, Hablitzia, Maurandia, Rhodochiton,* and the common climbing nasturtium (*Tropaeolum* species).

In the pitcher-plants of Malaysia (*Nepenthes* species) the midrib of the leaf is sensitive and curls around the first obstacle it encounters.

Similarly in some other vines, friction between a touch-sensitive stem and an obstacle, such as another stem, a branch, or a wire, will cause the entire stem to act like a tendril, encircling the obstacle and using it as a support. This is of common occurrence with *Bauhinia galpinii, Passiflora foetida, Argyreia speciosa, Congea tomentosa, Hippocratea, Machaerium, salacia, Securidaca, Uvaria,* some of the Cucurbitaceae, as well as with Annonaceosus and Connaraceous climbers.

## The Stickers

The stickers are vines equipped to glue themselves to a support. They are of three kinds:

Some of them, like *Phaedranthus buccinatorius,* have tiny branchlets that end in adhesive discs which fasten themselves, like vacuum cups, to walls or similar impervious, flat supports.

Similarly, certain vines with compound leaves replace the terminal leaflet with tri-partite tendrils which at their tips have adhesive discs. The cross-vine (*Bignonia capreolata*) is a good example. This is like the first except here the discs are on tendrils rather than on branchlets.

Other vines are equipped at branch nodes with adventitious roots that are adhesive and will stick to impervious surfaces. Examples are black pepper (*Piper guineese*), vanilla orchids (*Vanilla crenulata* and V. *planifolia*), and *Hoya carnosa*. (*See* Rooters.)

## The Clingers

The clingers are vines equipped with tendrils. These, to start with, are weak, tender, soft, curly, flexible organs. In response to friction they wind themselves around the cause of the friction and thus find solid support. In their early stages, tendrils exhibit strong circumnutation tendencies which markedly increase the likelihood of their finding support. Before they have made contact with a support, they are very sensitive and may respond to a touch stimulus lasting only a few seconds (28). Once the support is contacted, the side of the tendril opposite the point of friction is stimulated; this makes the tendril curl faster and faster as the inside surface stimulus builds up. Experiments have proved that when a tendril touches a support, it will not curl unless there is vibration (as by wind, etc.) to produce the necessary friction (42).

Once the tendrils have become attached, their tissues develop to such a degree that they become robust, tough, woody, and inflexible, supporting great weights and resisting high winds. Tendrils which fail to find a support usually wither and drop off.

Once fastened, that part of the tendril leading back to the plant gradually curls into a tight spiral. Since both ends of the tendril are fixed, the coils of the spiral are necessarily reversed at some midway point. This results in an elastic springlike connection, and the plant is less and less likely to be torn from its support.

Tendrils may be encirclers, which go around and around a supporting twig or wire; stickers (as previously described); or wedgers, which force their way into cracks, then swell their tissues to become hodfasts. *Hydrangea petiolaris* digs its tendrils into a tree's bark, and there they become fixed by swelling. *Bignonia capreolata* sometimes behaves like this instead of forming a disc at tendril tip.

Tendrils originate in many ways. Some are modified stems as in *Antigonon* and *Landolphia*. Some are modified stipules, springing directly from stem or branches, as in *Smilax,* although this vine often develops hooks also. Tendrils are sometimes true branches, as in the passion-flowers (*Passiflora* species), where they arise in the leaf axils.

The tendril may be leaf-opposed, with sympodial growth, developing from a modified terminal shoot, as in the Vitaceae. It is typical of this family that the tendrils are associated with the inflorescence, hence handy to hold the weight of a bunch of grapes when it develops.

In compound leaves, a terminal leaflet may be replaced by a single tendril (*Distictis, Arrabidea, Anemopaegma,* etc.), or by branched, 3-part tendrils (*Pyrostegia, Eccremocarpus,* etc.), or by tripartite tendrils ending in sharp claws (*Doxantha unguis-cati*), or by tripartite tendrils ending in discs (*Bignonia capreolata*). In compound leaves (*Vicia, Pisum, Cobaea*), only the terminal leaflet is replaced by a tendril.

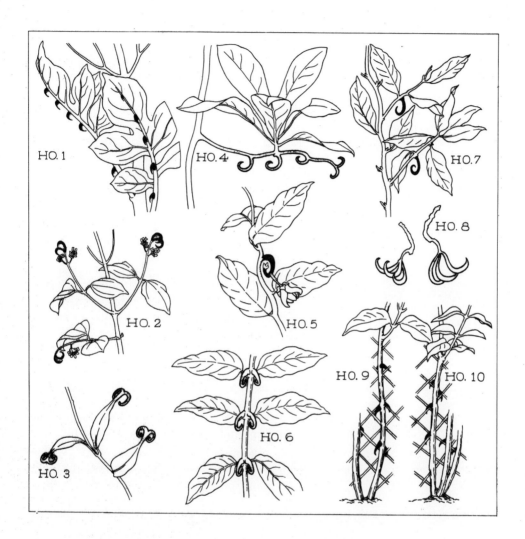

1)—*Solanum wendlandii*

2)—*Strychnos nigritana*

3)—*Triphyophyllum peltatum*

4)—*Ancistrocladus guineensis*

5)—*Artabotrys*

6)—*Uncaria*

7)—*Roucheria*

8)—*Doxantha unguis-cati*

9)—*Combretum grandiflorum*

10)—*Quisqualis indica*

The tip of a simple leaf is sometimes modified to become a tendril, as in *Gloriosa superba, Flagellaria guineensis,* and *Littonia.*

## The Hookers

Many vines develop hooks, sometimes sharp-pointed, often dull, which catch on some support and hold the weight of the climbers. These arise in a half a dozen ways:

(a) On the Costa Rican nightshade (*Solanum wendlandii*) and the gray nickers (*Guilandina crista*), the leaf petioles and even the back side of the leaf's midrib are armed with vicious, recurved hooks, catching on anything within reach.

(b) An African vine, *Triphyophyllum peltatum,* in addition to two other kinds of leaves, develops a third kind for climbing; the tips curve two ways, then harden to form tough hooks.

(c) In one of the strychnine climbers (*Strychnos nigritans*) in west Africa, the growing point of a leafy shoot, just beyond the inflorescence, becomes a double hook that hardens.

(d) A growing branchlet on the west African vine, *Ancistrocladus guineensis,* instead of depending on the support of tendrils as is normal in the family, may itself become a series or chain of hooks, with short lateral shoots produced at intervals with large leaves and spreading inflorescences of small flowers.

(e) Hooked peduncles are found in two widely separated families, the Annonaceae (*Artabotrys*) and the Rubiaceae (*Uncaria*). In the former, a branch-let forks; one fork curls into a dull-pointed hook and may produce flowers, while the other fork develops leaves. In *Uncaria* the small globular heads of flowers on peduncles arise in pairs on opposite sides of the stem, and each peduncle curls once; usually the peduncle hooks are sterile. This is similar to *Clematis* except that the curled peduncles of *Uncaria* harden into hooks instead of remaining green.

(f) With some vines that for long periods may remain unarmed, supporting hooks develop on old wood to help support the weight. On *Combretum,* for example, a leaf on a main stem may drop off at the base of the blade. The petiole that persists hardens and curls into a hook, often sharp-pointed. *Quisqualis* develops hooks like this on old stems.

Other vines which develop hooks are several kinds of *Caesalpinia,* a few feeble climbers among the 250 species of *Galium,* some of the 25 or more lianas called *Dipladenia,* the African genus *Hugonia* in which the lower twigs of the inflorescence are modified into hooks, all of the Malaysian palms of the genus *Plectocomia,* and some kinds of *Ventilago* in the Rhamnaceae.

## 5. THE ROOTERS

Many vines develop roots at each node as they go along. If prostrate on the ground, these plants are often called groundcovers. If growing on a tree trunk, they will bury their roots in the bark; *Hydrangea petiolaris* sends growths into the bark, but whether these are tendrils that swell and anchor, or whether they are roots, is a hairsplitter's delight. Ivy (*Hedera* species), growing on a chimney, will

38

bury its roots in every crack in the masonry. Usually this method achieves maximum security, but *Campsis radicans* grows thus without ever gaining a foothold secure against storm and strain; it must be tied to its support to be secure.

Most of the wild climbing figs (*Ficus* species) in the eastern tropics, are rooters. Other climbers in this category are *Begonia, Clusia, Hoya, Kendrickia, Norantea, Piper, Rhus, Salacia,* and some of the Sapindaceae, Araceae, Araliaceae, and a few of the Bignoniaceae.

Vines growing on impervious planes sometimes glue themselves fast, as above described, but they may decide instead to encircle the post or tree with a mass of hug-me-tight root fastenings; the chalice-vines (*Solandra* species) do this,

# IV

## *The Usefulness of Vines*

Most memorable of forest scenes is a stand of great wild trees beside a tropical river or seashore, the gaps between them filled with the trellising of a thousand vines and their hanging tresses festooned with flowers. Out of such equatorial exuberance a few climbers have worked their way into the Temperate Zones to add the same sort of garlanded draperies to gardens. Some of them survive out-of-doors in warm places; many others are prized features of a million glass-houses all over the world. Still others have developed cold-resistant species and have become established ornaments of the Temperate Zone.

Vines are popular in gardens because they are more useful than any other plant form. Considering the small amount of ground space that they require, their contribution to beauty and grace is unequaled, their fast growth gets quicker results in foliage and flowers, and they are capable of producing shade and flowers where these two garden essentials are wanted. In landscaping programs, such pinpointed results might be difficult or impossible to achieve with trees and shrubs. Many vines adapted to garden culture are evergreen under near-frost conditions, and the blooming cycles are often longer and more frequent than in other plant forms. These "plus factors" give the climbers a long lead as ornamental subjects, yet the number of available vines is so large, and their range of size is so extensive, it is exceedingly important to use good judgment in choosing the right one for a particular place.

Hume (59) suggests that the best thing about vines as garden plants is their ability to grow vertically in limited space and yet fulfill their three most important functions: (a) Provide a screen to hide unwelcome views or create a measure of privacy; (b) soften the harsh lines of buildings and tie them into the landscape plan; and (c) produce shade for outdoor living areas. When the vines selected for any of these purposes are flowering species, the householder gets double value. Foliage vines should be used in shady places under big trees, because flowering climbers under such conditions always rebel; either they will not flower, or they will climb out of the shade and display their wares elsewhere—usually in places where they are unwanted.

In selecting a vine for the garden, the householder must consider the natural vigor of the plant, its habit of growth, whether it is thorny (if that matters), its eventual size, the character of its foliage, the color and profusion of the flowers and whether they harmonize with the color of the house, the time of flowering, and the suitability of the soil in the chosen location. Some vines bloom at night, which makes them ideal subjects in a patio but often useless elsewhere. Another factor to be considered in the vine's location is moisture. Many herbaceous climbers such as *Thunbergia, Gloriosa,* and *Antigonon* have tuberous roots that are water-storage reservoirs, and these will survive in exceedingly dry places. Other vines with green stems ordinarily require an evenly distributed water supply. Woody climbers are less demanding.

The householder in selecting the right vine must decide whether it should be evergreen or deciduous, whether it will be possible to control the growth if it begins getting too big for the location, whether it is a seasonal or temporary filler to be removed in autumn and replaced in the spring, or whether it is to be a permanent part of the landscape. Temporary or seasonal vines are not unusual tools in landscaping; many gardeners prefer the fresh young growth of new plants rather than a struggle with an old specimen that is more difficult to make attractive. Many tropical climbers are too big and could not be used in Temperate Zone gardens at all, except they may be grown fresh from seed each year and destroyed when their usefulness has ceased. Frequently a vine that is valuable in the garden in summer to shield from a boiling sun, produces a cold, damp area in winter. Its value at all times of year must be assessed.

Because many tropical vines provide a profusion of brightly colored flowers, it is every homeowner's objective to get one or more of them to produce bursts of loveliness in his garden so he can call in the neighbors and show them the glories of its pink or gold or blue, and tell them the story of the vine's homeland far away. It is a tale of romance, fragrance, and tropic nights. Meanwhile the honeysuckle (*Lonicera* species) and the Carolina yellow jessamine (*Gelsemium sempervirens*) along the roadside in front of his place go unnoticed—they are natives and folks are used to them. Or perhaps a bulldozer will clear them away when the superhighway is built.

Fragrance is a plus value in gardens that is often overlooked, yet many climbers can supply it, sometimes in overpowering quantities. If not all the occupants of a house agree on the desirability of certain scents, the problem of plant selection become complicated. Often it might be better to grow certain vines in the glasshouse rather than in the open; then the fragrance can be confined for the pleasure of some without offending others.

Climbers are a further welcome addition to any garden because the flower colors are almost invariably in soft pastel shades that harmonize with any surroundings. The blossoms on vines are seldom, for instance, a flaming red. Gorgeous glowing pinks are available, good rich blues are to be found, and plenty of the whites and creams and golds are soft enough to add a special richness to a green, leafy background.

The sight of a well-tended, exotic climber abloom in a garden makes all who see it want vines of their own. Its unexpected eye-filling spectacle is an inspiration to visit the nearest nursery. Here may come a rude surprise, for vines are anathema to many nurserymen because of their uncontrolled enthusiasm for getting tangled in other plants. They complain that when the climbers grow together they become difficult to separate and to sell, so they prefer not to bother with them. On the other hand, plenty of nurserymen do grow ornamental vines and take great care with them to keep individual plants in salable condition. One Florida nurseryman wrote: "We grow all our smaller (gallon) vines with a 4-foot tomato

41

stake nailed to the container. When shifted to a 4 or 5-gallon container, we nail on a 6-foot ladder-like trellis support. Vines in general seem to be shy in blooming in the younger (gallon) sizes and bloom best in larger containers and in the ground. Flame-vines in particular almost never bloom before the second year in that container. However, some like the *Passiflora* often bloom in very young sizes, even as rooted cuttings."

The homeowner should not be discouraged if the first nurseryman he visits is short of flowering vines. He is only stimulated to search farther because he is determined to find a colorful climber for his own garden, so that he in turn will have a conversation piece stretching from ground to treetop. He usually succeeds because most vines are easy to grow from cuttings, from seeds if available, from layers of a stray branch on the neighbor's plant, or from a root sucker. The only other things needed are patience and good pruning shears.

Vines will do what the gardener wants them to do, and they might just as well be floriferous. Hoyt (58) suggests that color can be piled on, particularly when the climbers are used to block out undesirable objects of a necessary nature, such as outbuildings and waste areas. A fence, a shelter, or even a pergola may be tied in with the architectural lines of the house. Climbers make excellent blockades against dust, noise, and prying eyes. A patio may be protected from the evening sun by a screen in the right place; a porch may be cut off from the street by a lovely vine which those inside can see through without being seen; a covered passageway gets added protection from screening vines along the path. Property lines can be marked with plant-decorated frames, and many climbers will cover a rock wall in such locations.

The great danger here lies in overdoing, because good architecture should be embellished rather than concealed. A cardinal point that every gardener should keep in mind is that vines, more than any other plants, require constant, intelligent pruning. Such training must accommodate both the natural bent of the climber and the wishes of the gardener. It might be noted here that most vines keep their roots cool and their leaves out in the hot sun.

Vines do many other useful things. They can establish "quick effects"—temporary plantings that will be removed later when the shrubbery, tree, or other permanent planting can be put in place. Vines can be used as focal points to draw attention to a particular garden spot. They can be grown as groundcovers to blanket areas that later will be in lawn or tennis court. Frequently their use as groundcovers is extended to the permanent covering of sloping banks or as a lawn substitute in similarly difficult areas. Many of the groundcover plants are also hanging basket subjects of excellence and great ornamental value. While flowering vines are seldom used in containers except in the glasshouse, a great many outdoor kinds provide cut blossoms for the living room, and in this feature they excel many other plant forms in year-round availability and wide selectivity.

A lot of plants got into this book that should have been omitted, just because avid gardeners are often successful in creating remarkable climbing displays with plants that normally stay where they belong—on the ground. One of the most satisfactory screenings for service yards ever devised stands behind a Palm Beach hotel; a 12-foot heavy-duty wire screen on steel posts has been planted closely

42

with the Natal plum (*Carissa grandiflora*) which is certainly not a vine; yet it has covered that screen to the top and, kept closely sheared on both sides, combines its unfriendly thorns with a magnificent display of fragrant white flowers and bright red fruits among a heavy, covering greenery.

A similar effect can be created with the use of blue leadwort (*Plumbago capensis*). It is ordinarily a loose, rather neglected shrublet, and if it achieves any glory it comes with the frequent rash of heavenly blue phloxlike flowers, which can be astonishingly pretty. Yet consider the imaginative gardener who sets a row of plants along a high chicken-wire fence and keeps pruning to prevent them from spreading (their natural inclination) and thereby forcing them to climb. By this method it is not difficult to create a 10-foot screen simply covered with those blue flowers, an arresting sight in any garden, and the uninitiated will exclaim: "What handsome vine is that?"

The parrot's-beak (*Clianthus puniceus*), as any New Zealander will tell you, is a shrub and nothing but a shrub. Yet in Santa Barbara, California, on an old 15-foot wall, this author found the parrot's-beak simply covering the entire vertical surface with a rampant display of greenery embellished by the striking blossoms, creating unforgettably the effect of a vigorous flowering vine. Whenever vines are mentioned, that beautiful parrot's-beak pops into mind, even though it was undoubtedly hours of pruning and other care that helped in establishing the picture.

A striking scandent shrub now established in the United States is the Ashanti-blood (*Mussaenda erythrophylla*). In Africa it can often become a small tree with a definite trunk; ordinarily it is a big shrub. Its rather inconspicuous yellow flowers are followed by large, brilliant red, leaflike appendages that are very showy. To produce these red "tear-drops" the plant requires full sun, and if overhanging growth prevents the sun from getting to the plant, the plant will climb to the sun. Examples of the Ashanti-blood in Miami have sent their branches up tall trees and put on their displays in the sunny tops of prosaic mango (*Mangifera indica*) and tropical-almond (*Terminalia catappa*) trees that are not used to such colorful canopies.

Another common warm-garden shrub that will go viny if the supply of sunshine is cut off is the mandarin-hat (*Holmskioldia sanguinea*). Ordinarily a subdued 4-foot shrub with arching branches covered seasonally with quantities of orange flowers that look like Chinese hats, this plant is unable to display its wares in the shade. Planted in the wrong place, it will start climbing, and under suitable circumstances may produce great arching festoons of its brilliant orange flowers (the calyx of which is the prominent part) on the edge of a house roof or in some similar spot that gets full sun.

It is possible, as many authors have done, to prepare lists of vines for masonry, low climbers, high climbers, veiling vines, and so on, but such suggestions are for particular localities and are not suited to this book's consideration of vines for all over the world. The reader is referred to regional books for his area, to be found in the Bibliography preceding the Index.

The utilization of climbing plants goes far beyond the garden. Most widespread use of vines in the United States is by state highway maintenance and beautification departments, because climbing plants are invaluable on fences in median areas on four-lane highways. They are excellent for holding steep banks, checking or preventing erosion there. In areas near the sea many vines that resist salt spray and salt-laden winds are unexcelled in protecting roadways that are subject to these elements. And of course, in addition, many vines contribute substantially to roadside beautification.

A survey has been made of highway departments in most states and the following reports, written in the language of an official of the state road department in question, indicate the wide use which vines have in this connection.

### ARIZONA

*Bougainvillea* species have been used as a groundcover in the Yuma area, where winter temperatures seldom drop below freezing.

*Lonicera japonica* (Hall's honeysuckle) has been used in the Tucson, Phoenix areas as screening on freeway right-of-way fences as well as for groundcover.

*Jasminum mesnyi*, which is really a rambling shrub rather than a true vine, is frequently trained on fences for screening in zones with temperatures of between 10° and 20°.

*Ficus pumila* has been used in semi-shaded areas for tracery effect on concrete abutments on underpasses, as has *Hedera helix* and *Hedera canariensis*. The tracery effect of the two *Hedera* species is short-lived, since complete coverage is obtained rapidly under optimum conditions.

*Doxantha unguis-cati* (*Bignonia tweediana*), *Anemopaegma chamberlayni* (*Bignonia chamberlayni*), and *Bignonia capreolata atrosanguinea* are being experimented with for highway use. Of these plants, the *Doxantha* will likely prove most valuable because of its ability to self-adhere to masonry and in use as a groundcover for its tendency to root at each node and form a dense erosion-control blanket.

On some few installations they have placed a limited number of *Gelsemium sempervirens*, primarily on an experimental basis. The deep, evergreen foliage and the late winter, yellow bloom appeal to them. Possibly, this plant may make a suitable groundcover as well as a climber.

Of the few species discussed here, it is believed that the most important, for their rather specialized use, are *Lonicera* and *Jasminum* for all desert, warm winter areas, with the exception of Yuma, where *Bougainvillea* takes precedence.

### CALIFORNIA

In highway planting in California few vines are used. On depressed highways, several varieties of ivy are used as a groundcover, not only for soil erosion, but also for aesthetic reasons. Its use is restricted to those parts where the climate is not intemperate.

Some other vines and vinelike shrubs have been tried with varying success. These include some forms of *Plumbago* and *Jasminum* among others. In some older structures Boston-ivy and Virginia-creeper have been used, but for aesthetic reasons such planting has been discontinued.

### DELAWARE

Delaware is using 'Penngift' crown vetch as a primary plant for erosion control. It is likely that *Vinca minor, Hedera helix,* and *Pachysandra terminalis* will grow in special locations—such as certain traffic islands and slopes adjacent to residences.

### FLORIDA

Contract work is confined to plants available commercially:

        Hall's honeysuckle (*Lonicera japonica halliana*)
        Carolina yellow jessamine (*Gelsemium sempervirens*)
        confederate jasmine (*Trachelospermum jasminoides*)
        trailing lantana (*Lantana montevidensis*)

Also used are the native beach morning-glories, *Ipomoea pes-caprae* and *litoralis* on work in the Keys.

Overlooked are the trumpet creeper (*Campsis radicans*) and Virginia-creeper (*Parthenocissus quinquefolia*), which should do a good job in many locations but they are not available commercially.

Also used with some success are some semi-vine materials such as *Allamanda, Tecomaria capensis,* and *Cryptostegia* for groundcovers.

## INDIANA

From 1962 to 1964 Indiana used two types of groundcovers on slopes tending to erosion. Purple-leaf wintercreeper and fleece-vine, were planted every fall. Upheaving of plants caused by freezing and thawing resulted in the material being washed to the base of the slopes. Two reasons may be cited: (1) the root system was shallow; (2) time of planting may not have been favorable. Since that time the highway authorities have returned to designing slopes no greater than 3:1. This would allow for slope areas to be established with the use of only grass and at the same time allow these areas to be mowed without serious erosion effects. Crown vetch is used to establish covers for slopes.

## IOWA

Vines used in highway planting have been Hall's honeysuckle, purple-leaf wintercreeper and Virginia creeper. The Hall's honeysuckle was used on roadway embankments in several locations with little success. Several years after planting, only a few of the plots have become established. Hall's honeysuckle is now being replaced with crown-vetch.

The purple-leaf wintercreeper and Virginia-creeper were specified to be planted along concrete walls. The wintercreeper after 2 years is just beginning to make a showing.

## MAINE

Use of vines is closely tied in with roadside maintenance practices. These practices vary. In this area natural climax growth consists almost exclusively of dense stands of both hardwood and softwood trees.

During highway construction, most areas of disturbed ground are initially seeded to grass for erosion control. However, maintenance practice calls for mowing only a narrow strip directly outside the road shoulder. Grass will normally be crowded out by other plants unless constantly mowed. Therefore, the zone between the mowed strip and the usually wooded outer area presents a special problem. Growth of native groundcovers in this area is encouraged. On the interstate highway system, on steep embankments, some use is made of cultivated plants, usually vines or small shrubs.

Crown-vetch (*Coronilla varia*) seems most generally satisfactory. The only other good spreaders are rose acacia, a shrub, and Virginia rose, which I suppose would also be considered a shrub. However, *Rosa setigera*, though not a spreader, has been satisfactory. Other vine roses are not hardy here. Bittersweet has proved satisfactory. Maine would like to use honeysuckle but it does not flourish here. Such vines as *Pachysandra* and *Vinca minor* are too delicate to compete against native vegetation without excessive maintenance costs.

Other vines are not commercially available in the sizes and quantities needed. Experimenting with *Polygonum auberti* and *Lycium halimifolium* is under way. Much needed is almost any hardy, vigorous vine, the more ornamental the better—vigorous, inexpensive groundcovers for those large unmowed roadside areas.

## MARYLAND

Maryland's use of flowering vines has been limited because of the high cost of installation and maintenance. The most economical method for slope stabilization is seeding with grasses and legumes.

*Celastrus scandens* and *Rosa wichuraiana* have been planted with excellent results on steep bridge abutment slopes and certain other slopes. *Lonicera japonica halliana* has been used as an underplanting for shrubs and trees. *Lonicera* did very well, but after four years has only spread a few feet and has not formed a cover.

The only other vines successfully used are *Parthenocissus quinquefolia engelmannii* and *P. tricuspidata*. These were used on concrete walls to soften the harsh effect of concrete.

## OREGON

Oregon uses vines extensively in erosion control or as groundcover in lieu of grass. It has followed the practice, in the western portion of the state, of planting evergreen vines on the slopes adjacent to underpass and overpass structures, to improve the appearance and reduce maintenance costs. Varieties used are listed below in order of importance.

*Hedera helix,* English ivy

*Arctostaphylos uva-ursi* and *A. media,* kinnikinnick or bearberry.

*Hypericum calycinum*—Aaronsbeard or St. Johnswort

45

*Ceanothus gloriosus*—Point Reyes *Ceanothus*
*Vinca minor*—dwarf myrtle or common periwinkle

## RHODE ISLAND

Vines have proved successful in highway plantings. *Parthenocissus tricuspidata* provides excellent fall color, the outstanding flowers of *Hydrangea petiolaris, Lonicera* sp. and *Wisteria sinensis* are valuable for screening on retaining walls and along the miles of chain-link fence that delineate the highways.

Where a year-round screen is desired, and space does not permit the use of trees and shrubs, *Hedera helix* often fits; also *Celastrus orbiculata* and *Wisteria* where a ledge cut seems too obtrusive or to give a sense of stability to rock plantings. More vines could be used, and more often, as their diversity is not yet completely explored.

## WASHINGTON

English ivy has been employed as a groundcover on steep slopes, especially shaded ones, Virginia creeper as a groundcover, and Boston-ivy on retaining walls to break up that bare expanse of concrete. Its resistance to fumes and its tight-clinging habit make it well suited for this purpose.

A spectacular display of flowers might be unduly distracting for heavy traffic conditions but in other situations flowering vines—a very much neglected group of plants—could be very usefully employed.

## WEST VIRGINIA

Hall's honeysuckle (*Lonicera japonica halliana*) has been used successfully well over twenty years in all counties and almost all soil types in West Virginia. It is a vigorous spreader, soon covering a highway cut or fill and giving good erosion control and a green groundcover for most of the year.

Honeysuckle is so aggressive that it has become a pest in some of the private farms along the highway right-of-way, climbing over young trees and shrubs in pasture land and keeping the roadside from returning to native woody species. Where Hall's honeysuckle can be controlled or confined, it is hard to beat as an erosion-control groundcover.

A vine used to a limited extent is *Vinca minor*. It is less aggressive than honeysuckle and takes a longer time to form a good groundcover. It does better on the cool, north or east exposure but does fairly well on the south and west exposure. Most of the plantings go back to the labor surplus periods.

At the present time, they are using 'Kentucky 31' fescue, *Lespedeza cuneata* (*L. sericea*) and crown-vetch for erosion control.

Kudzu has been tried all over the state and is a pretty good bank cover, but is a pest in adjoining tree areas. It dies back and is not good protection in the winter.

Virginia-creeper is a decorative vine on rocky banks in the summer and fall, but only grows on the cool slopes.

Because of their fast-growing habit, many climbers found a special use in wartime as camouflage instruments. For example, morning-glories of several kinds were used to screen ammunition dumps and gun emplacements in Ceylon. T. B. Worthington of Kandy writes of these:

My whole plant of *Ipomoea briggsii* recently collapsed leaving only a stalk six feet high, and then suddenly it started to regrow and climbed another 18 feet within a week or ten days; all that 18 feet became a solid pole of red. This rapid growth is possible because of large tubers in the ground, holding big supplies of plant food. The vine was planted nearly twenty years ago and has been up two or three trees at one time or another. *Antigonon leptopus* is also like that and I made use of the fact in the last war to camouflage an ack-ack gun site—three months later an aerial photo failed to show up the site; i.e., coverage was complete three months after planting. *Ipomoea pes-caprae* is another wonder. When big coast guns are fired they blow every green thing off the concrete aprons in front. The battery commander said to me: 'Oh, yes,

46

we get the concrete aprons covered in a fortnight after firing; we persuade new runners from the old roots to grow across from both sides'."

In primitive mountain areas all over the world, vines are used frequently in the construction of footpath suspension bridges over deep chasms or turbulent streams. For example, in Ivory Coast several of the 100 species of climbers growing on river banks supply long lianas that are resilient and strong enough to be dragged across a stream as suspension cables on which swinging, living bridges can be woven. (See Photograph 291.) In many African countries *Hippocratea* vines are used to fasten bundles and to tie timbers together in buildings.

# V

## *How Vines Are Supported*

An examination of all the usual supporting structures for vines reveals their favorable possibilities along with their weaknesses and shortcomings.

Actually there is no ideal man-made support for a climber, especially a big one. The nearest thing to it is a rock wall that the vine can scramble over. Unfortunately not many homes have places for rock walls and big climbers, so consideration goes back to the devices that can be used temporarily, then replaced as they rust out, rot out, get wrecked by wind and weather, or need painting badly enough to remove the vine and start over.

In the wild, vines have selected trees as their ideal support. Trees are semipermanent, they are strong enough to sustain enormous weights, the trunks and branches are excellent things to cling to without hurting the trees in any way or interfering with their metabolism. They enable the vine to get off the ground and up into the sunlight, no matter how thick the undergrowth around the base of the trees.

But under cultivation the tree-climbing solution is not so simple or so satisfactory, either to the tree, to the vine, or to the gardener. If a climber is planted close to a tree, it gets little nourishment because the tree roots are too many and too aggressive; if away from the trunk it must be wired to its destination and such wires are often awkward in a garden. A few vines will flower low on the trunk, but most of them go to the top and then fall back out with their shower of blossoms, too high in the air to be enjoyed and susceptible to grave damage in every storm.

In the southern and southwestern states the only trouble-free perch for vines is the cabbage palmetto (*Sabal* species) which any self-respecting climber can mount unassisted. Tying to this upright support is unnecessary, and flowering along the trunk is promoted by the constant arching of branches away from the support. Even hurricane winds do not destroy or damage a palmetto. It is the only proper place for the night-blooming cacti. However, too few gardens can boast a palmetto, and man has not yet devised a substitute for it.

First suggested for big vines is usually the pergola—parallel colonnades supporting girders and cross rafters, with an open top. The pillars must be at least 10 feet high and 10 feet (or more) apart if anyone is to walk beneath the archways. They should be of rock if the structure is expected to last, although treated timbers on concrete footings would endure some years. But any such massive framework could not be tolerated anywhere near the average house without dwarfing it and looking badly out of place. Hence the pergola, perhaps suited to a public park, is impractical in ordinary gardens. The most serious objection to it anywhere is that if different vines are planted beside the different posts, they will grow at different rates to different heights, and what started out as a dream collection of beautiful climbers may turn out to be a nightmare of mismatchings.

The greatest objections to pergolas in public gardens is their perpetual untidiness and the unceasing maintenance expense. A Los Angeles plantsman, David Barry, Jr., has come forward with an entirely new idea how best to display warm-country vines in parks and similar places, and his idea can readily be adapted to other climates. Barry's presentation, which is applicable mainly to parks and public gardens, is substantially this:

One way to enjoy the beauty of vines is to display them so that their flowers can be seen at close hand from above, not from below, while keeping their growth conveniently under control. This can be done by planting each vine in the center of a level, wire-topped table, a 12-foot square, where it would be spread out and kept flat, as a horizontal espalier. The table would be at workbench height from the ground, 3½ to 4 feet, easy to work around for trimming and training. Tying and re-tying the branches of the vines to hold them flat against the wire could be minimized by using heavy hairpins bent from quarter-inch reinforcing bars. Dead leaves would fall through the wire to the ground (minimum mesh of 6-inch squares), well out of sight yet easy to collect from time to time with a rake. The legs of the tables would be located well in from the sides to give the illusion of floating squares.

The vines are to be viewed from elevated walkways that run between the table tops, a foot above them. The walkways are enclosed with railings 32 inches high. The railing areas are covered with wire mesh small enough to bar arms and hands. Stairs from the ground to the floor of the walkways would be easy to ascend with risers not to exceed 6 inches.

Among the vines for warm countries that might be grown on these horizontal floating panels of color are:

| | |
|---|---|
| *Allamanda* species | *Mandevilla* 'Alice Dupont' |
| *Adenocalymma nitidum* | *Norantea guineensis* |
| *Antigonon leptopus* | *Petrea volubilis* |
| *Bauhinia cumingiana* | *Phanera kockiana* |
| *Bauhinia galpinii* | *Pyrostegia ignea* |
| *Bignonia* species | *Odontadenia speciosa* |
| *Bougainvillea* | *Stigmaphyllon ciliatum* |
| *Clitoria ternatea*, double-flowered | *Thunbergia grandiflora* |
| *Congea velutina* | |

The structure described would not be suitable for vines that produce flowers on pendent racemes which are shyly hidden in the foliage. When these vines are grown on fences their beauty is lost. They should be maintained on horizontal planes and viewed from below. Pergolas may be used. Eliminate one side of the pergola and surround it with similar but smaller horizontal grids of wires to hold the vines about 12 feet from the ground, placing the hanging flowers just beyond arm's reach. Here should be planted the great tropical lianas, *Strongylodon*, the Philippine jade-vine, and the red *Mucuna* from New Guinea; *Thunbergia mysorensis*, *T. grandiflora* var. *alba*, and perhaps species of *Aristolochia*. Several of these vines have two flowering seasons. When they are forced to expose their flowers which otherwise are hidden, the effect is startlingly beautiful.

49

The most suitable garden devices for vines out in the open are individual trellises, posts with cross-arms, or pyramids, all built of treated timber or wire. A vine-clad arch over a gateway can be attractive, but of course none of these devices can accommodate a big climber. If vines are to be grown near the house they do best on wire frames built of termite-proof and rot-proof wood or galvanized iron pipe. Climbers must never be allowed to get on top of the house, mostly because they will quickly take root up there, monopolize the drains, unseat the tiles, and cause various other kinds of damage. Ivy on a rock chimney will cover the top and cut off all draft. *Ficus pumila* with its tiny leaves clinging to a masonry wall can be beautiful; once it reaches the top of the wall or edge of a roof, its leaves become large and the plant itself becomes treelike, quickly developing a trunk 20 feet above the ground. If the yard frames are made of iron, a boiling sun will cook the vines that touch them. Painting or mending an old trellis after a climber gets established is impossible without extensive damage to the vine.

Egbert Reasoner who, 85 years ago, with his brother Norman, established what is today Florida's oldest nursery, used to feel that discarded telephone poles were the best possible supports on which to grow heavy flowering vines because on them the beauty of the plants could be fully appreciated.

However, if no rock wall is handy and no telephone pole is available, perhaps the only way to accommodate a big climber in a garden may be on fences of galvanized wire, either barbed or ornamental, although split redwood or locust logs offer possibilities. Any other kind of wood fence is too short-lived. Fences can be common yard separators, 3 to 4 feet high, or they can be backstops on a tennis court. Of course a dead tree, so rarely cherished in gardens nowadays except as driftwood, makes a glorious perch for a big flowering vine, but why suggest the impossible?

Some thoughts about the growth habits of individual vines may aid in the selection of the right one and the best place in the garden for it. Climbers like Guinea/gold (*Hibbertia volubilis*) or those that grow from tubers like the glory lily (*Gloriosa* species) rarely ascend very high, usually 3 or 4 feet, and after blooming and fruiting seasons, they are ready to die back to the ground and rest. They behave like annuals. In the glasshouse tuberons vines are kept in pots and when the growing cycle has passed, these are turned on their sides under the bench and allowed to dry out. In a warm garden the tubers are usually left in the ground, although water and fertilizer are withheld during the resting season.

Most vines that twine are herbaceous and rarely climb to great heights, seemingly being content with covering a pillar or frame. These are comparatively easy to keep under control by pruning and usually produce their flowers from the ground up. A *Hoya* vine on a cabbage palmetto trunk in Florida is usually permitted to climb to the top of the exposed trunk; then it will be allowed to hang down until perhaps its tip reaches the ground; at this point the gardener turns its tip upward once again, so that it may go up and down its support endlessly. Some, like the Mexican flame-vine (*Senecio confusus*), in warm gardens are apt to develop strong lateral shoots extending into neighboring areas; these take root readily, and the vine may soon form a blanket, sometimes clambering over other vegetation to display orange daisies in the sun.

50

Many of the plants grown on fences and trellises are not true vines, but rather scandent shrubs. Their great virtue under cultivation is that, if they climb at all, ordinarily they show no inclination to go high or far and consequently are easy to keep under control. This might be rephrased to say that such "vines" invite neglect, and the lazy gardeners loves them for their indolence and undemanding nature. Plants in this category include both the yellow and the purple allamanda, many jasmines (*Jasminum* species), the Palay rubber-vine (*Cryptostegia grandiflora*), the "red orchid"—not a true orchid—(*Bauhinia galpinii*), and a host of similar plants. The failure of most gardeners, especially in warm countries, to prune often and well is responsible for these "vines."

Scandent shrubs in the garden require a pergola or similar support and flower mostly when they bend downward. Because they do not like to flower on shoots pointing upward, they are never happy on a trellis or on a fence. Just as twining vines do not succeed on walls, so these scandent plants should never be coaxed up the wrong sort of support.

Harry Blossfeld (8), São Paulo plantsman, wrote:

The Tupi Indians of ancient Brazil coined the word cipó (pronounced sipó with accent on the ó) to include such scandent climbers, and it is commonly so used by Brazilian gardeners. Cipó sends up a stout stem 10 feet or longer until it bends of its own weight, finally resting on any available support. Then a side shoot springs off from the highest point of the bow, again straight upwards, pushing through bushes and tree crowns, until it in turn bends over some support. There at the top of the bend, the process is repeated. When reaching the top of a tree, it branches out profusely, making a web on and between forest trees. When old, such cipó lianas often get flattened and curl, forming the famous 'monkey ladders' frequently mentioned in reports on tropical jungles. This curling is important. When the treetops bend in a strong wind, the curled cipó acts like a spring and will not break. *Thunbergia laurifolia, Adenocalymma comosum, Dioclea* species, several *Bauhinia* species, etc., are examples of this.

Climbers with woody stems require extra careful planning, pruning, and vigilance. On a big estate the herald's-trumpet (*Beaumontia grandiflora*) can be allowed to climb a giant oak tree and smother its top with a burst of white trumpets 50 feet in the air in a spectacle that stops traffic. However, the same vine can be flowered successfully on a 10-foot trellis if its enthusiasm is curbed. For essentially this same reason, most members of the Bignoniaceae (which develop extremely long stems) are grown in Florida on fences rather than on trees or trellises. The showy flowers are better seen and more easily controlled on a rock wall or a wire fence than if the vines are waving their glorious masses of flowers from some treetop.

These are some of the factors limiting the choice of vines for particular locations out-of-doors. The gardener must decide whether he wants a dense screen covering a building, wall, or trellis, or whether he prefers the softening of architectural lines by a graceful tracery of green growth which is enlivened from time to time with a floral display. For a shady place he must select a vine that will both grow and flower with little or no sun. If the chosen location is beyond watering limits, the climber selected must be drought resistant. Perhaps most

51

important in many places is the selection of locations that are protected in some measure from cold, either the lee of a wall, near an open body of water, or in a patio or similar enclosure.

It is not within the scope of this book to select vines for all these contingencies, nor to dwell on propagation, culture, or physical care. Bailey (3) reminds all gardeners that most vines require a certain amount of thinning and training, because if neglect permits the formation of thick, unsightly masses of stems near the top of the support, any decorative beauty the vine might possess is destroyed. Heavy pruning encourages coarse, rank growth. The best procedure is to begin training the plant even before it starts to climb, then choose strong stems as leaders, train them fanlike to cover the desired area, and always do the necessary pruning and thinning after the blooming season, not before.

# VI

## *Climbers in the Glasshouse*

The glasshouse finds a place in a vines book because climbers are the only plants that can fill the vast empty space between the bench and the glass far overhead. This represents two-thirds or more of the space in the conservatory, and considerable ingenuity is required to utilize this production area without sacrificing the bench plants by obscuring the sun which gives them life.

In general the glasshouse operator solves the problem of where to put his climbers in relation to his other plants in three principal ways:

(1) He can plant vines on both sides of a doorway partition because it is there anyway, and the foliage and flowers adhering to it will not increase the amount of shade cast by the partition. The climbers may be planted in the ground if evergreen, and they will be effective ornaments all the year without stealing any of the precious bench space. Plants thus used must of course be controlled and confined to the space assigned to them; this requires selection of screen, wire frame, fan, or other device to suit the habit of the plant as well as to fit the spot to be covered. If the climber is held flat against the partition, it can be flowered low down where it will attract a maximum of attention.

(2) Similarly, the operator can plant vines in the corners where, if stems are closely pruned, they will cast no shadows. These can be true climbers, or they may be scandent shrubs that are forced 10 feet in the air before being permitted to put forth their burst of foliage and flowers in a cascade near the top of the house. This is so distant from the bench that the amount of shade cast on the plants below is inconsequential. *Fuchsia* (photograph 6) is an ideal plant for this sort of display, but many others are similarly utilized. They may not be climbers in any sense, but they lend themselves to being trained on wires or frames, and they become vines in effect. Florists use hundreds of flowering plants in this way. In hanging baskets against north walls where no shading is involved, they get vine and cascade effects with many creeping or mat plants like *Browallia, Asystasia, Achimenes, Lantana,* etc. If they can place these so as not to rob other plants of their light requirements, the effect can be breathtaking.

(3) The glasshouse operator uses another device to achieve similar results. He puts a container on the floor or even buries it, and cultivates a suitable vine on a frame of wire or other materials, keeping foliage and flowers so low in the house that other plants are not affected. This device also keeps the flowers near eye-level where they can be most appreciated, and it has the added advantage of being portable; in off-season the entire container may be removed to a rest area where it will be out of the way, or even set out-of-doors, and a different container with flowers abloom can be wheeled into the display space.

53

Of course all climbers grown in the glasshouse must be pruned regularly to check vegetative growth and to preserve the flowering parts. Frequent spraying is required to maintain a healthy growth pattern. These maintenance practices require skill and experience and the successful grower is a busy man, for each plant is an individual with distinctive habits and needs, and a knowledge of these requirements is essential to successful production of bloom. Some climbers require a 50° cool greenhouse to force bloom, others require a 65° warm house. Some need special rest periods. Some must be fertilized at fixed intervals. Many climbers in the glasshouse must be treated as annuals and propagated anew each season, because only thus can they be controlled. The glasshouse operator with fingertip management of shade, temperature, moisture, and other factors is in a better position than any other grower to produce flowers exactly when and where he wants them.

Part of the fun of glasshouse gardening is hunting for plants to try. Tropical climbers are a special temptation because they are uncommon, many of the flower forms are strangely beautiful, and some of them flower over long periods. But whether the glasshouse operator chooses one of these exotics or something more familiar, it is important that he limit his selection to vines that are not too rampant in growth habit. Otherwise he is apt to harvest too much foliage and too few flowers. With tropicals he can achieve success only as he imitates the warm and humid conditions under which the vine thrives half the year in its native land and the six-month dry season or resting period that most of these require.

It is not within the province of this book to discuss greenhouse culture or practices or to suggest what climbers should or might be grown; this author would only cite the important factors to be considered when either true climbers or man-made "vines" are cultivated under glass. Several good glasshouse manuals that are available are listed among the references which precede the index.

5. STREPTOSOLEN JAMESONII

6. FUCHSIA CASCADE

7. TRACHELOSPERMUM JASMINOIDES

# VII

## *Espaliers*

A vine growing on a trellis against a wall or building has only two significant dimensions—height and width. If properly trimmed it has minimal thickness. Among its chief advantages are that it displays all its flowers in a single plane, toward the viewer, and that it steals almost no ground space from the garden in which it stands.

A century ago, European plantsmen dreamed of growing trees and shrubs in this vinelike manner, because it was ornamental and hence a challenge to enterprising horticulturists to create new forms in small garden plots, and because it provided a way to produce more flowers and fruits with less investment in space.

Originally such plants were merely pruned into a flat fan shape and tied to a trellis here and there to preserve this form. But when alert gardeners grasped the idea of moving the trellis away from the wall and letting it stand independently in the garden, they decided to train their plants to fit the angular outlines of the framework of which they became a part. If the framework was tall, the branches could be trained vertically in parallel lines if desired; if low, the branches were trained to grow horizontally, often in parallel lines, and all vertical growth was checked. Experimental work with these two patterns over the years resulted in the development of a special technique. Many intricate designs grew out of the original efforts, and these took their name from the French word for trellis— *espalier*. Adopted into the English language both as a noun and as a verb, the word is now pronounced es-*pal*-yer with the accent on the *pal*.

Espaliers really do not belong in this book at all because basically they are never vines. They are trees or shrubs trained on frames to grow in a vinelike manner. (Photographs 8-11.) The true espaliers are works of art with single and multiple patterns in the form of the letters T, U, V, W, X, Y, and inverted U. Unfortunately most of the so-called espaliers in the United States are haphazard creations of a frenetic, overworked gardener and are nothing more than trees or shrubs trimmed to fan shape.

The true espalier must be grown very slowly, and a truly good one requires nurturing for fifty years. It must be grown on dwarfing rootstock, or be naturally a slow-growing plant, or the roots must be trimmed twice a year to keep the plant from getting too much nourishment. It requires as much care and attention as a bonsai creation. Major pruning of the entire plant is required twice a year, and incidental clipping, twisting, tying, and retying are continuing necessities.

Very few gardeners have the time or inclination for such niceties nowadays, so that well-established espaliers, such as those in the accompanying photographs

56

8. HORIZONTAL ESPALIERED PEAR TREE IN BELGIUM

9. YEARS ARE REQUIRED TO TRAIN THIS PEAR TREE

10. ALMOND, APPLE, AND PEAR ESPALIERS IN LIMBURG, HOLLAND

11. A CENTER UPRIGHT MAKES THIS A PALMETTE VERRIERE ESPALIER

from Holland, represent the handiwork of patient people for a lifetime. Anything approaching their elegance is seldom seen in this country.

Occasionally parallel wires are strung, and the long runners from a wisteria vine are tied to them, thus effectively decorating a blank wall. This is not an espalier, just a tailored vine. Other climbers are often similarly trained around windows or over doorways, but the mere fastening of such plants to a fence or frame is a long jump from the art of a gardener who envisions and creates an espalier.

The woman who tells her garden club associates that espaliering is easy means that she had a carpenter drive a few nails in a design on the side of her house, and she tied the rambling branches of her firethorn (*Pyracantha* species) to the nails. One of the accompanying pictures (Photograph 15) depicts such a performance with a Barbados-cherry (*Malpighia glabra*). This is not an espalier, just monkey-business. The accompanying photographs (12-14) show other aspects of the craft.

The various classic, symmetrical patterns of espaliers came down to this generation from the middle of the 19th century and bear the names of their originators—Verrière, Goucher, Losange, Arcure, etc. Any good textbook on espaliers (see List of References preceding the Index) portrays the standard designs and their modifications, shows how they are created with living plants, suggests trees and shrubs that lend themselves best to satisfactory displays when utilized as espaliers, and outlines the regimen of maintenance, pruning, feeding, pest control, etc. All these things are outside the purpose of the present book, which recognizes espaliers only as artistic, man-made efforts to imitate the grace and beauty of the vine.

# VIII

## *The Most Beautiful Vines in the World*

Any attempt to select the most beautiful flowering climbers in the world is inevitably fraught with difficulties. Therefore, this chapter can only hope to force the reader to seek new horizons and to challenge him to get more widely acquainted with the twisty world of vines.

Any selection of climbers is limited by the experience of individuals who take part in the preparation of a list. What each one has seen is all that counts. Therefore, for the purposes of this book a questionnaire was sent to a hundred plantsmen throughout the world who have been places, who know plants, who have seen many climbers in many countries under a wide variety of circumstances. The result is rather a diverse list and most of those plants named by the contributors are entirely unknown to most readers.

Differences of opinion about which climber is most beautiful necessitate an analysis of beauty. What is it? How can it be defined? Joseph Addison in the *Spectator* papers 250 years ago laid a foundation when he wrote: "Beauty as apprehended by the imagination, is only an idea in the mind, and has no qualities that have any existence in matter."

Beauty is entirely within ourselves, the expression of a moment of exquisite harmony that is awakened by a combination of exterior factors and interior receptivity—all parts of a picture suddenly fused together in an unforgettable vision of delight.

This definition can be taken apart so that some of the stimulating factors can be analyzed. We usually think of color as having a part in its creation, but this is not necessarily true. Symmetry or rhythm is important. Elegance and grace (which flower arrangers call "line") play a leading role. Comeliness and concord of composition are requisite. The surroundings which establish a contrast or make a frame for the picture are essential. Put these all together and we begin to conceive of beauty.

Very important are the effects of light and shadow. The background can make or break the entire concept. Bright sunshine and a brilliant blue sky bring out the best in red and yellow flowers, but place a gorgeous yellow-flowered vine against a lowering sky and it is not worth a second glance. White flowers are often prettiest at night. The richness of blue flowers is accentuated by a bright-green background; but the handsomest of blue-flowered vines is only indifferently appealing against a blue sky.

These are the chief exterior factors; now consider the interior reactions.

Beauty exists only in the eye of the beholder, not in the object. There its register is influenced first of all by the mood of the observer. It is controlled to some extent by the environment of the moment:

> The waving of the fronded palms,
> The sleepy hush at noon,
> The wonder of the tropic night,
> The magic of the moon.

Things such as these underlie beauty. It is possible in some instances that fragrance plays a part in the beholder's reaction. Many are the shifting factors inside each experience of beholding beauty. Consciousness takes in all of these factors and with the speed of an electronic computer, comes up with an answer. We call it beautiful!

The poet John Milton was blind, but he did not need physical sight to write his poetry. In one of his masterpieces he calls beauty "nature's coin" that must not be hoarded, but currently enjoyed. At the same time, he said, it was "nature's brag," for it must be displayed for all to glory in. Beauty is not something we keep secret; we spread it freely before all who will look.

B. Y. Morrison, long-time head of the U.S.D.A. Division of Plant Introduction, and Secretary of the American Horticultural Society, wrote the foreword in this author's book on *Flowering Trees of the World,* in which 425 color plates depict some of the most beautiful. Morrison wrote in part:

> It is true, perhaps, that many of the trees shown will be of no value to many a reader as plants for his garden, and that some may never even find a single place in these United States where they may repeat the miracle of their flowering. Does that matter too much? No, a thousand times no, for a mere examination of the pictures alone will open one's eyes to beauty and urge on one's zeal toward new efforts to know and experience, within the possible realm of one's own garden life, things he had never dreamed of.
>
> In this day and age, dare one dream? A thousand times yes, for without a dream there is no vision, and without vision the people perish.

\* \* \*

Here follows a list of the most beautiful flowering climbers in the world in the opinion of men and women who have seen them to their best advantage:

*Aeschynanthus*—Gesneriad in Indonesia that forms flower curtains.
*Agalmyla*—Another showy-flowered gesneriad in Indonesia (see also *Dichrotrichum,* below).
*Allamanda hendersonii*—Scandent shrub of tropical America, grown from Florida to Cape Town.
*Antigonon*—Coral-vine, several species in pink, red, and white.
*Bauhinia galpinii*—South African beauty grown in California and Florida.
*Beaumontia grandiflora*—Herald's-trumpet, with loveliest of large white blooms.
*Blakea florida*—"One of the fanciest things I have seen."
*Bougainvillea*—Most widely grown of any tropical vine.
*Butea superba*—"The vegetable world offers no more gaudy show."
*Camoensia maxima*—Great white flowers banded in gold, from southwest Africa.

*Camptosema grandiflorum*—Leguminous vine with pea flowers, South America.
*Chonemorpha*—*Allamanda* relative with clusters of white flowers.
*Clematis* 'Ramona'—One of finest of these climbers in the Temperate Zone.
*Combretum coccineum*—"One of the handsomest ornaments of Indian gardens."
*Congea tomentosa*—Indomalaysian, clouds of mauve bracts that resemble flowers.
*Dichrotrichum*—Another gesneriad in the forest of Indonesia.
*Dimorphanthera species*—Vines in heath family in mountains of New Guinea.
*Dioclea purpureum*—Among 50 species of this legume in tropical America.
*Doxantha unguis-cati*—Cat's Claw vine. Hanging clouds of golden flowers.
*Duparquetia orchidacea*—Tropical African climber with orchid-like flower.
*Epiphyllum quezaltecum*—"A cactus, one of the fanciest that I know."
*Friderica speciosia* –A trumpet-vine in Brazil, the only species.
*Gelsemium sempervirens*—Carolina Yellow Jessamine, a favorite everywhere.
*Heteropterys beechyana*—Brazilian climber now grown in the United States.
*Hibbertia volubilis*—California's most popular vine, from Madagascar.
*Hibiscus rostellatus*—One of the few *hibiscus* species that climb.
*Hydrangea petiolaris*—Popular porch vine throughout the United States.
*Hylocereus undatus*—Best known of the NIGHT-BLOOMING CEREUS type of cacti.
*Ipomoea species*—Many blue and purple, "exceedingly attractive in the tropics."
*Lundia multiflora*—Another trumpet-creeper, in Brazilian mountains.
*Medinilla waterhousei*—The most beautiful flower in the Fijian flora.
*Metrosideros carminea*—Handsomest climber in the New Zealand flora.
*Mucuna bennettii*—Best known of half-dozen brilliant New Guinea climbers.
*Mutisia*—Masses of daisy-like flowers cover treetops in Peru.
*Odontodenia grandiflora*—Among the spectacular members of Dogbane family.
*Parafridericea obidoensis*—Recently discovered trumpet-climber in Brazil.
*Passiflora caerulea*—Best known of 500 different passion-flowers.
*Pentapterygium serpens*—Heathlike vines, native from Himalayas to Malaysia.
*Petrea kohautiana*—Among the finest of the Queen's-Wreath climbers.
*Phanera kockiana*—Malayan *Bauhinia* relative with brilliant yellow flowers.
*Podranea ricasoliana*—South African pink-flowered trumpet-vine.
*Porana paniculata*—Clouds of white flowers make this the Christmas-vine.
*Pyrostegia ignea*—The flame-vine—most popular of all in the tropics.
*Quisqualis indica*—The Rangoon creeper, with flowers that change color.
*Rosa gigantea*—A spectacular climber in the Burmese mountains.
*Securidaca species*—Several kinds of South American climbers.
*Senecio chinotegensis*—In full flower over the trees, certainly attractive.
*Solandra maxima*—Most popular of the so-called chalice-vines.
*Solanum wendlandii*—The Costa Rican nightshade, in clouds of blue.
*Souroubea*—In Amazonian Peru, tops of trees are painted red by it.
*Stephanotis floribunda*—Much loved as the finest for bridal bouquets.
*Strongylodon*—The famous Jade-vine, native from the Philippines to Malaya.
*Thunbergia grandiflora*—Cascading blue flowers; also a white variety.
*Wisteria sinensis*—Most widely grown of the garden Wisterias.

# IX

## *Descriptions of the Vines*

The remainder of this book up to the Supplement (Chapter X; *see* page 341) consists of descriptions of 2,000 climbing plants, the handsome flowers of which make them worthy of garden use. The climate for which each is best suited is indicated in the text. Photographs are shown of some 600 of the species mentioned, some of them in color.

The book's objective is to present not only the principal vines in cultivation, but also many others that deserve horticultural recognition. Yet the book cannot pretend to be exhaustive. There are too many climbers and creepers and clamberers in the world to be 100 per cent included.

The families to which these climbers belong are handled in alphabetical order, from Acanthaceae (the Acanthus family) to Zygophyllaceae (the caltrop, bean-caper, or *lignum vitae* family.) Similarly under each family, the genera are mostly in alphabetical order. Where disarrangement has seemed preferable for the sake of comprehending the relationships within the family, the index will solve the problem of a genus's location. (To get twisted a bit in a book on vines seems no more than logical.) Within each genus, where several species are described, after the principal one of the group, which is given first place, these too are generally alphabetized.

The personal name that follows the botanical name of a plant tells who gave that kind of plant its scientific designation. This personal name is often in abbreviated form, such as L. or Linn. for Carl Linnaeus, famous 18th-century Swedish botanist who was responsible for the present system of plant classification. R. Br., as another example, stands for Robert Brown, whose botanical work was produced in Great Britain largely in the early 19th century. HBK refers to the famous trio of Humboldt, Bonpland, and Kunth, who prepared an important work on New World plants, published between 1815 and 1825. Other names are spelled out in full, such as G. Don and D. Don, Scottish brothers of the early 19th century; Vahl for Martin Vahl, Danish botanist, also Miers for John Miers of Great Britain, both of the 19th century. Any reference book on the plants concerned will give all names in full.

Since 1753, when Linnaeus' definitive work on species of plants was published, the first scientific name to be bestowed on a plant is considered its correct name—provided certain technical qualifications have been met in accordance with the International Code of Botanical Nomenclature. A botanist with more up-to-date information, however, will sometimes amend the work of his predecessor. The botanical name of a species, it should be understood, consists of two words—the first being the name of the genus to which it belongs. If the second word of the name, the specific epithet, is transferred to a new genus, the original author's name is carried along in parentheses before the name of the present author. The original name, no matter how it is changed, is then looked upon as a synonym. In this book it follows the current name, in, brackets, with the abbreviation "Syn."

Common names of plants also need some explanation, for many green-growing things are called by names of plants to which they are not related. For example, the Hottentot-fig (*Carpobrotus edulis*) of the carpet-weed or mesembry-anthemum family, has no connection with the true fig (*Ficus carica*) in the mulberry family, so the word "fig" follows a hyphen, instead of standing alone. Similarly, sweet-pea (*Lathyrus odoratus*), while in the pea family, is not considered a true pea, the garden pea, which is *Pisum*. This name is also therefore hyphenated. Other examples will be found throughout the book. The hyphen indicates that the name does not represent the "true" plant by that name.

Numbers in parentheses that follow names of botanists or of specific writings mentioned in the text refer to the List of References that immediately precedes the index.

## ACANTHACEAE—ACANTHUS FAMILY

### *Acanthus leucostachys*  WALLICH
*Common Name:* BEAR'S-BREECH

Most of the 25 species of these showy-flowered herbs and subshrubs in warm areas are erect, but in Burma this white-flowered form and also *A. volubilis* Wallich, with red blossoms, are climbers.

### *Adhatoda cydoniaefolia*  NEES
*Common Name:* BRAZILIAN BOWER-PLANT

Although most of the 20 or more species of *Adhatoda* are shrubs, a few, including this one, *A. cydoniaefolia* (Color Plate 1), with purplish flowers, are scandent. It is cultivated in California and also frequently seen in Hawaii. The other species are largely native to Asia and tropical Africa, as, it has also been said, this one is too.

Chittenden (22) calls this a scrambling, slightly downy shrub for training up pillars and rafters, or "a pretty basket plant when in flower." Under cultivation at the Fairchild Tropical Garden in Miami it is a robust shrub. The showy flowers are in dense clusters at branch tips, the corolla tube white, its upper lip white tipped with purple, its large lower lip a rich deep purple with white median stripes.

### *Asystasia gangetica*  T. ANDERS
[Syn. *A. coromandeliana*  Nees]
*Common Name:* COROMANDEL

*Asystasia* comprises some 20 species of creeping herbs or subshrubs that root

63

at the nodes and hence are useful as groundcovers, but they will climb to 6 feet at the first opportunity. This Indian species, *A. gangetica* (Color Plate 2), with its bright mauve funnelform flowers is common in American glasshouses and out-of-doors in Florida and California. The evergreen, papery, heart-shaped leaves are opposite on slender stems.

The South African *A. bella* [syn. *Mackaya bella*], with white or lilac, bell-shaped flowers in clusters 5 to 8 inches long, is commoner in Cuba (43), in Madeira (47), and in English glasshouses (94).

*A. scandens* Hooker [syn. *Henfreya scandens* Lindley] is a scandent shrub from Sierra Leone with smooth 5-inch lanceolate leaves. In March it bears handsome, large, white, thimble-shaped flowers.

## *Aphelandra aurantiaca* LINDLEY
*Common Name:* TIGER-PLANT

About 200 species of this herb from tropical America have been described. A few of them are cultivated primarily as glasshouse plants. They have a great tendency to become leggy, with the result that glasshouse operators usually grow them as annuals from seed. This species, often found out-of-doors in warm climates, is a coarse trailer, frequently with quantities of attractive flowers. Bailey (4) says of the tiger-plant: "Grown in hothouses with a fine foliage and very showy four-sided terminal spikes of red or yellow, gaudy-bracted flowers."

## *Crossandra undulaefolia* SALISBURY

This is typical of some 50 species of trailing or scandent shrubs in the genus *Crossandra*, native from India to Madagascar. They are 1 to 3 feet tall and bear brilliant salmon or orange flowers overlapping one another in dense clusters 3 to 5 inches long. *C. undulaefolia* is often seen in Florida gardens, but as a low herb, rarely scandent.

## *Geissomeria schottiana* NEES

This Brazilian vine bears beautiful upright 5-inch racemes of red flowers, somewhat resembling a salvia, writes Harry Blossfeld from São Paulo, but it "is still rare in our gardens." The flowers of all ten evergreen species of *Geissomeria*, which are also found in the Guianas and Jamaica, are red, often velvety, the corolla tube widening into 2 lips. On the smaller *G. coccinea* T. Anders, the one Jamaican species, these are white.

## *Goldfussia iamiifolia* NEES
[Syn. *Strobilanthes lamiifolius* T. Anders]

A small, slender trailer in India that is exceptionally pretty with numerous little pale lilac, thimble-shaped flowers in winter.

## *Meyenia hawtayneana* NEES
[Syn. *Thunbergia hawtayneana* Wallich]

Although this was originally reported from the West Indies, it is called by

1. ADHADOTA CYDONIAEFOLIA

2. ASYSTASIA GANGETICA

3. RUELLIA AFFINIS

4. THUNBERGIA CRISPA

5. THUNBERGIA BATTISCOMBEI

6. THUNBERGIA GRANDIFLORA ALBA

7. THUNBERGIA LAURIFOLIA

8. THUNBERGIA GRANDIFLORA

9. DROSANTHEMUM FLORIBUNDUM (Pink)

10. LAMPRANTHUS SPECIOSUS
(in three shades)

11. CYLINDROPHYLLUM SPECIOSUS (red);
HYMENOCYCLUS LUTEOLUS (yel.);
DROSANTHEMUM HISPIDUM (pink)

12. BAISSEA SP. (Malawi)

13. CARPOBROTUS CHILENSE

14. CYDISTA AEQUINOCTIALIS

Firminger (37) a native of the Nilgherries (India). He described it: "A neat, pretty, climbing plant with slender, threadlike stems and very rigid, heart-shaped 1½-inch leaves, bearing at nearly all seasons large azure-blue flowers with a white tube; succeeds better in the open ground than in a pot."

## Peristrophe speciosa  Nees

This is one of several creeping herbs in this genus that are grown in glasshouses for their showy flowers. In this plant they are bright purple, 2 inches across. Some 30 species have been described, ranging from tropical Africa to Malaya.

## Pseuderanthemum ludovicianum  (Buettn.) Lindau

This weak, scrambling shrub to 12 feet or more makes pure stands in the forests of central Africa from Ghana to Kenya. The white, pale blue, or purplish tubular flowers, 1½ inches long, are borne in 10-inch, spikelike clusters at the branch tips. Irvine (65) calls it a decorative plant. It was cultivated at Kew in 1952.

## Ruellia makoyana  Hort.
Common Name: Trailing Velvet-plant

This Brazilian plant bears bright red or rose-color funnelform flowers 2 inches long. It is a trailing herb with thin, hairy stems to 18 inches or more, suited to basket use. The dark green leaves have silvery veins above and are purple beneath.

Edwin F. Steffek of *Horticulture* wrote: "It is what professional gardeners call a basket plant, but it doesn't hang down. Rather, it billows gracefully over the pot to make a low mound, and is a better shelf than a hanging plant. The leaves have a soft look, almost velvety, with a purple cast beneath, which seems to add sparkle to the 2-inch rosy-red trumpets borne generously in the axils of the new growth for the biggest part of the year."

Another species, perhaps better known in the West Indies than in the United States, *R. affinis* T. Anders is a shrub with flexuous, pendent branches that may be 20 feet long in their native land, Brazil. (Color Plate 3). Scarlet flowers are 3½ inches long, solitary in the leaf axils, the corolla funnel-shaped.

## Thunbergia grandiflora  Roxburgh
Common Names: Sky-flower; Bengal Clockvine

## Thunbergia laurifolia  Lindley
Common Name: Laurel Clockvine

These two magnificent climbers, that rise to 50 feet or more, bearing an abundance of sky-blue flowers, must be numbered among the world's most beautiful. They will quickly cover a trellis or lofty tree with a luxuriant growth of dense foliage that is decorated with hanging ropes of blossoms. The vines can also be made to flower when small by judicious close pruning.

Both the sky-flower and the laurel clockvine are commonly cultivated in California and Florida. Their general aspect is very similar, but they have these distinguishing characters:

12. PYRUS KAWAKAMI   13. CALLIANDRA GUILDINGII

14. CARISSA GRANDIFLORA   15. MALPIGHIA GLABRA

*T. grandiflora* (Color Plate 8). The leaves are dark green, very rough on both surfaces, broadly heart-shaped, usually 4 to 5 inches long by 3 to 4 inches wide, 7-nerved, coarsely toothed, the margins getting more irregular as the leaves get older. The cuplike corolla tube is 2½ inches long; its lower half is whitish, changing to yellow with blue stripes in the throat. This suddenly flares to five sky-blue lobes, the upper two erect, the others spreading. The flowers, usually 3 inches across, may be solitary but are commonly in narrow drooping clusters of 8 or 10. Blooming season in India is March to November, right through the rains. Seed is seldom set.

*T. laurifolia* (Color Plate 7). The leaves of this Burmese species are long and narrow, often to 7 by 2 inches, rounded at the base, 3-nerved, usually smooth but sometimes slightly rough on both surfaces. The flowers are very similar to those of the foregoing, though the corolla tube is more conical at the base, more swollen above, obliquely funnel-shaped, very wide at the mouth. The lobes are sometimes a deeper blue, and the throat is yellowish. Flowers appear in India through the cold season. Seeds are produced abundantly.

Both plants climb by twining their leaves around any available support, as does *Clematis*. Their stems are brittle and hence rather difficult to train. The lovely blue flowers wilt quickly when picked and do not lend themselves to decorative work. Both vines sustain temperatures down to 20 degrees and even when frozen to the ground will send up new shoots to bloom the same year.

A white-flowered form of *T. grandiflora* (Color Plate 6) is occasionally cultivated, but its 5 by 5 inch or larger leaves are coarse and harsh to the touch, rather like those of garden squash. The flowers are pure white, much larger than on the blue vine, often 4 inches across; the mouth of the tube is a dainty yellow.

*T. crispa* J. ANTON-SMITH, which comes from Malawi in Africa, is a purple-flowered species hitherto undescribed (Color Plate 4.)

*T. coccinea* WALLICH, in India, is another tender, wide-spreading climber with thick, heavy leaves, 5 inches long by 3 wide, toothed and palmately 5-nerved, smooth green above and somewhat glaucous beneath. The funnel-shaped flowers, in hanging clusters up to 18 inches long, are orange in the throat, the 5 lobes bright scarlet and flared backwards. Flowers appear from December to March.

Another extensive climber in India is *Thunbergia mysorensis* T. ANDERS (Photograph 16). It too has large flowers, borne in long, hanging, interrupted sprays. The 2-inch purple corolla ends in 4 lobes, one erect and the others reflexed. These lobes are bright yellow, orange, or maroon, spotted with yellow or brown. Holttum (54) called it "a most attractive plant for a large arch or pergola."

This climber is also extensively cultivated in Brazil. Harry Blossfeld, plantsman of São Paulo, writes:

> "*M. mysorensis* is not seen frequently here, because it requires a large space and a very high pergola. When it has both, the plant is in bloom 365 days of the year and curtains of flowers of yellow and fox red hang down thirty feet."

The other *Thunbergia* vines in cultivation are mostly trailers or creepers, found both in warm gardens and in glasshouses.

The black-eyed clockvine (*T. alata* BOJER), sometimes called black-eyed-susan or pullet's-eye (Photograph 17), is a lovely perennial from South Africa that usually is grown as an annual. The soft, dark green leaves of satiny texture are shaped like an arrowhead, 2 inches long by 1 inch wide with 3 sharp points, and the petiole is winged. The vine is usually covered with flowers from June to October; these may be orange, yellow, or white, with maroon or jet-black centers. On banks or trellises the vine has a tendency to grow down unless guided upward.

The white clockvine (*T. fragrans* ROXBURGH), (Photograph 18) is an Indian herbaceous trailer with snow-white flowers about 1½ inches across. It much resembles *T. alata* but differs in these respects: (1) the petiole is shorter than the leaf and is not winged; (2) the tube of the funnel-shaped flower is 1 inch long and slender as a match; the tube of *T. alata* is only ¾ inch long and bigger than a pencil.

*T. fragrans* is common as a trailer or groundcover in California and Florida, and in glasshouses is often grown on a screen. The Latin epithet *fragrans,* meaning fragrant, is misleading as the flowers have no odor. Seeds are freely produced and distributed by birds, with the result that the plant may become a weed.

The orange glory (*T. gibsonii* S. MOORE) in Kenya has a winged petiole on 3½-inch leaves that are covered with harsh hairs. Its plain glowing orange flowers make it "far more beautiful than *T. alata* and less pushing" (67), although in California it is often 7 feet tall and may go to the housetops (69).

*T. gregorii* S. MOORE (Photograph 19), in tropical Africa (67), also has plain orange flowers, but it makes a heavier vine, climbing over trees and shrubs, often to 20 feet—"very striking."

*T. primulina* HEMSLEY has lovely primrose-yellow flowers with violet throats.

*T. affinis* S. MOORE, in Hawaii (84), is a seldom seen scandent shrub to 6 feet tall, similar to the better-known *T. erecta* T. ANDERS, except that the deep violet flowers are twice the size, and the plant often climbs.

*T. battiscombei* TURRILL, native near Lake Victoria, is a low trailing herb bearing 2-inch flowers of blue or pale lilac. (Color Plate 5.)

ACERACEAE—MAPLE FAMILY

## *Acer circinatum* PURSH
*Common Name:* VINE MAPLE

Despite the common name, this California maple is not a climber. Ordinarily a round-headed tree to 40 feet, it intermittently decides to sprawl on the ground, sometimes 20 to 30 feet (91), like a running lasso. In this condition it is occasionally trained on a trellis.

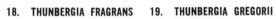

16. THUNBERGIA MYSORENSIS 17. THUNBERGIA ALATA

18. THUNBERGIA FRAGRANS 19. THUNBERGIA GREGORII

## *Actinidia chinensis* PLANCHON
*Common Name:* CHINESE GOOSEBERRY

Although several species of *Actinidia* are in cultivation in the United States, chiefly for their beautiful foliage, *A. chinensis* (Photograph 20) is the only one distinguished for its attractive flowers, and the vine is even more highly prized for its edible fruit. Regrettably, it is very seldom found in the United States. The creamy-white flowers are larger on the male plants than on the female.

## *Clematoclethra integrifolia* MAXIMOWICZ

This is one of a dozen species of these deciduous climbers, mainly from western China, cultivated for their profusely produced white flowers ½ inch across and sometimes for the berries that follow. The flowers, which are fragrant, are occasionally solitary but usually in clusters. The plants may grow to 30 feet or more.

 *C. hemsleyi* BAILLON is a climber to 20 feet with half-inch white flowers in clusters in the leaf axils. Other species cultivated in England are described by Pearce (90). He says:

> "Two species, both natives of China, are useful and of easy culture and thrive in most soils. *C. actinidioides* MAXIMOWICZ is a vigorous grower with rounded leaves and small flowers that are white flushed with pink. *C. scandens* MAXIMOWICZ is also vigorous, and has its young growths covered with bristly hairs. Leaves up to 5 inches long with bristles on the margins and on the veins. The flowers are small, white and produced in clusters from the leaf axils."

This group of climbers is confused in the literature; some authors place it in the Clethraceae, while others put it in Dilleniaceae.

## *Agdestis clematidea* SESSE & MOCINO

This Florida native is an exceptionally handsome vine with its many starlike flowers, but it is rarely grown because the foliage has such an objectionable odor, that it can be used only over outbuildings and similar places. Bailey (4) says:

> "Grows 40 to 50 feet in one season and is covered in September with masses of small white blossoms in dense racemes, very sweet-scented. The red stems come from a tuber which grows half out of the earth, and which is sometimes 100 and 150 pounds in weight. These tubers look like solid rocks. They are of a gray granite color. To do its best, this plant requires very rich soil and an abundance of moisture."

## *Mesembryanthemum*   DILLENIUS EX LINN.

This composite genus has been broken down into more than 100 genera and upwards of 2,000 species. The following are characteristic of the species with elongated, prostrate stems that lend themselves to use as groundcovers, sand binders, and bank climbers. Mostly South African, they are much cultivated in California and other warm climates. A few are hardy enough to grow in England.

The heart-leaved noon-flower or dew-plant (*Aptenia cordifolia* SCHWAN-TES) sends many branches over the ground. This South African succulent bears numerous half-inch purple or pink daisy-like flowers that make a brilliant display in the sun. It is prized in Australia as a sand binder on steep slopes, but it is equally useful in the glasshouse as a basket plant.

The ice-plant (*Cryophytum crystallinum* N. E. BROWN) is a succulent groundcover much cultivated in southern California. The 1-inch flowers are whitish or rose.

The Hottentot-fig (*Carpobrotus edulis* L. BOLUS), which has prostrate woody stems 3 feet or more long, is cultivated in California as both a ground-cover and sand binder. It is useful for carpeting large areas and is frequently beautiful when in bloom. It is characterized by thick, fleshy leaves, 3-inch yellow or rose-purple flowers, and large edible fruits. In California this plant is called *Mesembryanthemum edule*. Hoyt (58) rated this and *Drosanthemum floribundum* SCHWANTES [syn. *M. floribundum* Linn.) as the toughest of these suc-culents grown in California. Next toughest, in resistance to salt spray and wind battering, he placed *Cryophytum crystallinum* [syn. *M. crystallinum* Linn.] and then *Carpobrotus chilensis* N. E. BROWN [syn. *M. chilense Molina*]. (Color Plate 13.)

*Drosanthemum floribundum* (Color Plate 9), with solitary pink flowers is one of 100 species in South Africa. *D. hispidum* SCHWANTES has lavender-pink flowers. (Color Plate 11.) *D. speciosum* SCHWANTES has flowers 2 inches or more across, orange-red with a green base. All these species are trailing suc-culent plants running over the ground.

*Lampranthus spectabilis* N. E. BROWN (Color Plate 10) is an evergreen woody vine from South Africa, prized as a sand binder on embankments, because of the stems that lie flat while the 3-inch flowers of purple, crimson, or white stand erect.

The trailing iceplant (*Hymenocyclus luteolus*) is one of 9 species in South Africa, now usually included in *Malephora*. (Color Plate 11.)

The redspike iceplant (*Cylindrophyllum speciosum* SCHWANTES) is one of 6 species of these prostrate plants in South Africa. (Color Plate 11.)

## *Sericostachys scandens*   GILG & LOPR. EX LOPR.

This is a creeper in the forests of western Kenya and Uganda. It flowers only every 7 or 8 years; then it covers huge trees with the creamy foam of its delightfully

71

scented blossoms. The blooming time is associated with omens and portents, and the young men of some tribes are initiated into manhood when these flowers appear.

AMARYLLIDACEAE—AMARYLLIS FAMILY

## Bomarea caldasiana  HERBERT

Some 120 species of *Bomarea,* with flowers resembling those of the related genus *Alstroemeria* but the plants themselves differing in their climbing habit, are native from Mexico to Chile, but come mostly from the Peruvian Andes. Their great clusters of colorful flowers over a long growing season make them most rewarding glasshouse plants and even outdoors in climates like San Francisco's.

*Bomarea* is astonishing as an Amaryllid that climbs, often to 15 feet or more. It has many twining stems that are clothed with leaves their full length, like bamboo, and these protect the new flowers as they open but never hide them. The bell-like flowers of *B. caldasiana* come in clusters of 5 to 36 at ends of branches, the outer segments of the perianth generally scarlet with yellow, the inner ones yellow, dotted with dull red. There are, however occasional variations in these tones.

*B. kalbreyeri* BAKER (Color Plate 15) grows out-of-doors at Malahide Castle in Dublin, also at Tresco, where it goes underground in winter but climbs its support again the following spring. It bears large rounded clusters of inch-long flowers with 3 outer segments to the corolla brick-red and 3 longer, inner ones orange-yellow spotted with red.

*B. multiflora* MIRBEL (Photograph 21) carries even larger umbels of 1-inch flowers, the outer segments tinged red, the inner ones reddish-yellow spotted with claret-brown within.

In Kenya gardens *B. lehmannii* BAKER has been most successful (67), its deep orange flowers speckled with brown.

Bailey (4) says the most beautiful species are *B. carderi* MASTERS, with 2-inch, rose-colored flowers splotched with purple, and *B. shuttleworthii* MASTERS, with pale yellow flowers spotted green.

This vine climbs by twisting and must have adequate support.

ANONACEAE—ANONA FAMILY

## Artabotrys odoratissimus  R. BROWN
*Common Name:* CLIMBING YLANG-YLANG

This plant, frequently cultivated in Florida, is one of 200 species found from tropical Africa to Indomalaysia, most of them climbers and all of them prized not for the beauty of their flowers but for their intense fragrance. In *A. odoratis-*

*simus* (Photograph 22) the flowers are 6-petaled, a greenish-yellow color with a pleasant fragrance sufficient to perfume a whole garden. The plants have a curious manner of climbing. The flowers develop on a stalk opposite one of the leaves. This stalk curls around any available support, and after the flowers are gone the stalk becomes woody and turns into a hook which holds the vine in place.

Other species are occasionally found in glasshouses, particularly *A. uncinatus* SAFFORD. This plant has creeping branches which can be trained in the manner of a vine. Howard (57) says:

> "The bright green leaves are glossy and attractive, and the flowers and fruit, though not ornamental, are highly and sweetly fragrant. For this reason, the plant is a welcome addition to patios or other restricted areas, where it may be trained on a trellis or allowed to cascade over walls, distributing its fragrance widely. Height, 6 to 10 feet. Evergreen. A fairly dense, woody plant with many wide-spreading branches. The leaves are alternate and untoothed, 5 to 10 inches long, and oblong-lanceolate. They are clear bright green, smooth, and highly polished."

APOCYNACEAE—DOGBANE FAMILY

## *Aganosma marginata*   G. DON

This genus of a dozen species of showy-flowered, shrubby climbers in India and Burma differs only technically from the tropical American vines, *Echites* and *Dipladenia*.

*A. marginata* produces loose terminal clusters of large, white, fragrant blossoms. Although the flowers of most species are white and often large, those of *A. elegans*   G. DON are small and purple; those of *A. caryophyllata*   G. DON are pale yellow tinged with red, and supposed to be clove-accented, hence the specific epithet. Roxburgh described the plant he saw as having a woody stem as thick as a man's thigh, with dark rust-colored bark rough with fissures. Hooker (*Curtis's Bot. Mag.* 1919) said the flowers were "very agreeably fragrant, somewhat aromatic; but in our opinion the scent does not resemble that of cloves."

## *Alafia scandens*   (THONNING) DEWILD

This scandent shrub or lofty woody climber with glossy foliage, common in the Gold Coast, bears white, bell-shaped flowers with pinkish-red centers in January, April, June, and November. These are heavily scented like carnations. Irvine (65) reported it well worth cultivating because of the handsome appearance of the flowers.

## *Allamanda cathartica*   LINN.

The allamanda is the best loved and one of the most widely planted of evergreen flowering plants in warm gardens. It can be shrub or climber, canopy or hedge,

20. **ACTINIDIA CHINENSIS**  21. **BOMAREA MULTIFLORA**

22. **ARTABOTRYS ODORATISSIMUS**  23. **ALYXIA OLIVAEFORMIS**

and its glossy foliage and gorgeous yellow cup-shaped flowers are always on parade, their beauty never dimmed by pests or neglect.

Most of the cultivated forms appear to be varieties of *A. cathartica* (Photograph 27), a Brazilian climbing shrub with 5-parted flowers in small clusters at the branch tips. The golden corolla is 2 inches deep and 3 inches across. This plant has escaped in south Florida and is rarely cultivated. There are too many improved, prettier, larger-flowered forms that are just as easy to grow. The allamandas are all too tender for outdoor culture in California.

Henderson's allamanda (*A. cathartica* LINN. var. *hendersonii* RAFFILL, or *A. hendersonii*) commonly called brown-bud by nurserymen because its 3-inch buds are a rich, bright yellow-brown, is a free-flowering form with thick leathery leaves and flowers 4 to 5 inches across (Photograph 26). This is the largest-flowered allamanda, hence most in demand, but it is tender and if frozen to the ground it usually fails to sprout again. It is often grown as a shrub, but with support it will mount to the housetop.

Williams allamanda (*A. cathartica* LINN. var. *williamsii* RAFFILL) has somewhat smaller leaves not so glossy, and flowers 2 to 3 inches across, yellow, the throat deeper and stained with reddish brown. (Photograph 25) They have a lovely light fragrance; other allamanda flowers have none at all. The Williams allamanda produces twice as many flowers as does Henderson's, albeit they are only half as big. If frozen to the ground, it quickly recovers. Unlike any of the other species, the Williams allamanda has produced a double-flowered form, hose-in-hose, a mutation that appeared in the 1950's in the garden of Mrs. J. M. Stansill of Samoset, Manatee County, Florida. It was first propagated by Miss Paula Dillman of the Oneco Nursery. Ed Brown of Goochland Nurseries, Pembroke, Florida, advertised it in his catalogs in the 1950's and distributed it nationwide. Today it is seldom found although for 10 years it was a great novelty. The inner corolla of the flower often does not unfurl until the second or third day. The plant is not as floriferous as the parent, but it retains the same fine fragrance.

The bush allamanda (*A. neriifolia* HOOKER) is described by Bailey (5) as half-climbing, but in Florida gardens it is nothing but a 4-foot shrub with smaller golden flowers (2 inches long, 1½ inches across the mouth) that are striped orange-brown in the throat. It is the only allamanda that sets seed regularly, in prickly burrlike capsules, a little larger than a golf ball, that turn brown on ripening. They are prized for dried flower arrangements.

The purple allamanda (*A. violacea* GARDNER) is an erect, sometimes scrambling shrub from Brazil, bearing handsome purple flowers 2 inches long, often 3 inches across, usually appearing in pairs (Photograph 24). It is a poor grower on its own roots and for commercial distribution is usually grafted on Henderson roots.

The foregoing are the only allamandas commonly grown in continental United States. In Hawaii sometimes seen is *A. cathartica* var. *schottii* RAFFILL, bearing large yellow flowers with a darker throat that is beautifully striped. Occasionally seen in collections are *A. cathartica* var. *grandiflora* Raffill, of dwarf, compact growth and lemon or primrose-yellow flowers 4 to 4½ inches across; also

75

*A. cathartica* var. *nobilis* Raffill, a pubescent form with purple twigs and bright yellow flowers 4 to 5 inches across, reported by Bailey (4, 5) to have a "magnolia-like odor."

Each variety has its own special leaf shape and color, so nurserymen can distinguish them without seeing the flower. The white spot at the base of the lobes in some flowers is not characteristic of any one kind of allamanda; it is often found on any of them.

All the allamandas are subject to nematode damage to their roots, which explains why they must so frequently be replanted.

The so-called "pink allamanda" is *Mandevilla* (q.v.), also in the dogbone family.

## *Alyxia olivaeformis* GAUDICHAUD-BEAUPRE
[Syn. *Gynopogon olivaeformis* Safford]

This straggling or somewhat twining shrub is one of 50 species, some of which are evergreen trees scattered from the islands of the Pacific through eastern Asia to Madagascar. The salverform yellowish flowers of *Alyxia olivaeformis* (Photograph 23) are very small but the plant is conspicuous because of the intense fragrance of leaves and bark. Bailey (4) says:

> "Interesting tropical woody plants worth cultivating under glass . . . nearly all of which have the agreeable fragrance of coumarin. . . . This [species] is perhaps the most cherished plant of the Hawaiians, who weave its fragrant glossy foliage into garlands, or leis, with which to adorn their friends, and with its branches decorate their houses and lanais on festive occasions; and they also celebrate its fragrance in their songs."

## *Baissea caudiloba* STAPF

This 80-foot woody climber of the Gold Coast produces in February and March pyramidal clusters of white, pinkish, or yellow funnel-shaped flowers. These are ¾ inch long with narrow petals, and they are fragrant. Irvine (65) calls the plant "of distinct decorative value." (Color Plate 12.)

## *Beaumontia grandiflora* (ROXB.) WALL
*Common Names:* EASTER-LILY VINE; HERALD'S TRUMPET; NEPAL TRUMPET

This outstanding large-flowered climber from northern India is one of 8 species cultivated in glasshouses and out-of-doors in warm areas over all the world. (Color Plate 29.) Under favorable conditions it will climb a 50-foot tree and deck the crown with its fragrant white flowers that are 5 to 7 inches long; but with severe pruning the same plant can be bloomed in a glasshouse. While plants have been known to produce 500 of these huge trumpets at once, ordinarily they do not appear in sufficient numbers to make a mass effect.

The flowers come in clusters of 3 to 9, opening first one here, then one there over a long period, often six weeks or more. Nehrling (85) reported that on one occasion a cluster of the blossoms given to him became so overpoweringly

24. ALLAMANDA VIOLACEA     25. ALLAMANDA WILLIAMSII

26. ALLAMANDA HENDERSONII     27. ALLAMANDA CATHARTICA

fragrant that they had to be removed from the house. Both flowers and leaves will stand up briefly in bouquets, but they are somewhat too bold for indoor use.

Some idea of the massiveness of the vine appears when its single stem in a year becomes an inch in diameter, woody with a corky feeling. The first year the new growth of reddish-brown buds will be only new leaves. The same-appearing red-brown growth the second year will be flower buds. The lateral branches clothe themselves with magnificent, heavy, leathery leaves to 10 inches long and 4 inches wide, soon overlapping each other. If the trellis provided for the vine is too small, extensions to a treetop will soon be necessary unless heavy pruning is resorted to. In East Africa (67) the plant is often kept shrublike, but the long curling growths, like small pinkish-green snakes, get to twining in all directions.

Splendid as this vine is, few gardens have it because of difficulties in propagation.

*B. jerdoniana* WIGHT (Photograph 28), known in the Philippines as moon-vine or moonflower, is one of the finest of the genus. Steiner (106) reported that its silvery white blossoms are about 8 inches in diameter with a spicy fragrance "resembling that of a lily." Only strong woody branches will bloom. This species succeeds in northern Malaya, but *B. multiflora* TEIJSMANN & BINNENDIJK flowers more freely in Singapore. Holttum (55) called *B. murtoni* CRAIB, from Thailand, "the finest of them all, but each species seems lovelier than the last." *B. fragrans* PIERRE has sharp-pointed yellow buds that open fully to a pure white cup. This species is native to Vietnam. Herklots (130) says *B. fragrans* (Photograph 29) and *B. grandiflora* are the best known species and adds that *B. fragrans* "grows best in countries in which the climate is tropical all year around—it flowers best after a dry period. I have seen it flourishing in Ghana and in Trinidad." Chittenden (22) says the flowers are white, shallowly bell-shaped, very fragrant. Jex-Blake (67) calls the vine in Ghana "very charming."

## *Carissa grandiflora* DC.
*Common Names:* NATAL PLUM; AMATUNGULA

A spiny African shrub, *Carissa grandiflora* (Photograph 30) is not a vine at all, but by training and pruning it can be compelled to cover a trellis in the vine manner. It is evergreen in warm climates, has pretty, fragrant, white, star-shaped flowers, and bright red plumlike fruits that are edible.

Widespread in East Africa up to elevations of 6,500 feet, *C. edulis* FORSKAL VAHL, when in bloom, much resembles one of the jasmines with its bunches of red buds and small white starlike blossoms. It is a scandent, thorny shrub bearing quantities of fragrant flowers that are followed by edible fruits that can be made into jelly.

## *Chonemorpha macrophylla* G. DON
[Syn. *C. fragrans* (MOON) ALSTON]

Although it starts out as a small scandent shrub, *Chonemorpha* develops into a large and powerful liana in Indian and Malayan forests, climbing to the tops of the tallest trees. (Color Plate 16).

Three species, all much alike (55), are found in Malayan gardens, where they are cultivated for their large, creamy-white, fragrant flowers that are borne profusely in clusters from May through July. The blossoms are about 4 inches across, with a short tube that flares into 5 large petals set obliquely, rather like the blades of a ship's propeller. Bor (9) described the lobes as triangular or trapezoid, from a very narrow base.

The leaves of *Chonemorpha* are exceptionally large, often 15 inches long and up to 10 inches wide, varying from ovate to round. The vines in gardens are so bulky that they must be supported by stout pergolas or trees.

*Chonemorpha* has been in cultivation in south Florida and southern California for 25 years, but its entire career has been a masquerade. Florida nurserymen and gardeners through all the years have been calling it*"Trachelospermum fragrans grandiflorum,"* an invalid name that ties the plant to a garden favorite in the southeast, the star- or Confederate-jasmine (*Trachelospermum jasminoides* LEMAIRE), an evergreen climbing shrub with 2½-inch leaves and clustered white fragrant flowers an inch across. California plantsmen have been more alert, discovering this mix-up in nomenclature a few years ago, so that the plant now is commonly known there under the correct name.

## *Echites coalita*　VELLOZO

Among the 40 species of *Echites* native from Brazil to Florida are many handsome climbing shrubs that are closely allied to *Dipladenia*. Outstanding among them is *E. coalita* from São Paulo, Brazil. It will stand some frost, more than allamanda will; it is a profuse bloomer, the blossoms smaller and a clearer yellow than on allamanda, in bunches, opening one after another, over a period of several months. The plant seems to be insect-free but not too vigorous in growth. The stems become woody and they arise from a sort of tuber which helps the vine withstand drought.

Cultivated in Rio de Janeiro is *E. sulphurea* MUELLER OF AARGAU, with large light yellow flowers, a red tube and rose eye.

*E. andrewsii* CHAPMAN, a native of Florida, has 2-inch, yellow, bell-shaped flowers. The blossoms of *E. stellaris* LINDLEY are rose and yellow, in 10- to 12-flowered clusters.

*E. umbellata* JACQUIN [syn.: *E. echites* (Linn.) Britton] is a vigorous native vine in south Florida and the Keys, rising from a tuberous root, the branches intricately intertwined. (Photograph 31.) The 2-inch salverform flower is white or greenish-white. It is commonly called devil's-potato although sometimes misnamed rubber-vine, which confuses it with *Cryptostegia*.

*E. tomentosa* VAHL has been introduced into California where it is sometimes called Trinidad Savannah-flower.

## *Forsteronia corymbosa*　G. F. W. MEYER

Of the 30 species of this climber in the West Indies and tropical America, most have inconspicuous white flowers. However, this species introduced to Florida by the United States Department of Agriculture (Plant Introduction No. 145860)

28. BEAUMONTIA JERDONIANA    29. BEAUMONTIA FRAGRANS

30. CARISSA GRANDIFLORA    31. ECHITES UMBELLATA

in 1943 proved to be an excellent garden ornament. It continuously produces ample clusters of small, bright lipstick-red flowers that are accented often by yellow stamens, and as it is of slender growth, it makes a fine climber in a limited space. The plant requires full sun and is hardy only to 27°Fahrenheit.

## Ichnocarpus frutescens AITON

This woody climber, native from southeast Asia to Australia, bears compound clusters of tiny cream-colored flowers. The Philippine species, *I. volubilis* MERRILL, has small white fragrant flowers. Both plants are prized commercially for the fibre in their stems, which is used to make rope. The genus is closely allied to *Aganosma,* but the flowers are not so pretty.

## Landolphia florida BENTHAM
[Syn. *L. comorensis* (Bojer) K. Schumann var *florida* (Bentham), K. Schumann]

Some 36 species of evergreen climbing shrubs in tropical Africa, include several that are prized as a source of rubber. All of them have glossy dark green leaves and rather large flowers, the funnel-shaped corollas white or yellowish with narrow contorted lobes. Jex-Blake (67) calls the native East African *L. florida* highly ornamental, clambering over the trees in the river gorges and making a beautiful showing with its large clusters of fragrant flowers.

There are borne at the branch tips, the densely hairy corolla tube about 1 inch long and stained orange toward the center. The blooming season is March to May and again October to December. The 4-inch yellow fruit is edible.

*Landolphia capensis* OLIVER (Photograph 32) is another of the 60 or more species known in Africa.

## Mandevilla splendens (HOOKER) WOODSON
[Syn.: *Dipladenia splendens* WOODSON]
*Common Name:* PINK ALLAMANDA (erroneous)

This Brazilian climber is one of several species in cultivation in glasshouses and warm gardens and one of 50 kinds scattered from Mexico to Argentina. *Mandevilla splendens* (Color Plate 19) is easily distinguished by its flowers growing larger from day to day and changing color. Its opposite leaves of dark lustrous green with sunken veins are oblong-elliptic, 3 to 8 inches long and 2 to 4 inches broad.

Clusters of as many as 20 flowers hang from the leaf-axils with 1 to 4 blossoms open at a time. Huttleston (64) wrote:

> "When each funnel-shaped flower opens it is about 2.5 inches in diameter and is dawn pink (RHS Horticultural Color Chart 523/3 with a flush of rose madder (23/3) and a darker (23/1) throat. During the three or four days that a flower lasts, it expands and darkens, reaching a diameter of 4 inches and becoming a dark rose madder (23/1). A plant bearing numerous inflorescences is a striking sight, and its long flowering season, from April through November, makes it a very desirable greenhouse plant."

81

*N.M. bolivensis* (HOOKER F.) (WOODSON) (Color Plate 18) is a Bolivian climber that was formerly called *Dipladenia bolivensis.* It resembles *Odontadenia* (q.v.) in many ways, but differs from it in having smaller flowers, only 2 or 4 together, the corolla white with a yellow throat, and smaller leaves, to 3½ inches long. The half-inch tube is thin and cylindrical, the 1-inch throat is half again as large, also cylindrical. Then the outspread flower is only 1½ inches across.

The savannah-flower *M. hirsuta* MALMA, has funnel-shaped, 2-inch yellow flowers with a red center. In Trinidad it is a rambling, native, very hairy vine, seen commonly by the roadsides in poor soil. The blossoms are borne several together on 2-inch stalks.

The Chilean jasmine *M. suaveolens* LINDLEY, [syn. *M. laxa* Woodson; *Echites laxa* Ruiz & Pavon] from Argentina (not Chile!), is less rampant than some of its relatives and is more widely grown in glasshouses and warm gardens. The pure white, fragrant, trumpet-shaped flowers with 5 broad rounded lobes, are 2 inches across and borne in clusters (Color Plate 17). Occasionally they have a pinkish tinge.

The stalked, soft leaves are obovate with a heart-shaped base, about 2 to 3½ inches long, smooth and grayish beneath. The vine is deciduous and even during the growing season the foliage often looks shabby rather than vigorous. Its quick growth requires attention to keep it from climbing over other plants.

All *Mandevilla* plants are easy to propagate from cuttings but difficult to transplant because of their tuberous roots. Blossfeld (8) wrote:

> "They are native here (southern Brazil) but hard to get because they have tuberous roots and lie a yard deep in the soil. You just cannot dig them out, and if one just bruises the thin root, the climber will not stand transplanting."

## *Melodinus monogynus* ROXBURGH

This *Melodinus* (Photograph 35) is one of 30 species in Indo-Malaysia, all of them climbing, woody shrubs with white, starlike, usually fragrant flowers in short clusters. The corolla is a cylindrical tube topped with 5 sickle-shaped, oblique, spreading lobes, and a coronet in the throat of 5 to 10 small erect scales that are sometimes united. The fruit is a round berry 3 inches in diameter, yellow or orange.

Bor (9) reported that this large climber with milky juice in the stems and bright, dark green, lanceolate leaves is well suited to growing over arches or on pergolas, and added: "The pure white very fragrant flowers are produced in spring and make this plant very ornamental."

## *Odontadenia grandiflora* MIQUEL

Among the most beautiful of scandent shrubs in the tropics is this smooth evergreen from Trinidad, powerful enough to climb the jungle's tallest tree but susceptible to training in the glasshouse or on a warm garden trellis.

The simple, opposite, glossy leaves of *Odontadenia grandiflora* (Color Plate

20) have wavy margins and are up to 12 inches long by 5½ inches broad. The delicately fragrant, velvety flowers are bell-shaped, 2 inches long and 3 across, with 5 apricot-colored lobes, the tube lined with scarlet. On some plants the flowers are yellow on the outside, shading to orange in the throat. They grow in loose, often large clusters, frequently produced. Holttum (55) called this "one of the finest woody climbers to grow in Malaya." It is cultivated also in east and South Africa, Ceylon, Hawaii, and many glasshouses.

Writing from Kew, England, G. A. C. Herklots said: *"Odontadenia* is distinguished by the perfection of the flower shape and coloring and the exquisite fragrance."

*O. nitida* MUELLER OF AARGAU, also from South America, is occasionally cultivated. The flowers, 1½ inches across, nodding in clusters, are pale yellow with a band of vermilion below the middle of the narrow tube.

About 20 species of *Odontadenia* have been described. They are closely allied to *Mandevilla* (q.v.).

## *Oncinotis glabrata*　(BAILLON) STAPF EX HIERN

This climbing shrub, native from Liberia to the Cameroons, in April bears fragrant, yellowish-white flowers that are brighter yellow within, in laxly-flowered clusters. Irvine (65) called it a plant of "distinct decorative value." Irvine described two other species that he called "decorative climbers": *O. gracillis* STAPF, a climbing shrub with small, fragrant, greenish-golden blossoms, and *O. nitida* BENTHAM, a woody climber from Ghana with clusters of heavily scented yellow flowers on which the petals recurve.

## *Parsonsia corymbosa*　R. BROWN

*Parsonsia corymbosa* stands out as a beautiful twiner. Firminger (37) called it "a very ornamental, scandent shrub, about 4 feet high, with slender stems requiring the support of a trellis and with rich, dark green foliage of oval, smooth, (opposite), rigid leaves, 1 to 2 inches long; bears during all the season, beautiful closely-crowded corymbs of very small, bright crimson flowers:" The funnel-shaped corolla has 5 lobes that are bent back.

*P. heterophylla* A. CUNNINGHAM [syn. *P. albiflora* Raoul], of New Zealand is a small ornamental climber with small, sweetly scented white flowers. About 100 species of *Parsonsia* have been described from South China, Indo-Malaysia and southward through Australia and Polynesia.

## *Pentalinon suberectum*　VOIGHT
[Syn. *Halmadictyon suberectum*　G. Don]
*Common Names:* DEADLY POISON-PLANT; SAVANNA-FLOWER

The Savanna-flower from the Burma border of India is a heavy climbing shrub requiring substantial support. Through the hot season it continuously bears large showy, yellow, flowers very much like those of allamanda. Sir Joseph Paxton, distinguished English horticulturist, wrote that in its native land, "whilst other vegetation is perishing from drought, this preserves the beautiful verdure of its leaves, and even continues to flower with the greatest vigor." The vine is not native to Jamaica, as reported by Firminger (37).

## *Prestonia contorta* (MARTIUS & GALEOTTI) HEMSLEY

This is typical of 5 species of *Prestonia* that are scandent shrubs in Mexico. It produces dense clusters of red salverform flowers which individually are only 1 inch long, the 5 broad lobes all twisted to the right.

## *Rhabdadenia biflora* (JACQUIN) MUELLER OF AARGAU
Common Name: RUBBER-VINE

Mexico, the West Indies, and the coastal hammocks of lower Florida are the native habitat of this far-climbing vine. It is rarely found in gardens, and the name rubber-vine is confusing because this is applied to other plants as well. *Rhabdadenia* has 4-inch oblong leaves. The 3-inch trumpet-shaped flowers, white with a yellow tube, the lobes an inch or more wide, are in few-flowered clusters. A smaller plant (*R. corallicola* SMALL) with yellow flowers an inch long is found in pinelands and Everglades of south Florida and the Keys. It is more shrub than vine.

## *Rhynchodia wallichii* HOOKER F.

T. K. BOSE

This beautiful evergreen climber grows very well in the moist and tropical part of India. The leaves of *R. wallichii* (Photograph 37) are elliptic-lanceolate, acuminate, green, glabrous, and opposite, and they alternate in pairs at right-angles. The flowers are very showy, axillary or terminal, and arise even on a newly developed shoot; the whole plant looks as if covered with large sprays of flowers. Each cluster contains 4 to 8 flowers about 1 to 1½ inches across. The petals are white on the outer portion, the center deep red.

This heavy climber grows well on trees, pergolas and high walls and serves the purpose of screening in addition to its colorful display of flowers in the summer months. It also responds well to pruning and can be kept under control.

## *Streptothachelus poinglei* GREENMAN

This large woody vine from the mountains of Mexico at Cuernavaca produces greenish-yellow or purplish salverform flowers about 1 inch long, the tubes twisted.

## *Strophanthus gratus* (HOOKER) FRANCHET
[Syn. *Roupellia grata* Hooker]

This plant from tropical Africa is a vigorous scandent shrub with shiny dark green leaves, dark crimson, waxy flower buds, and close clusters of large, attractive, fragrant pink flowers (Color Plate 23.) Holttum (54) reported that in sunny places in Singapore it flowers fairly freely and continuously.

32. LANDOLPHIA CAPENSIS    33. STROPHANTHUS PREUSSII

34. STROPHANTHUS DICHOTOMUS    35. MELODINUS MONOGYNUS

The plant is a robust evergreen, shrublike or climbing to the tops of forest trees. Dalziel declared it "a beautiful climber with shining foliage and clusters of rose-pink flowers, occasionally white or pink-tinged, sweetly scented in the evening." Bor (9) admired the large, leathery, bell-shaped flowers, white tinged with rose purple, "attractive just as they are expanding" (37). The significance of those final 6 words is apparent from Firminger's further observation that the flowers are "not very agreeable on near inspection when fully opened." In fact, Sir Joseph Paxton, distinguished English horticulturist, took one look at greenhouse-grown blossoms and exclaimed: "It is difficult to imagine a flower with a more uninviting appearance."

Among the 60 species of *Strophanthus* (Color Plate 26) grown experimentally by the United States Department of Agriculture for their medicinal potential, the only one which stood out as a promising ornamental was *S. preussii* ENGLER & PAX, EX PAX. (Photograph 33.) This is a sprawling, viney shrub on which the tips of the 5 flower petals stream down a foot or more, like a beard, and persist for a long time. The flowers, borne in clusters, are white at time of opening, but they turn yellow with age. The throat of each blossom bears reddish-brown stripes, and this color is repeated in the hanging streamers.

Another species of *Strophanthus* that offers promise is *S. dichotomus* DC. (Photograph 34.) T. K. Bose of Calcutta writes:

> "*S. dichotomus* is a large straggling shrub or climber. The stem and branches are woody. The evergreen leaves are opposite, decussate, ovate-elliptic, 2 to 3 inches long, 1 to 2 inches wide, glabrous; the midrib and veins are whitish. The flowers are in terminal clusters of 6 to 20 flowers in each. The flowers are peculiar because the lower half of each petal is about 1 inch long, funnel shaped, purplish white; the upper part of each lobe of the petal develops into a narrow twisted appendage, deep purple in colour, 3 inches long."

## *Temnadenia violacea* (VELLOZO) MIERS
[Syn. *Echites violacea* Vellozo]
*Common Name:* SAO FRANCISCO

Blossfeld (8) reported from Brazil that this vine grows abundantly in the valley of the São Francisco river where the residents use the kapok-like fibre from the seed capsules to stuff their pillows. It is a pubescent plant with reddish stems and leaves that are velvety on both sides. It produces clusters of funnel-shaped flowers in the leaf-axils; they are violet on the outside and yellow in the throat.

## *Thenardia floribunda* HBK.

*Thenardia* is a large vine in Mexico with thin, narrow leaves 2 to 6 inches long. The half-inch corolla of the greenish-white, pink, or purplish flowers of *T. floribunda* (Photograph 36) has 5 lobes that are twisted to the right. While these blossoms are tiny, they are produced in many-flowered clusters 3 to 5 inches across. Hoyt (8) reports that in California the plant makes a satisfactory ground-cover and that the light purplish flowers have the fragrance of ripe apples.

## Trachelospermum jasminoides LAMARCK
[Syn. *Rhynchospermum jasminoides* Lindley]
Common Name: CONFEDERATE-JASMINE

This seems to be the favorite of the several species of *Trachelospermum* that are prized for the delicious fragrance of their flowers. They are of course no kin to the true jasmine (*Jasminum*); their white blossoms are somewhat similar except that those of *Trachelospermum* twist to one side, which never happens on *Jasminum*.

The Confederate-jasmine (Photograph 7, 38) is named for the Federation of Malay States where it is native. In foliage and growth habit the vine much resembles *Alyxia* (q.v.) which is favored by Hawaiians for the vanilla-scented leaves and bark.

The leathery, glossy, dark evergreen leaves of the Confederate-jasmine, an inch wide and 2½ inches long, make a handsome background for the quantities of star-shaped, 1-inch, pure white flowers that come in April and May. These are borne in clusters that extend beyond the foliage, the individual blossoms opening in succession over a long period. The 5 lobes of each flower are oblique, spreading, waved, and are distinguished by their margins being rolled back along the edges. The calyx lobes also are turned back.

The vine is often planted to climb over pergolas and arches. It grows slowly at first, throwing up thin, whiplike stems that ascend by weaving in and out of any support they find, preferably a wire net. The plant starts to bloom when only 2 feet high, and if well tended, will continue to display its wares for many years. It sustains temperatures down to 24 degrees Fahrenheit and appears to be hardy throughout the South and in protected places as far as Washington, D. C.

*T. fragrans* HOOKER F., native of China and Japan but much cultivated in India and elsewhere, has much larger leaves, up to 6 inches long by 2 inches wide, and it bears quantities of fragrant white flowers like the other except that the edges of the petals do not reflex backward. They overlap to the right but twist to the left. The vine is most frequently used as a covering for an embankment and it prefers moist, shady places. The blooming season is later than that of the Confederate-jasmine, running into the summer.

*T. asiaticum* (SIEBOLD & ZUCCARINI) NAKAL, from Japan and Korea, is a similar climber except that it grows faster. The calyx lobes are erect, the leaves are shorter, broader, and blunt at the tip, and the yellowish-white flowers have protruding stamens.

*T. difforme* (WALTER) GRAY, native of the southern United States from Texas to Delaware, is a slender climber with small, greenish-yellow flowers that are striped orange-red within. (113)

36.  THENARDIA FLORIBUNDA

37.  RHYNCHODIA WALLICHII

38.  TRACHELOSPERMUM JASMINOIDES

39.  URECHITES LUTEA

## *Urechites lutea* (LINN.) BRITTON
[Syn. *Echites andrewsii* Chapman]

*Common Names:* WILD-ALLAMANDA; HAMMOCK VIPERTAIL

This high-climbing pretty vine of the woods in south Florida and the Keys has small bright green leaves, 1½ to 2 inches long that are typically slightly hairy. The vine of *U. lutea* (Photograph 39) produces quantities of bright yellow campanulate flowers about an inch wide. It is almost never found in cultivation, as it does best in wet ground.

Standley (104) described 2 species of *Urechites* in Central America, both of them scandent shrubs with large white flowers, 2 inches or more long, in clusters. The flower buds and tender young shoots of *U. karwinskii* MUELLER OF AARGAU are used as vegetables in Guatemala and Salvador.

## *Vallaris heynei* SPRENGEL
[Syn. *V. dichotoma* Wallich]

This Burmese evergreen climbing shrub is sparingly cultivated in south Florida and in English glasshouses. *V. heynei* (Photograph 41) is a heavy, high-climbing woody vine, with pale bark and dark green, prominently veined, 4-inch leaves. It bears clusters of small, fragrant, cup-shaped, creamy-white flowers with 5 lobes about 2/3 inch in diameter.

## *Vinca minor* LINN.

*Common Names:* PERIWINKLE; RUNNING-MYRTLE; BLUE-MYRTLE; TRAILING-MYRTLE

This vigorous, widespread, evergreen creeper from Europe with oblong leaves and erect, blue, half-inch funnelform flowers makes a good groundcover in shady places, is used in baskets, and will hang or trail to great lengths. If neglected it may become a weed. Bailey (4) says that *Vinca minor* (Photograph 40) is a "hardy, trailing plant with shining evergreen foliage . . . It forms a dense carpet to the exclusion of other herbs . . . It is a capital plant for clothing steep banks, covering rocks, and carpeting groves."

Among the several other useful species is *V. major* LINN., which is somewhat larger and more tender than the common periwinkle. A variety with ivory markings on the leaves is frequently seen hanging from boxes and baskets.

## ARACEAE—AROID FAMILY

## *Anthurium andreanum* LIND.

Most of the 2,000 kinds of aroids have inconsequential flowers, but many are utilized ornamentally for their bold and handsome foliage. (*See* Chapter X, Part 9.) An outstanding exception is *Anthurium andreanum* from Colombia, which makes a stunning floral display. It is a low plant with erect stems to 2 feet, a

40. VINCA MINOR 41. VALLARIS HEYNEI

42. ARISTOLOCHIA BRASILIENSIS 43. ARISTOLOCHIA GALEATA

creeper at heart, but it lends itself to pot culture under glass and in borders in warm areas. The arrow-pointed spathes, 4 to 6 inches long, highly glossed, range from metallic dark red through orange, pink, and even white. (Color Plate 37.)

ARISTOLOCHIACEAE—BIRTHWORT FAMILY

## *Aristolochia elegans* MASTERS
*Common Name:* CALICO-FLOWER

BIRTHWORT is the common name for the genus *Aristolochia,* comprising 300 perennial herbs and shrubs, mostly climbers with astonishingly ugly flowers that often stink. These blossoms, resembling a crumpled ice cream cone, range in length from 1 inch to 3 feet. They have no corolla (no petals, that is)—just a twisted calyx that flares funnel-like, and its exposed interior is usually a livid purple or greenish brown on a cream background.

The calico-flower (*A. elegans*) (Photograph 45) is the least offensive of the genus. It is a graceful, slender, twining climber from Brazil with 3-inch, heart-shaped leaves, and in warm areas it blooms freely all summer. The long-stalked, solitary blossoms have a short tube, about 1½ inches, and a kidney-shaped limb (mouth) 3 inches across, white with purple veining outside and purple-brown inside. It lacks the unpleasant odor of most birthworts.

The swan-flower or pelican-flower (*A. grandiflora* SWARTZ), from the Antilles, is at the other extreme. (Photograph 44.) The blossom mouth becomes a foot long and 8 inches wide. The lips are mottled deep maroon over a cream base. A variety (var. *sturtevantii* W. WATSON) produces tremendous buds 20 inches long with a 3-foot tail. Dr. Konrad Guenther in *A Naturalist in Brazil* says that the flower is the color of "bloody flesh." It has a repulsive odor the first day it opens, and it attracts numerous flies that get trapped inside. After that the odor disappears.

The Dutchman's-pipe (*A. durior* HILL), a woody vine to 30 feet, is sometimes grown as porch shade. It is native from Kansas to Pennsylvania and south to Georgia.

The rooster-flower (*A. galeata* MARTIUS & ZUCCARINI) from Brazil is grown out-of-doors in Florida. (Photograph 43.) It has a 2-lobed mouth, the upper lip 3 inches long, clawed, and the lower lip 5 inches long. The unpleasant odor is not overpowering.

*A. brasiliensis* SIEBOLD & ZUCCARINI (Photograph 42) is one of the oddest of all, the large lips and the tube of its flower, especially on the variety *macrophylla* DUCH., giving aspects of various birds, all in shades and mottlings of purple.

Birthwort vines rarely succeed in pots, but if planted in the ground are useful in glasshouses where the astonishing flowers attract much attention. For this purpose Hottes (56) suggests: *A. cymbifera* MARTIUS & ZUCCARINI, on which the flower is boat-shaped; *A. ornithocephala* HOOKER, the bird's head flower;

44. **ARISTOLOCHIA GRANDIFLORA**     45. **ARISTOLOCHIA ELEGANS VAR.**

46. **ARAUJIA SERICOFERA**     47. **DREGEA SINENSIS**

*A. tricaudata* LEMAIRE, the flower of which is 3-tailed; and *A. ridicula* N. E. BROWN, which has blossoms with 2 long lobes like donkey ears.

ASCLEPIADACEAE—MILKWEED FAMIILY

## *Araujia sericofera*  BROTERO

*Common Names:* WHITE BLADDER-FLOWER; MOTH-PLANT; CRUEL-PLANT; KAPOK-PLANT

This evergreen climber from South America, hardiest of a dozen species, thrives out-of-doors in the southern states and in warmer parts of England. Its strongly twining urge produces twisted ropes of its own stems. The white or pale-pink, 1-inch, bell-shaped flowers, according to Bailey (5), are not scented, but this is contradicted by most observers (22, 67, 76, 78). The blossoms of *A. sericofera* are in groups of 2 or 3 at every node; these mature at different times, which prolongs the blooming period. Katherine Jones (68) found the flowers so exquisitely formed architecturally, she wondered "why they have not found their way into artistic stone work or other arts." (Photograph 46.)

The corolla tube is inflated at the base, the 5 lobes overlapping in bud, a crown with 5 scales attached at the middle of the tube. The waxy pollen catches moths at night when their proboses get stuck in it. Most of them die but some are released when the morning sunshine softens the wax. The plant does not digest the moths. *Araujia* is less frequently planted now in the United States than formerly, perhaps because the bruised leaves are malodorous.

## *Ceropegia succulenta*  E. A. BRUCE

*Ceropegia* comprises 100 species of African and Asian creepers usually found in glasshouses, with twining succulent stems and small milkweed flowers. Hottes (56) explains that the flowers of *Ceropegia* are a combination of two kinds of traps; a spring trap such as in other asclepiads, and a cage trap, such as occurs in *Aristolochia,* constructed on the same principle as an ordinary mouse trap with inwardly pointing elastic wires.

## *Cryptostegia grandiflora*  R. BROWN

*Common Names:* PALAY RUBBER-VINE; INDIA RUBBER-VINE

## *Cryptostegia madagascariensis*  BOJER

*Common Names:* MADAGASCAR RUBBER-VINE; LOMBIRA RUBBER-VINE

These 2 woody climbers are so much alike and so much confused that some unemployed botanist should combine them into one species. They are grown as ornamentals, without distinction, in tropical gardens all over the world, for their leathery, dark glossy-green 3 to 4-inch leaves and bright handsome flowers above the foliage.

The twisted buds in forked clusters open to 3-inch purple or reddish-purple, funnel-shaped flowers (much like those of allamanda). The color of the flowers on both species of Cryptostegia changes with age and exposure to the sun, from purple to reddish-purple and lavender. (Color Plate 27.) A white form is known. (Color Plate 28.) The seed pods of the climbers are identical, 4 inches long, like a 3-sided cigar ending in a sharp tip, in widely divergent pairs like the horns of a Texas steer.

Usually the rubber-vines are cultivated as shrubs, but their scandent urge carries their twining stems up and over every possible nearby support. The technical distinctions between the two vines are these:

(1) The Madagascar vine has purple flowers, the calyx is only ¼ inch long, and the scales of the crown are not divided.

(2) The Palay rubber-vine has slightly larger and paler flowers, the calyx is ½ inch long, and the scales of the crown are deeply divided. Incidentally, this climber is a native of Africa but is called "Indian" because it has been cultivated in that country for a fibre derived from the stems, also for the heavy latex from which a kind of rubber is made. This latex is poisonous to livestock.

Uninformed gardeners sometimes call these rubber vines "purple allamanda."

## *Dictyanthus pavonii* DECAISNE

This is probably the showiest in flower of all 6 species of *Dictyanthus* described by Standley (102), although the flowers on all of them are large. The others are less conspicuous because of their brownish or purplish cast. This scandent shrub, native from Sinaloa to Jalisco (Mexico), with 5-inch leaves, bears usually just a few clusters of flowers. The corolla is white, 3 inches across and broadly campanulate, with brown-purple veins marking the lobes.

## *Dregea sinensis* HEMSLEY
[Syn. *Wattakaka sinensis* Stapf]

This is one of a dozen climbing shrubs found from tropical Africa to China, allied to *Marsdenia,* and cultivated much like *Hoya.* This Chinese species, *D. sinensis* (Photograph 47), is cultivated in New Zealand and against warm walls in England. The flowers come 10 to 25 in long-stalked, downy clusters 2 to 3 inches across; the 5-lobed corolla is ½ inch wide, the lobes white, dotted with red.

Pearce (90) wrote:

> "This twining shrub is hardy when grown against a wall. It will climb to 10 feet or more when growing well, and produce its sweetly scented flowers in axillary umbels 2 to 3 inches across, during June and July. They are creamy-white spotted with pinkish-red."

*D. abyssinica* (HOCHSTETTER) K. SCHUMANN is a "pretty shrub, or more or less woody climber," as reported by Irvine (65). It bears whitish fragrant flowers, 1/3 inch across, in big clusters, in tropical Africa between Ghana and Rhodesia. Another species, *D. crinita* (OLIVER) BULLOCK, is a stout climber with fragrant white flowers in April and October, from Sierra Leon to Angola.

48. FUNASTRUM CLAUSUM 49. STEPHANOTIS FLORIBUNDA

50. TELOSMA CORDATA 51. ADENOCALYMMA PAULISTARUM

## *Funastrum clausum* (JACQUIN) SCHLECTENDAHL

This native Florida evergreen vine, *Funastrum clausum* (Photograph 48), has small white star flowers. It is found in coastal hammocks in the lake regions all over the peninsula, and in the Keys. It is one of about a dozen species of this milkweed scattered through tropical America. Standley (102) describes this and other species from South America northward to Florida and westward to Texas and California. Most of them are scandent; some are herbaceous, while some have woody stems and may be bushy. Their flowers, mostly white, are occasionally in large clusters. The corolla's 5 lobes are usually twisted. *F. crispum* (BENTHAM) SCHLECHTER has yellow-purple flowers. In Salvador the tough stems of *F. cumanense* (HBK) SCHLECHTER are used by fishermen as cords on which to string fish. Most of the flowers are small but those of *F. pannosum* (DECAISNE) SCHLECHTER. are up to an inch across in many-flowered clusters. In *F. bicolor* (DECAISNE) STANDLEY the flowers are greenish-yellow and brownish-purple.

## *Gonolobus edulis* HEMSLEY
*Common Name:* GUAYOTE

This genus comprises some 200 species of trailing or climbing plants, herbaceous or woody, of North and South America, chiefly tropical. The flowers are mostly dull or dark-colored, medium to large in size, and in clusters.

This particular species appears to be the only one of horticultural interest. It is cultivated in Guatemala and Costa Rica. The white corolla is of medium size, densely hairy inside. Bailey (4) reports it hardy in Santa Barbara, California, where it blooms profusely but sets no fruit. Standley (102) describes 40 species of *Gonolobus* in Mexico under the generic name *Vincetoxicum*. Some of these have flowers 2 inches or more across. He reports that the young fruits are eaten either raw or cooked and that sweetmeats are sometimes made by boiling them in syrup.

## *Gymnema geminatum* R. BROWN
[Syn. *G. sylvestre* R. Brown]

About 40 species of *Gymnema* have been described from West Africa to Australia, and Hundley (60) found 9 species in Burma. *G. geminatum,* which is often cultivated, is a Queensland climber to 15 feet. It bears clusters of white flowers in the leaf-axils.

## *Holostemma rheedii* WALLICH

Firminger (37) reported that this climbing shrub in India, with large, heart-shaped leaves 5 to 6 inches long, bears during the rains heavy clusters of large, thick, fleshy, 5-lobed flowers of a beautiful color mixture of green and white. Lindley & Moore (75) reported that the twiner has "largish flowers, deeply colored inside" in clusters.

15. BOMAREA CALBREYERI

16. CHONEMORPHA MACROPHYLLA

17. MANDEVILLA SUAVEOLENS

18. MANDEVILLA SP. (Ecuador)

19. MANDEVILLA SPLENDENS

20. ODONTADENIA SPECIOSA

21. MANDEVILLA X ALICE DU PONT

22. HOYA CARNOSA VARIEGATA

23. STROPHANTHUS GRATUS

24. HOYA X SILVER STREAK

25. HOYA BELLA

26. STROPHANTHUS LUTEOLUS

27. CRYPTOSTEGIA GRANDIFLORA

28. CRYPTOSTEGIA GRANDIFLORA ALBA

## *Hoya carnosa* R. BROWN
*Common Name:* WAX-PLANT

An unspectacular climber that nevertheless is highly prized in glasshouses and out-of-doors in warm areas is this wax-plant from Australia. (Color Plate 22.) Not only does it bear hanging symmetrical clusters of waxy, star-shaped, fragrant, white flowers, tinged pink in the center, but it does this so delicately that the result looks like porcelain instead of blossoms. The individual flowers are ½ inch in diameter, and the center is a convex, 5-pointed star.

The climber is slow growing, less rampant than many tropicals, and it needs the shade of a tree trunk or something similar for most successful cultivation. The succulent, oval, shining leaves, 2 to 4 inches long, hang a long time on the thin stems.

The flowers probably make their most startling display when hanging from the rafters of a glasshouse, but, as they exude a honeylike liquid, they often drip on spectators.

More than 100 species of *Hoya* have been described from Australia, Malaysia, and India, and a good many are in occasional cultivation, including a host of cultivars. (Color Plate 24). Most frequently seen are *H. australis* R. BROWN white flowers tinged with pink, and *H. bella* HOOKER (Color Plate 25) pure white flowers, the crown segments purple and boat-shaped.

## *Leptadenia reticulata* WIGHT & ARNOTT

This diffuse, much-branched, robust climber in India is common in hedges, in shrubberies of gardens, also around telephone poles and wires. It has rough leaves and produces many-flowered clusters of pale yellow blossoms. Seed pods are usually solitary straight, hard, almost woody, and smooth, with a thick curved beak.

## *Macroscepsis obovata* HBK.

This shrub with scandent stems in eastern Mexico, with deeply cordate leaves 3 to 7 inches long, bears short-salverform white flowers an inch or more across in few-flowered clusters.

## *Marsdenia erecta* R. BROWN

Bean (6) says this is a "deciduous twining climber to 20 feet whose stems and leaves exude a poisonous milky juice when cut. . . . The flowers are white, fragrant, 1 to 3 inches wide, borne numerously in terminal clusters."

This plant from Asia Minor is one of probably 30 species of climbers in the genus *Marsdenia,* some of which have unattractive purplish or pale pink flowers, quite different from the beautiful *Stephanotis* to which it is related. *M. imthurnii* is a twining species in British Guiana with flowers 1½ to 2 inches wide. This and another twiner, *M. flavescens,* are described in *Botanical Magazine* plates 3289 and 7953.

## *Metastelma bahamense* GRISEBACH

*Common Name:* BAHAMAN MILKWEED

This slender vine of south Florida sand dunes, with small whitish flowers often makes copious growth over other plants.

Standley (102) describes 14 species in Mexico. They are slender herbaceous vines, occasionally bushy, with small leaves and very small flowers. Some of the flowers are sweet scented and are prized locally for this feature.

## *Oxypetalum caeruleum* DECAISNE

[Syn. *Tweedia caerulea* G. Don]

This tender, weakly twining perennial from Brazil is usually treated as an annual in glasshouses, where it quickly produces its pretty sky-blue star flowers that darken with age. It is one of 125 species of herbs or subshrubs of this milkweed genus in northern South America.

## *Oxystelma esculentum* R. BROWN

*Oxystelma* is a semi-aquatic herbaceous creeper with narrow leaves and rather large cup-shaped, purplish flowers that are veined pink. The 5-lobed corolla is rotate. Lindley (75) expressed doubt that the plant, native of Malabar, is actually eaten by the people there, despite the specific epithet.*

Chittenden (22) says the flowers are white with rose tinge, large, the corolla fringed with hairs. The flowers are usually in clusters. Macmillan (78) calls this an ornamental climber with cream and pink flowers.

## *Parquetina nigrescens* (AFZELIUS) BULLOCK

"The plant has distinct decorative possibilities," wrote Irvine (65) of this slender, glabrous, twining shrub that may climb to the tops of forest trees. The flowers which come in April and May in clusters in the leaf-axils, are pinkish in bud, cream-colored outside and reddish-black to chocolate-colored within, the corolla rotate, with triangular, reflexed lobes.

## *Periploca linearifolia* DILLON & A. RICHARD

In Kenya this is a climber to the tops of the tallest trees. It is held sacred by many tribes. The Wakamba feed the latex from its roots to cows to increase their milk production. Flowers have 5 fuzzy white petals and give off an unpleasant smell.

## *Philibertia clausa* SCHUMANN

About 40 species of *Philibertia* are native to Florida and the West Indies. This plant, *P. clausa,* is a twining perennial with glossy evergreen leaves and very sweet-scented white flowers.

*P. gracilis* D. DON. This twining shrub from South America bears larger flowers, more than an inch across with 5 triangular segments. They are cream-

---

*According to *Wealth of India,* leaves, flowers and fruits, in times of scarcity, are human fare, and leaves and roots, fodder for animals.

colored, dotted and streaked with purple inside. Bailey (4) says this is cultivated to some extent in Europe.

## *Physostelma wallichii* WIGHT

*Physostelma* is a smooth climbing shrub from Malaya with opposite, fleshy, leathery, shining leaves and clusters of "rather large" flowers. The pale yellow corolla is very broadly bell-shaped, marked with green, with 5 fleshy corona sales. By some authors this is placed in *Hoya*.

## *Raphistemma pulchellum* WALLICH

This big climber, *Raphistemma pulchellum,* from Assam and Burma has heart-shaped, smooth, flaccid leaves 4 to 8 inches long. Its waxy-white, rotate, sweet-scented flowers in large clusters were described by Wallrich (37) as the largest-flowered Asclepiad with which he was acquainted. Lindley & Moore (75) reported that both this and a Java species have "rather showy white campanulate flowers" in clusters.

## *Rothrockia cordifolia* GRAY

This perennial, twining herb grows along water-courses on the Mexico-Arizona border and nearby and is cultivated in southern California. Bailey (4) says the stems of *Rothrockia cordifolia* are somewhat woody at the base, with leaves opposite, cordate, acutely acuminate. The 1-inch white flowers are in clusters.

Standley (102) describes this and 2 other species as native to the Cape region of lower California. *R. umbellata* T. S. BRANDEGEE has flowers up to 1 inch across in clusters of 2 to 6 *R. fruticosa* T. S. BRANDEGEE, native of the same region, has tiny flowers that are purple-black.

## *Sarcostemma grandiflorum* DECAISNE
[Syn. *Philibertia gracilis* D. Don]

This Cinderella of a dozen species found through the tropics was flowered at Kew a century ago. Hooker described it as "an extremely handsome plant," native of Argentina. *Sarcostemma grandiflorum* bears umbels of "large, handsome, downy flowers, the corolla more than an inch across, with five triangular segments, and a small tooth between them, cream-colored, prettily dotted and streaked with purple within." (The flowers are like *Stapelia* in construction.) The leaves were described as opposite, cordate-acuminate, longer than the petioles.

In South Africa *S. viminale* R. BROWN is a vigorous, leafless climber with succulent green stems that strangle and twist, festooning themselves over other vegetation. The creamy-white flowers are inconspicuous.

## *Stephanotis floribunda* BRONGNIART
*Common Names:* MADAGASCAR-JAMINE; CLUSTERED WAXFLOWER

Widely known because of the use of the pure white, fragrant flowers in bridal bouquets, this evergreen glasshouse climber from Madagascar, *Stephanotis flori-bunda* (Photograph 49), is also grown out-of-doors on trellises in all warm areas. It rarely extends more than 15 feet. Its leathery, dark green, shiny, 4-inch leaves are abruptly pointed at the tip, more or less heart-shaped at the base.

*Stephanotis* climbs by twisting its stems and must be supported, for it has no hooks or tendrils to help itself. The waxy blossoms are funnel-shaped, 1 to 2 inches long with 5 pointed lobes, the open blossom 1 to 2 inches across. The flowers are in clusters of 8 to 10 on short stalks from the leaf-axils. They stay fresh for a long time, both on the plant and when cut for decoration.

Usually the flowering is in 2 main flushes, March and April and again in September and October, although scattered blooming in between is not unusual. The 6-inch seed-pods, like ribbed cucumbers, hang on the vine nearly 2 years in the process of ripening.

The climber is deliberate, very slow growing and difficult when small, which may explain its rarity in gardens. Cuttings root with difficulty, and many mature vines fail to produce seed.

Regarding *Stephanotis,* G. A. C. Herklots wrote from Kew, England: "This is notable for the purity and fragrance of the white flowers, which are borne in great profusion."

## *Tacazzea apiculata*   OLIVER
[Syn. *Zacateza pedicellata* Bullock]

"The flowers are quite decorative," wrote Irvine (65) of this woody climber or twining undershrub in tropical Africa, from Senegal eastward. The flowers in May and June are small, yellow-green, sometimes tinged with purple, reddish-green outside and green inside, ¾ inch long, in lax panicles up to 4 inches long. The generic name derives from the Taccaze River in Ethiopia.

## *Telosma cordata*   (BURMAN F.) MERRILL
[Syn. *T. odoratissima* (Loureiro) Coville]
*Common Names:* CHINESE-VIOLET; TONKIN-CREEPER; PRIMROSE-CREEPER; COWSLIP-CREEPER; WEST COAST-CREEPER

This climber from China and India is much cultivated in Hawaii because the delightfully fragrant flowers are prized in leis. The corolla of the yellowish-green 5-parted flowers is only ½ inch long, with spreading oval lobes. The leaves are thin, dull green, heart-shaped, pointed.

*Telosma cordata* (Photograph 50) is described by Chittenden (22) and other authors under the name *Pergularia odoratissima.* Holttum (54) calls it "a slender climber, reaching no great height, bearing continuously small clusters of inconspicuous greenish yellow cup-shaped flowers which have a most delightful fragrance." Firminger (37), much less enthusiastic, calls it "a very extensive climber (in India); bears bunches of flowers resembling those of the cowslip, but of a dead, heavy greenish-yellow, scenting the air when in blossom during the hot months, with most delightful fragrance; not an agreeable-looking plant at any time, and therefore best planted in some situation a little out of notice."

## *Impatiens repens* MOON

*Common Name:* TOUCH-ME-NOT

*Impatiens* comprises a large group of garden and glasshouse herbs, tender, succulent, and often with very fleshy stems. *I. repens* in Ceylon is an herbaceous creeper with purplish-crimson stems and bright yellow flowers, often cultivated.

## *Anredera* species JUSSIEU

To this genus have been transferred 5 or perhaps 10 species of *Boussingaultia* described from the southern United States and West Indies on southward to the Galapagos Islands and Argentina. The best known of these is the madeira-vine (previously known as *B. Leptostachys* MOQUIN-TANDON or *B. baselloides* HBK), originating in Ecuador. This is often found in Florida in warm hammocks and occasionally along the roadsides.

Another species, *B. gracilis* MIERS var. *pseudo-baselloides* BAILEY is also commonly called Madeira-vine, as well as mignonette-vine, silk cururu, or Bertalha of the garden. This is a common porch vine to 20 feet that has escaped through the southern United States. It originated in Ecuador, got established in Madeira, then was returned to the Americas. Being fast growing and much branched, it is often used to cover summer houses from Florida to California. In late summer it produces quantities of airy white, fragrant flowers on 1-foot, spikelike clusters at branch tips; these turn black with age, and the vine dies off with frost. Little tubercles grow in the leaf axils and from these the vines are grown; fruit is never produced. The tuberous roots are hardy far north.

## *Basella rubra* LINN.

*Common Names:* MALABAR-NIGHTSHADE; COUNTRY-SPINACH

*Basella* is an attractive, profusely branched, rampant climber from tropical Asia with purplish, dark red, or yellow-green stems that may be 30 feet long. The smooth, yellow-green or purplish leaves may be tiny, or may be as much as 5 inches long by 4 inches wide. The small white, pink, or purple flowers are in very loose 4-inch clusters. (Color Plate 31.) Although 4 species have been described, they are generally regarded as variations of a single kind. The form with white stems and light green leaves is cultivated in India, Puerto Rico, and the Virgin Islands for the succulent, edible leaves and stems which are eaten like spinach.

## *Begonia* LINN.

*Common Names:* BEGONIA; ELEPHANT-EAR

Of the 800 species of these tropical American plants that are cultivated in glasshouses for their handsome flowers and foliage, several climb by aid of roots like ivy (*Hedera* species). The following are typical:

*B. nelumbiifolia* CHAMISSO & SCHLECHTENDAHL from Mexico, has creeping prostrate stems, rounded, short-pointed leaves to 18 inches long, and many small white or pinkish flowers on stalks that rise above the leaves.

*B. conchaefolia* A. DIETRICH, from Central America, has a creeping rhizome and fragrant pink flowers on penduncles 1 foot or more long.

*B. fuchsioides* HOOKER, from Mexico, is a semi-climber with drooping scarlet flowers.

*B. glaucophylla* HOOKER F., var. *scandens,* from Brazil, with rosy flowers, is often used as a rafter plant in glasshouses.

EDITED BY

BIGNONIACEAE—BIGNONIA FAMILY       ⚛ ARMANDO DUGAND & RUSSELL J. SEIBERT ⚛

## *Adenocalymma comosum*    (CHAMISSO) DC.
[Syn. *Bignonia comosa*   Chamisso]

Blossfeld (8a) reported 3 species common in Brazilian gardens, chiefly *A. comosum,* "a notably beautiful vine," with bright yellow campanulate flowers 2½ inches across, in clusters. It is a rampant grower needing ample room.

In Singapore gardens Holttum (55) reported *A. marginatum* DC. "a very handsome species," with rather large dark green glossy leaves and long hanging clusters of bell-shaped, orange-yellow flowers. The leaves, as in certain other species of *Adenocalymma,* have a distinctive pale margin.

Another of these Brazilian climbers with trumpet-shaped flowers is *Adenocalymma paluistarum.* (Photograph 51.) All require hot, moist conditions for successful culture.

## *Amphilophium paniculatum*    (LINN.) HBK.
[Syn. *Bignonia paniculata*   Linn.]

This South and Central American species of *Amphilophium* is a small woody vine with pink to whitish flowers that are not very handsome, in clusters at branch tips.

## *Anemopaegma chamberlaynii*    (SIMS) BUREAU EX K. SCHUMANN
[Syn. *Bignonia chamberlaynii*   Sims]

This vigorous evergreen climber from Brazil, according to Bailey (5), is "one of the freest [flowering] and most beautiful" of tropical vines. Its dark green, glossy, ovate-acuminate leaves that are paler beneath produce tendrils with hooks that facilitate the escalading process. A heavy mass of foliage develops early and is held onto the stems to the ground, so small buildings can be quickly covered.

*Anemopaegma* somewhat resembles the cat's-claw vine (*Doxantha*), but the flowers are borne in larger clusters. Hume (59) wrote that in Puerto Rico "the bright yellow flowers are produced at irregular intervals, usually in sufficient numbers to attract the attention of visitors. The period of flowering lasts only a few days, after which the flowers fall like a shower to blanket the earth below."

This flower color agrees with Bailey (5) and Chittenden (22), but Holttum (54) says that in Singapore the vine bears primrose-yellow flowers which "seem to be only a color variety." Jex-Blake (67) reported from Kenya that the flowers are pale creamy yellow, and Hottes (56) in California wrote: "The pale yellow flowers are lighter in color than most of the other vines with which it might be confused."

Two other noteworthy species of *Anemopaegma* grow in Trinidad. G. A. C. Herklots of the University of the West Indies wrote this author that *A. chryso-leucom* (HBK) SANDWITH was a rare vine there with "large yellow flowers with the fragrance of roses." The ovate leaves are 3½ to 4 inches long, the flowers are 4½ inches long, pale yellow on the outside and deep yellow within.

Williams (41) reported that *A. carrerense* ARMITAGE is a pretty Trinidad native with leaves 2½ to 3 inches long, funnel-shaped flowers 1½ to 2½ inches long, pale to deeper yellow, not scented.

About 20 species of *Anemopaegma* have been described from northern South America. One of the most striking is *A. chrysanthemum* DUGAND from the west coast of Colombia, with golden-yellow flowers. It is also found on the coast of Ecuador.

## *Arrabidea rotundata*  (DC.) BUREAU EX K. SCHUMANN
[Syn. *Bignonia rotundata*  DC.]

Holttum (50) reported from Malaya that this is a deciduous climber, "very attractive when in flower . . . after a complete leaf-fall, when the plant is bare." The small pale pink trumpet flowers are borne on *Arrabidea rotundata* in great profusion. The corolla is bell-shaped, the lobes overlapping in bud. The leaf tendrils are simple. The calyx is without glands, cup-shaped, short-toothed.

Steiner (106) wrote from the Philippines that the cherry-vine *A. mollissima* (HBK) BUREAU EX K. SCHUMANN, is a "remarkably beautiful vine" that drapes windows and trellises with showers of rose-pink flowers. It is common in the dry forests of northern Colombia. "Even in the dark it is noticeable, for its sweet delicate fragrance fills the air around it. In the morning a carpet of these fugacious flowers covers the ground." Stems and leaves are covered with stiff, coarse hairs, but the flowers are soft and downy. The rounded leaflets, in twos or threes, have long pointed tips which are sometimes used as tendrils to grasp a support.

*A. candicans* (L. C. RICHARD) DC. [syn. *A. pachycalyx* Sprague] is a native to the Pacific slopes of Central America, and Hume (59) wrote that in its native habitat it is so showy that it can be seen from a long distance when in bloom. It is woody at the base, grows vigorously, and makes a big shrub if unsupported. The flowers are lavender with white throats on flowering stalks from the leaf axils often several feet below the branch tips. Individual blossoms are 1½ inches across and 1½ inches long, the 5 petals spreading from the funnel-like throat. Clusters of up to 50 flowers may arise from a single stalk.

For the common *"Arrabidea magnifica"* of gardens, see *Saritaea* in this family.

## Bignonia capreolata  LINN.
[Syn. *Anisostichus capreolata*  Bureau; *Doxantha capreolata*  Miers]
*Common Names:* CROSS-VINE; QUARTER-VINE

The Cross-vine (Photograph 54), which grows to 50 feet or more, is native in the southeastern United States from Maryland west. Bailey (5) found that it is not hardy north as a climber, though it survives in Massachusetts as a creeping plant. *Bignonia capreolata* is a handsome vine for outdoor use, covering walls and fences, though it often becomes a pest in orchards, climbing the trees. Dickey (30) attributed its common name to the appearance of a cross section of the stem, which shows a 4-parted or crosslike arrangement of the water vessels. The evergreen leaflets, 2 to 5 inches long and oblong-lanceolate, are usually borne in twos. The tubular flowers are yellow-red on the outside and lighter within, 2 inches long, and borne in clusters of 2 to 5. The 3-part tendrils usually cling by discs, but Hottes (56) reported that they creep into crevices and then swell, thereby wedging themselves into the crack.

Bor (9) called this a "handsome vine very suitable to covering walls and embankments." Lord (76), who believed this the "hardiest of the *Bignonia* family" said the flowers in Australia are orange; Eliovson (32) reported from South Africa that the blossoms are "spectacular orange or terra-cotta colored," 3 inches long, 2½ inches wide at the mouth.

Bailey (5) described the variety *atrosanguinea* HOOKER F., as having longer and narrower leaves, flowers dark purple, "handsome."

## Callichlamys latifolia  (L. C. RICHARD) K. SCHUMANN
[Syn. *C. riparia*  Miquel]

Among the fine native woody climbers of Trinidad is *Callichlamys* with beautiful yellow flowers 3½ inches across, resembling allamanda but of a slightly different color and having brown lines in the throat. Williams (41) says they are borne in profusion several times a year, lasting only a few days at a time. The vine climbs by simple tendrils at the tips of compound leaves. Seed pods seldom form.

*C. latifolia* is common in northern South America. The characteristic calyx is very large, spongy-tissued, inflated, 1½ to 2 inches long and about 1 inch broad. The fruit is large (up to 3 by 10 inches), woody, compressed, and ellipsoid.

## Campsidium chilense  SEEMANN & REISS
*Common Name:* CHILE TRUMPET-VINE

Firminger (37) reported this "fine climber" from Chile to have in India dark green foliage and tubular orange flowers.

*Campsidium valdivianum* (PHILIPPI) SKOTTESBERG [syn. *Tecoma valdiviana* Philippi] also from Chile, is cultivated in Australian gardens where it produces tubular creamy-orange flowers in spring. Lord (76) said it was "worth growing if only for its handsome glossy, fernlike foliage."

52. CAMPSIS GRANDIFLORA

53. CAMPSIS RADICANS

54. BIGNONIA CAPREOLATA

55. DOXANTHA UNGUIS-CATI

## Campsis radicans  (LINN) SEEMANN
[Syn. *Bignonia radicans*  Linn.]
*Common Names:* TRUMPET-CREEPER; TRUMPET-VINE

## Campsis grandiflora  (THUNB.) K. SCHUMANN
[Syn. *C. chinensis*  (Lamarck) Voss]
*Common Name:* CHINESE TRUMPET-VINE

The genus *Campsis* comprises two species of rampant, hardy, woody vines, sometimes climbing to 40 feet.

The American trumpet-vine, *C. radicans* (Photograph 53), is native from Texas to Florida and north to Pennsylvania, where it often becomes a troublesome weed in cultivated fields (101). It produces quantities of funnel-shaped 3-inch flowers with 5 spreading lobes, usually orange with scarlet limb, in August and September. Scarlet and yellow-flowered forms are known.

The Chinese species, *C. grandiflora* (Photograph 52), will withstand most severe climatic conditions and will tolerate salt-laden winds and almost any atmosphere.

Both vines climb with roots like ivy. They fasten to any rough surfaces including tree trunks, but may need support as the stems can be whipped loose by strong winds. The Chinese climber forms fewer aerial roots and is a better garden subject. The flowers appear in July, August and September. The corolla is 2 inches long, shorter and broader than on the American vine, the color scarlet or orange, sometimes with scarlet stripes in the throat. Bor (9) called "this graceful climber . . . very beautiful . . . and an ornament to any garden." Both climbers produce their flowers in lovely big clusters at the branch tips. Jex-Blake (62) complained that in East Africa the Chinese vine "has a distressingly strong habit of suckering, new plants constantly springing up many yards away from the parent." This is the same weedy nuisance cited for the American vine.

A cross between *C. chinensis* and *C. radicans*, *C. tagliabuana* (VISIANI) REHDER, combines the good qualities of both parents. *C. tagliabuana* (sometimes listed as *C. hyloida*) was named after two celebrated gardeners, the brothers Tagliabue. This cross, usually known in the trade as 'Mme. Galen,' has found a useful place in southern gardens. The large, trumpet-shaped red blooms stand out boldly against a background of dark green leaves. Blooming starts in June and continues through the summer. One of the most valuable characteristics of Mme. Galen is that it does not sprout and become a nuisance. This species is most valuable for covering unsightly power, telephone, and clothesline posts. With a little training it makes an interesting "living post."

## Clytostoma callistegioides  (CHAMISSO) BUREAU
[Syn. *Bignonia callistegioides*  Chamisso]
*Common Name:* PAINTED TRUMPET

The painted trumpet from Argentina (Color Plate 34) has been a favorite garden vine all over Florida for many years, usually growing on fences, its slender stems clinging by leaf tendrils. It has attractive, glossy, evergreen foliage, always 2 leaflets with an unbranched tendril between that drops off if not needed. The young foliage is bronzey. The trumpet flowers in early summer are 3 inches long, light purple or lavender with strong purple veins and a yellow throat, and the flowers are borne in pairs. In South Africa this vine is used as a bank covering (32). Bor (9) wrote: "This is a very showy and ornamental species." Its half-hardiness is one of its advantages.

## *Colea colei*   (BOJER EX HOOKER) M. L. GREEN

The genus *Colea* comprises some 15 species of climbing plants on islands in the Indian Ocean, all with compound, unequally pinnate leaves and funnelform flowers with 5 spreading lobes. *C. colei* blossoms are dark rose, in clusters. (Color Plate 35.) The flowers of *C. floribunda* BOJER are yellowish-white, clustered on the old wood, almost sessile. *C. undulata* REGEL in Madagascar has whorled leaves 2 to 4 feet long. The flowers, yellow and lilac, appear in clusters on the trunk and big branches.

## *Cuspidaria pterocarpa*   (CHAMISSO) DC.

This husky vine in Brazil and northeastern Argentina, has simple leaves and bears tubular lilac flowers 1 to 1½ inches long in loose clusters at the branch tips. The flowers are abundant throughout the growing season.

## *Cydista aequinoctialis*   (LINN) MIERS
[Syn. *Bignonia aequinoctialis*   Linn.]

This climber, native to the West Indies and from Central America to Brazil, is confused by many with the garlic-vine (*Pseudocalymma alliaceum* Sandwith). In fact, in Florida *Cydista aequinoctialis* (Color Plate 14) is commonly erroneously called "garlic-vine," though its foliage does not have a garlic odor. G. A. C. Herklots reported that in its native land this vine is planted near the sea because of high resistance to sand battering and salt spray. The compound leaves, with shining, ovate to ovate-oblong leaflets 3 to 4 inches long, sometimes end with an unbranched tendril. Sandwith (in A. Pulle: *Flora of Suriname* IV: 2:28) describes *Cydista* as having more or less tetragynous branchlets, the young ones.

> "dry black with 4 distinct paler ribs; leaflets 16 x 7.5 cm., shining but minutely lepidote, 6—8 nerves either side of midrib raised on both surfaces; flower clusters to 15 cm. long, branches of thyrses 3-flowered. Corolla pale lilac or rose with darker veins, sometimes white, or white with mauve streaks, lepidote outside, the limb 4—6 cm. diameter and pubescent within; capsule 30—40 cm. long, 2—2.5 cm. broad."

## *Distictella elongata*   (VAHL) URBAN  ⚜ RUSSELL J. SEIBERT ⚜

This is a white-flowering shrubby vine appearing in second-growth areas along roadsides. Its home is French Guiana and Surinam.

Stems are terete (that is, circular in cross-section), the tendrils trifid (branched halfway down into 3), and the leaflets obovate, obtuse, coriaceous, and densely tomentose.

The inflorescence of *D. elongata* (Color Plate 38) is a terminal racemose panicle, the white flowers making a contrast with the very dark color of their tomentos, truncase calyces. The buds stand erect in the young inflorescence. Fruit is an elliptical capsule with woody valves, somewhat sickle-shaped in out-line, densely brownish tomentose.

## *Distictis lactiflora* (VAHL) DC.
[Syn. *Microdiscus laftiflorus* (Vahl) Bureau]

## *Distictis laxiflora* (DC.) GREENMAN
[Syn. *Distictis cinerea* Greenman]
*Common Names:* VANILLA DISTICTIS; VANILLA TRUMPET-VINE

These two similar vines are confused in the trade and in many reference books. Their foliage looks like *Phaedranthus* and their corolla's resemble *Clytostoma,* although the calyx is quite different.

*D. lactiflora* from the West Indies has white trumpet flowers with yellow throat, less than 2 inches long. The oval leaflets are more or less 2 inches long. The seed-pods are 3 to 4 inches long by 1 inch wide.

*D. laxiflora* from Mexico has 5 by 6-inch funnel-shaped flowers 3½ inches long and 2½ inches across. Blossoms in different parts of the cluster come out at different times and thus prolong the blooming season. In bud the flowers are rich purple, and as they open they turn first lavender, then almost pure white, all 3 colors displayed on the vine at the same time in perfect harmony (69). The tube is almost white, streaked with lavender. The flowering continues more or less all year in warm areas, and a vanilla fragrance pervades the air all around the vine. The leaf tendrils are in threes, and the leaflets, to 2½ inches long, are ovate to oblong.

In South Africa a South American species, *D. riversii* (Color Plate 42) with showy purple flowers, is found in gardens.

## *Dolichandra cynanchoides* CHAMISSO
[Syn. *Macfadyena cynanchoides* Morong]

This vine, grown in California, is a liana from Brazil and the Argentine. It is similar in foliage to *Macfadyena,* but has red 2¼-inch flowers, singly or a few in a cluster, the calyx cut to the middle.

## *Doxantha unguis-cati* (LINN) REHDER
[Syn. *Bignonia unguis-cati* Linn.; *B. tweediana* Lindley non Grisebach]
*Common Name:* CAT'S-CLAW VINE

The cat's-claw is an evergreen, fast-growing climber from South and Central America with slender stems and comparatively thin leaves 2 to 3 inches long. On *Doxantha unguis-cati* (Color Plate 31), these come in pairs that are equipped with 3-parted cat's-claw-like tendrils. (Photograph 55.) These cling tenaciously to stone, brick, or wood so that the vine soon provides a dense cover. The trumpet-shaped flowers are borne in pairs in profusion during March and April in Florida. They are 2 inches long, golden yellow, the throat striped with orange lines, the spreading lobes making the flower 2 to 4 inches across. This is essentially a climber and cannot be grown as a bush. It will escalade to great heights if opportunity offers, and as it seeds very freely it often becomes a pest.

One form of this vine is described in some reference books under the name of *Bignonia argyreo-violescens*. In Singapore this South American vine grows vigorously on a framework but flowers rarely. Holttum (55) stated that when it does flower "the display is the finest that could be wished, the whole plant being covered with gold." This author added that there is no doubt that flowering is caused by dry weather, but not every spell of dry weather has the desired effect. "If the plants were a little more susceptible to such stimuli, they would be in demand for every garden."

This second climber is distinguished from *Doxantha unguis-cati* by the foliage of sucker shoots, which is purplish, later turning green, with pale veins; the flowers are rather smaller and a lighter yellow. It is distinguished from *Macfadyena dentata* in having a cup-shaped calyx and leaves that are not toothed. The statement in Bailey (4) that *B. argyreo-violescens* has purple flowers seems to be in error.

## *Eccremocarpus scaber*   RUIZ & PAVON
*Common Name:* CHILEAN GLORY-FLOWER

*Eccremocarpus* is a genus of 4 evergreen, shrubby, half-hardy climbers in Chile and Peru, of which one species, *E. scaber* (Photograph 56), has come to be much cultivated under glass over all the world. Since it is a bit too rampant in the cool house, it is usually grown as an annual. It is often found out-of-doors in the United States, Australia, and England because it blooms readily from seed the first year.

This attractive climber to 15 feet or more bears clusters of 1-inch bright orange tubular flowers with swollen throats. The leaves are bipinnate, the alternate leaflets are obliquely cordate, entire or notched on the edges. Scarlet and golden-yellow forms are known.

## *Fridericia speciosa*   MARTIUS                                    ⚘ HARRY BLOSSFELD ⚘

*Fridericia* is a beautiful climber but I do not know if it is ever cultivated in Brazil, where it is native, though it should be. In fact, it is worthy of cultivation anywhere. The leaves are 2- or 3-foliolate, with oval leaflets 3 to 4 inches long and 1 to 2 inches. broad. The plant blooms on terminal panicles which have red pedicels: The red calyx is inflated, 5-angled, the red corolla, protruding in a star is almost an inch long. The vine lasts a long time in flower and is still showy later in seed.

The name of the genus is sometimes spelled *Fredericea*.

56. ECCREMOCARPUS SCABER   57. PSEUDOCALYMMA ALLIACEUM

58. PANDOREA JASMINOIDES   59. PODRANEA RICASOLIANA

## *Haussmannia jucunda* VAN STEENIS
[Syn. *Haussmannia jucunda* F. v. M.]

This tall smooth climber of the Queensland coast has compound foliage with 3 leaflets 2 to 4 inches long. It bears tubular, purple flowers in short clusters, each blossom about 1 inch long in the tube and with short lobes. Harris (51) calls this "a very handsome plant."

## *Lundia corymbifera* (VAHL) SANDWITH
[Syn. *Lundia umbrosa* (HBK) Bureau; *Bignonia corymbifera* Vahl; *B. umbrosa* HBK]

*Common Name:* WHITE BIGNONIA

Williams (41) reported that in Trinidad this native climbing plant, "often completely covering shrubs and small trees, is very pretty when flowering in August." The foliage is compound, usually 2 leaflets with a tendril between. The funnelform flowers are pure white and slightly hairy, about 1½ inches long and 1 inch broad, produced in axillary and terminal clusters. This climber is also found growing wild in Venezuela and Colombia.

In southern Brazil there are several beautiful climbing species of *Lundia,* such as *L. cordata* DC, with rosy-purple flowers in umbels, *L. nitibula* DC, with white flowers, and *L. umbrosa* (HBK) BUREAU, with rather showy white blossoms. They have some similarity to *Pyrostegia* in their habits but are less conspicuous in flower.

## *Macfadyena dentata* SCHUMANN
[Syn. *Bignonia fraseri* Hort; *B. tweediana* Grisebach non Lindley]

This strong climber from Brazil and Argentina is one of several species of *Macfadyena* introduced into the United States. It climbs with 3-forked leaf tendrils and has glossy toothed leaves 1½ to 2½ inches long that have scurfy scales on both sides. The funnelform, solitary, yellow flowers to 2½ inches long have minute scales on the outside of the corolla. The calyx is split, which distinguishes this plant from *Bignonia argyreo-violescens.*

In habit the vine resembles *Doxantha unguis-cata* (LINN.) REHDER, but the leaflets are rounder with distinctly toothed edges. The calyx cut to the base instead of being cup-shaped prevents these from being confused.

In the Guianas a much cultivated vine is *M. uncata* (Andrews) Sprague and Sandwith [syn. *Bignonia uncata* Andrews], which also climbs with cat's-claw tendrils. The pale yellow flowers, less than 2 inches long, are in small clusters in the leaf-axils.

## *Nyctocalos cuspidatum* (BL.) MIGUEL

*Nyctocalos* (taken from two Greek words signifying "beautiful at night") comprises 3 species of tall climbing shrubs in Malaysia. This one from Assam has exceedingly long (7-inch) white corolla tubes with spreading, oblique, gloxinia-like limbs. These dangle in clusters at branch tips, opening at night, falling off next morning. Macmillan (78) calls it "a beautiful plant."

## *Parafridericia obidoensis*   A. SAMPAIS

This native of the Amazon region is not in cultivation elsewhere.

## *Phaedranthus buccinatorius*   (DC.) MIERS
*Common Name:* MEXICAN BLOOD-TRUMPET

The blood-trumpet is one of the loveliest and showiest of evergreen climbers in the warm gardens of the earth, reaching 25 feet or more and covering itself for months at a time with a spectacular floral display. The clustered flowers of *Phaedranthus buccinatorius* (Color Plate 39) are 4-inch narrow trumpets that are yellow at the base and flushed a glowing crimson at the mouth. Some of the flowers are blood-red all over. Two forms have been observed, one with smaller flowers and foliage than the other. The leaves are opposite, consisting usually of 2 oval or oblong leaflets 3 inches long with a terminal, 3-parted tendril. Often these tendrils develop directly from the multiple stems, each tipped with an adhesive disc that fastens itself to the support, whether tree, wall, or building.

## *Phryganocydia corymbosa*   (VENTURS) BUREAU
[Syn. *Macfadyena corymbosa*]

This South American climber is cultivated in Singapore. Holttum (55) called attention to the distinctive calyx, which is cut to the base on one side while it is long and pointed on the other. This separates it from other Bignons cultivated in gardens. The tendrils among the leaves are simple and unbranched. The trumpet flowers are pink or purplish, in large spreading bunches at the tips of branches.

In Trinidad *Phryganacydia* has flowers 2½ to 3 inches across the mouth and 3 inches long, funnel-shaped, mauve with a white throat, the hooded calyx a greenish yellow. Williams (41) reports it a rampant climber that "when allowed to grow on trees or arbors clothes them with a dark green foliage and several times of the year with masses of flowers."

## *Pithecoctenium cynchoides*   DC.
[Syn. *P. clematideum*   Grisebach]
*Common Name:* MONKEY-COMB

The Argentine MONKEY-COMB derives its name from the spines that cover the 8-inch seed pods. It is a pretty evergreen vine that uses tendrils to climb and bears in spring clusters of 2-inch, tubular white flowers at the branch tips.

The Colombian monkey-comb, *P. echinatum* (JACQUIN) K. SCHUMANN [syn. *P. muricatum* DC.] common in central and northern South America, is a similar evergreen vine with bell-shaped white flowers half the size of those on the Argentine plant. They appear in drooping clusters and turn yellow the second day. Both of these climbers are sparingly grown in Florida.

## *Podranea ricasoliana*   (TANFAUNI) SPRAGUE
[Syn. *Tecoma riscasoliana* Tanfani, *Tecoma Mackeni* (W. Wats.); *Pandorearicaso ricasoliana* Baillon]
*Common Names:* PODRANEA; RICASOL PODRANEA; PORT ST. JOHN CLIMBER

29. BEAUMONTIA GRANDIFLORA

30. SARITAEA MAGNIFICA

31. BASELLA RUBRA

32. DOXANTHA UNGUIS-CATI

33. PYROSTEGIA IGNEA

34. CLYTOSTOMA CALLISTEGIOIDES

35. COBAEA SCANDENS

36. PSEUDOCALYMMA ALLIACEA

37. ANTHURIUM ANDREANUM

38. DISTICTELLA ELONGATA

39. PHAEDRANTHUS BUCCINATORIUS

40. PODRANEA BRYCEI

41. TECOMANTHE DENDROPHILA

42. DISTICTIS RIVERSII

**43. TRADESCANTIA BLOSSFELDIANA**

**44. LEYCESTERIA FORMOSA**

**45. ABELIA GRANDIFLORA**

**46. ZYGOCACTUS TRUNCATUS**

**47. LONICERA SEMPERVIRENS**

**48. CAPPARIS MICRANTHA**

**49. LONICERA HECKROTTI**

50. COMBRETUM MICROPHYLLUM

51. CANARINA CAMPANULATA

52. COMBRETUM FARINOSUM

53. COMBRETUM GRANDIFLORUM

54. COMBRETUM COCCINEUM

55. COMBRETUM PLATYPTERUM

56. QUISQUALIS INDICA

## *Pandorea jasminoides* (LINDLEY) W. SCHUMANN

[Syn. *Bignonia jasminoides* Lindley]

*Common Name:* BOWER-PLANT

These two climbers are described together here because they are similar in many ways, their anagram names are confusing, and references to them in some books are mixed. Here are the outstanding distinctions between them:

*Podranea* vines (Photograph 59) are from South Africa; *Pandorea* (Photograph 58) comes from Australia.

*Podranea* leaves have 7 to 11 leaflets, 1 inch long, elliptic-ovate, dark green above, pale beneath, smooth, toothed on edges. *Pandorea* has 5 to 9 ovate to lanceolate, smooth, thick, bright green leaflets, not toothed 1 to 1½ inches long.

*Podranea* flowers are light pink striped with red, the funnels 2 inches long. (There is also a white-flowered form of *Podranea ricasoliana* with a purple spot in the throat.) When planted in full sun the flowers are produced vigorously and profusely in large clusters. *Pandorea* blossoms are white with pink or red in the throat, smaller (1½ to 2 inches long) narrower, in few-flowered clusters, growing less vigorously.

The calyx on *Podranea* is large and inflated. On *Pandorea* it is small and not inflated.

On *Podranea* the seed-capsule is long, narrow, and leathery. On *Pandorea* it is short and woody.

One other species of *Podranea* is known in South Africa. This is *P. brycei* REHDER, often called Queen-of-Sheba or Zimbalwe climber. (Color Plate 40.) It is a variable plant (see Introductory Chapter) with showy pink flowers much like *P. ricasoliana* except that the throats are hairy and the color more mauve.

In Indomalaysia there are six species of *Pandorea* of which the bower-plant is best known and most widely cultivated around the world. Another species sometimes seen in warm gardens is the Australian *Pandorea pandorana* (ANDREWS) VAN STEENIS [syn. *Tecoma australis* R. Brown], commonly called wonga-wonga vine. Its dark green glossy foliage is lovely, bronze when young, but the funnel-shaped, yellowish-white flowers, spotted with purple in the throat, though heavily scented are so small (½ to ¾ inch long) as to be too inconspicuous to attract attention.

## *Pseudocalymma alliaceum* (LAMARCK) SANDWITH

[Syn. *Bignonia alliacea* Lamarck; *Adenocalymma alliaceum* (Lamarck) Miers]

*Common Name:* GARLIC-VINE (This is the real garlic-vine)

Steiner (106) wrote that in the Philippines some plants seem to have a calendar in their system.

"Watch the garlic-scented *Pseudocalymma alliaceum* [from tropical America]. (Photograph 57 and Color Plate 36.) When one of these vines starts to bloom you can be sure that all the others will do so on the very same day . . . The garlic-vine has become very popular in the Philippines. Its dark green, glossy leaves have two ovate leathery leaflets, with or without

113

tendrils between them . . . . Its purple blossoms are five-lobed and funnel-shaped, and have a characteristic garlic scent, which is however not penetrating and is noticeable only at close range. After a few days the blossoms fade, turning pale lavender and eventually almost white. The vine . . . flowers several times a year . . . and always 23 days after a temperature minimum."

The compound leaves, often consisting of 2 dark green, shining leaflets up to 4 inches long, with a long unbranched tendril between them, are distinctive in that their sides bend upward from the midvein in a wide "V" while the tips are curling downward.

The light purple, funnel-shaped, 2½-inch flowers with wide-flared mouth have darker lines running down into the creamy throat. Usually the blossoms are in clusters of 6 to 25, opening only a few at a time so that the flowering extends over a long period and is repeated several times a year.

This climber is commonly grown in Florida under the incorrect name of *Cydista aequinoctialis,* a Trinidad plant (q. v.) with foliage that is not garlic scented.

In Puerto Rico, according to Hume (59), *P. alliaceum* is a semi-woody climber that continues to bloom much of the year. It is called "bejuco de ajo" (garlic-vine) in Colombia, from the slight garlic odor of the flowers or crushed leaves.

## *Pyrostegia venusta*   (KER) MIERS
[Syn. *Bignonia venusta*  Ker; *Bignonia ignea*  Vell.; *Pyrostegia ignea*  (Vell.) Presl.]

*Common Names:* FLAME-VINE (Florida); GOLDEN SHOWER (India); FLAME TRUMPET (California); ORANGE TRUMPET (Hawaii); ORANGE-FLOWERED STEPHANOTIS (Malaysia); TANGO (Colombia)

"Probably no plant in the world presents so gorgeous an appearance when in full bloom," wrote Bor (9) of this Brazilian and Bolivian evergreen climber that covers fences, walls, and even buildings in warm gardens everywhere. By tendrils and by discs when necessary, *Pyrostegia venusta* (Color Plate 33) rambles extensively, often to 70 feet or more, knows no pests, but needs a rest period if it is to flower most successfully. In Singapore it never blooms.

Unlike most Bignons, the brilliant orange flowers of the flame-vine are long tubes, gradually enlarging toward the mouth, which for a time scarcely opens, though the lobes are marked by white stripes. When the mouth does open, the lobes curl backward and form 2 lips, the upper 2-lobed, the lower 3-lobed, the stamens well exserted. These 3-inch blossoms are produced in greatest profusion in large, hanging clusters through the winter months in southern California and in early spring in Florida. The light green leaves, borne opposite in twos and threes, are smooth, sharp-pointed, and 3 to 4 inches long.

In the glasshouse this is usually planted in a container, kept to a single stem, and trimmed to follow the rafters above, so that when flowers appear they hang in bunches overhead. Out-of-doors the vine is hurt by temperatures below 28° Fahrenheit, which limits its usefulness to warmest areas.

60. TECOMANTHE VENUSTA    61. TECOMANTHE SPECIOSA

62. TECOMARIA CAPENSIS    63. ACANTHOCEREUS PENTAGONUS

## *Saritaea magnifica* (W. BULL) DUGAND

[Syn. *Bignonia magnifica* W. Bull; *Arrabidaea magnifica* (W. Bull) Sprague ex van Steenis]

*Common Names:* PALO NEGRO; SARITEA (Colombia)

This scandent shrub is cultivated in gardens everywhere in the tropics, climbing to 100 feet if opportunity offers, but usually remaining much smaller. It has smooth, stalked, obovate, leathery, shiny leaflets customarily in pairs, up to 4 inches long. Several times a year *Saritaea magnifica* (Color Plate 30) bears clusters of tubular-campanulate flowers 3 inches long and 3 inches in diameter when fully open, pale purple with purple streaks within the tube.

Most gardeners refer to this woody plant loosely as *Bignonia magnifica*. Actually it is the type of a very distinct new genus, *Saritaea,* described by Dr. Armando Dugand in 1945. Dr. Dugand lives in Colombia where the plant is native and is an authority on the Bignoniaceae of that area.

The large showy flowers are usually in clusters of 4 but the flowering branches may have several clusters at their ends. The blossoms are freely produced, 2 to 4 times a year, and their mauve color sometimes varies to a rich reddish purple, offset with light primrose within the throat.

## *Tecomanthe venusta* S. MOORE
## *Tecomanthe dendrophylla* (BLUME) K. SCHUMANN

[Syn. *T. dendrophila* Blume]

Both of these beautiful climbers from New Guinea have been established in cultivation in the United States and are beginning to be seen in gardens. They are handsome plants, not too rampant, producing big clusters of highly colored trumpet flowers from the old wood. Both are frost tender.

Despite some early confusion in nomenclature, these two species of *Tecomanthe* are easily distinguished by both the foliage and flowers. The Fairchild Tropical Garden in Miami suggests these points of difference:

On *T. venusta* (Photograph 60) the flowers are about 6 cm. (2¼ inches) long. The corolla inside is creamy, on the outside rosy purple. The compound leaves are supposed to be 5-foliolate but many of the leaves have 7 leaflets, and a few of them have 6 leaflets plus a lop-sided terminal one. All leaflets are 2½ to 3 inches long.

On *T. dendrophylla* the flowers are about 8 cm. (3¼ inches) long, not including the limb. The inside of the corolla is a milky white, and the outside of the funnelform tube is reddish with yellow markings. The leaves are compound, always with 3 leaflets, the 3-inch terminal one much larger than the other two.

Dr. W. H. Hodge brought *T. venusta* from Australia in 1958. In the *American Horticultural Magazine* (July 1960) he described the "beautiful, pendent, trumpet-shaped flowers which appear in axillary umbelllike clusters (up to 16 in a cluster) on old wood." He said further:

"The flowers are a light magenta rose on the outside of the tube, fading

116

to a paler rose, and creamy yellow on the inner surface of the spreading lobes and the inside of the tube."

Maximum over-all length of the individual flowers is about 3½ inches, and each is about 2 inches across the flaring, somewhat irregular lobes."

(This climber was described in *Journal Royal Horticultural Society,* London, July 1958, under the erroneous name *T. dendrophila.* The flowers were described as "rich, fiery orange-red.")

*T. dendrophylla* (Color Plate 41) was introduced to Florida by D. J. McSwiney of Fort Lauderdale and distributed through the Florida Federation of Garden Clubs.

Ten other species of *Tecomanthe* have been described from New Guinea. *T. amboinensis* (BLUME) VAN STEENIS, is cultivated in Singapore where it produces bunches of beautiful pink flowers on the old wood. *T. speciosa* W. R. B. OLIVER (Photograph 61) was discovered in 1945 in New Zealand and now is sparingly cultivated there. It was described August 21, 1954, in the *Gardeners' Chronicle:*

"Each compound leaf consists of 3 to 5 leaflets . . . . The flowers are produced on the older stems. The number of individual flowers in the corymb varies from 10 to 27, often borne in groups of 3 on a common stock. The individual flowers measure up to 2½ inches long and are creamy white, overlaid with a refreshing tinge of green."

## *Tecomaria capensis*   (THUNBERG) SPACH
[Syn.: *Bignonia capensis*   Thunberg: *Tecoma capensis* (Thunberg) Lindley]
*Common Name:* CAPE-HONEYSUCKLE

The woody climber from South Africa known as Cape-honeysuckle is cultivated in subtropical gardens everywhere, sometimes as a shrub, more frequently as a shrubby climber. *Tecomaria capensis* (Photograph 62) is a handsome plant of luxuriant growth, knows no pests and produces frequent flushes of the 2-inch, orange-red or scarlet, slender tubular flowers in clusters at stem tips. The foliage is evergreen; the compound leaves are opposite, shining, and bearing 7 to 9 leaflets, usually with sawtooth edges. A yellow- flowered form is widely cultivated in Florida. The plant is badly hurt by temperatures below 25° Fahrenheit.

## *Tourretia lappacea*   (L'HERITIER) WILLDENOW
[Syn. *T. volubilis*   J. F. Gmelin;   *Dombeya lappacea* L'Heritier]

*Tourretia* is a charming little tendriled annual creeper, native from Peru to Mexico, with bright green, fernlike foliage and small scarlet flowers. The seed-pods are covered with reflexed prickles. It is very common in tropical thickets and waste places.

## *Lithospermum diffusum* LAGASCA
[Syn. *L. prostratum* Loiseleur-Deslongchamps]

This rock-garden perennial from the Mediterranean, especially the variety called 'Heavenly Blue,' is a beautiful prostrate shrub with creeping stems that seldom exceed 12 inches, massed half-inch leaves, and producing in spikes at branch tips the 1-inch, funnel-shaped, deep blue flowers, striped reddish-violet.

CACTACEAE—CACTUS FAMILY ⚜ LADISLAUS CUTAK ⚜

## *Acanthocereus pentagonus* (LINN.) BRITTON & ROSE
[Syn. *Cereus acutangulus* Otto]
*Common Name:* BARBED-WIRE CACTUS

*Acanthocereus* is a genus of weak, elongated cacti that clamber or trail over bushes and rocks. They are strongly 3-angled, although 4 or 5 or more angles sometimes occur, particularly in the juvenile forms. *A. pentagonus* was known to Linnaeus as early as 1753. Its distribution extends from Florida to Texas, down through Mexico and Central America, to northern South America. It produces a truly magnificent nocturnal blossom, up to 8 inches long, glistening white and fragrant. (Photograph 63.) The genus contains about 10 species, the most plentiful being *A. pentagonus* and the stoutest one *A. horridus.*

## *Aporocactus flagelliformis* (LINN.) LEMAIRE
[Syn. *Cereus flagelliformis* Miller]
*Common Name:* RATTAIL CACTUS

*Aporocactus* is widely cultivated in most tropical countries, usually as a basket plant. Presumably the genus is of Mexican origin, although the oldest known species, *A. flagelliformis,* was introduced from Peru in 1690. Five species are recognized and usually these are grafted on the stouter stock of *Selenicereus, Nyctocereus, Monvillea,* or *Cereus.* Lush growth in umbrella-like fashion results.

This species is noted for its slender, cylindric stems, inconspicuously 10- to 14-ribbed, and covered with small weak spines in clusters. Flowers are of a crimson pink. They usually appear near the tips and last several days. (Photograph 64.)

## *Cryptocereus anthonyanus* ALEXANDER
*Common Name:* FISHBONE CACTUS

*Cryptocereus* is a monotypic genus from Mexico and one of the most attractive novelties discovered in the past 20 years. It has a climbing habit of growth. The deeply-lobed branches attain great lengths and develop some aerial roots at the midrib. Plants with phylloid stems belong chiefly to the *Epiphyllanae,* but strangely enough *Cryptocereus* is more closely related to the *Hylocereanae* and

64. APOROCACTUS FLAGELLIFORMIS

65. CRYPTOCEREUS ANTHONYANUS

66. EPIPHYLLUM OXYPETALUM

67. ERIOCEREUS GUELICHII

apparently serves as the missing link between the two groups. *C. anthonyanus* produces waxy, fragrant, night-blooming flowers, cream-colored, with purple sepals. (Photograph 65.)

## *Epiphyllum oxypetalum*   (DC.) HAWORTH
[Syn. *Phyllocactus oxypetalus*   Link]

*Common Name:* DUTCHMAN'S PIPE CACTUS

*Epiphyllum* is a genus of about 20 species of epiphytic cacti growing in the rain forests of tropical America from Mexico to Brazil. *E. oxypetalum* is the best known member of this group and it is almost always erroneously called "night-blooming cereus." Most species of *Cereus* are cylindric-stemmed and fluted, while *Epiphyllum* plants, in contrast, are characterized by flattened, leaflike stems.

E. oxypetalum (Photograph 66) is widely cultivated in the tropics and is often found as an escape. It often roots at the tips and can attain great lengths. The large flowers curve above the ovary like a smoker's pipe and last but one night. Epiphyllums have been hybridized extensively and now possess flowers that vie with the orchid in coloration.

E. quezaltecum (STANDLEY & STEYERMARK) L. WILLIAMS. Of this colorful species, Dr. L. O. Williams at the Field Museum of Natural History, Chicago, wrote: "This cactus is one of the fanciest that I know. It is an epiphytic vine hanging down from the trees where it occurs in Guatemala."

## *Eriocereus guelichii*   (SPEGAZZINI) BERGER
[Syn.: *Harrisia guelichii*   Britton & Rose]

*Common Name:* CHACO NIGHT-BLOOMING CEREUS

*Eriocereus* is a genus of about 7 species, all native to South America, characterized by a red fruit which often splits upon ripening. The plants branch more or less profusely, at first growing quite erect, later becoming pendent or prostrate on rocks or clambering into trees. In the trees of Chaco province in Argentina, *E. guelichii* (Photograph 67) is a very high-climbing cactus. It branches extensively and flowers freely there. The stems are 3 or 4-angled and contain 4 or 5 radial spines with one much thicker central one in each areole. The flowers are quite large, greenish on the outside and white inside.

E. martinii (LABURET) RICCOBONO [syn. *Harrisia martinii* Britton & Rose], Argentine Night-Blooming Cereus, is probably the commonest species seen in cultivation. Because it is such a vigorous grower, with sprawling stems, it is often used as a rootstock for grafting. Its stems are almost cylindrical but with prominent tubercles arranged on low broad ribs. The nocturnal flowers, about 8 inches long, are white, the petals often tinged with pink. The fruit is red and very tuberculate. (Photograph 68.)

E. bonplandii is another widely cultivated species, often used in homeopathic medicine. *E. tortuosus* is probably the most vicious looking. *E. jusbertii* is thought to be a natural hybrid.

120

68. ERIOCEREUS MARTINII 69. HYLOCEREUS LEMAIREI

70. HYLOCEREUS UNDATUS 71. HARIOTA SALICORNIODES

## *Hylocereus undatus* (HAWORTH) BRITTON & ROSE
[Syn. *Cereus tricostatus* Gosselin]

*Common Name:* QUEEN OF THE NIGHT

*Hylocereus* is a genus of climbing cacti, of which there are about 18 species. The plants are suitable for trellises in outdoor gardens in the subtropics or for the greenhouse elsewhere, when allowed to climb up to and over the rafters. Hylocerei are native to the West Indies, Mexico, and Central and South America. The large spineless edible fruits are found in the marketplaces and relished by the natives.

The stems and branches of all species emit aerial roots which enable the elongated stems to climb over rough cliff faces or into the tops of trees. The joints are 3-winged or angled and the areoles bear very short spines. *H. undatus* has been in cultivation for a long time, in some instances as a hedge plant, like the famous half-mile-long hedge about Punahou College in Honolulu, Hawaii. The large white flowers, nearly 12 inches long, are fully open at night and remain partially open on cool mornings. (Photograph 70.)

Trinidad night-blooming cereus, *H. lemairei* (HOOKER) BRITTON & ROSE [syn. *Cereus trinitatensis* Lemaire & Herment], is one of the most beautiful, the pure white flowers flushed pink or purple. (Photograph 69.) Another interesting one is *H. costaricensis,* which can be recognized by the whitish powder on its stems.

## *Hariota salicornioides* (HAWORTH) DC.

*Common Name:* DANCING BONES CACTUS

*Hariota* is a genus of three species of plants with an epiphytic habit. At first the plants are quite bushy but eventually they tend to be pendent and copiously branched. The ultimate joints are often much elongated. *H. salicornioides* (Photograph 71) is the most remarkable member of this group, with peculiar clavate or bottle-shaped joints which grow in whorls, branching and rebranching as the plant grows older. Small yellow to salmon-colored flowers are produced on the blunt tips of new joints. Another interesting species is *H. bambusoides* which has joints that look like miniature bamboo stems. The genus is also known as *Hatiora,* an anagram of the official name.

## *Mediocactus coccineus* (SALM-DYCK) BRITTON & ROSE
[Syn. *Cereus setaceus* Salm-Dyck]

*Mediocactus* is a genus of 2 species found in Brazil and Argentina, also in the Andes of Peru, Colombia and Bolivia. The long triangular stems have aerial roots and the plants usually climb on trees or clamber over rocks or walls. The stems and flowers resemble a *Hylocereus* but have a tuberculate ovary and felted spine-bearing areoles on the fruit like a *Selenicereus*. *M. coccineus* (Photograph 72) came to the notice of botanists in 1828 and *M. megalanthus* in 1907. Both bear very large flowers which are white and nocturnal in habit.

72. **MEDIOCACTUS COCCINEUS**    73.  **MONVILLEA CAVENDISHII**

74.   **PERESKIA ACULEATA**    75.  **RHIPSALIS CAPILLIFORMIS**

## *Monvillea cavendishii*    (MONVILLE) BRITTON & ROSE
[Syn. *Cereus saxicola*    Morong]

*Monvillea* is a genus of 6 or 7 species that form thickets, the spiny stems often high-clambering or drooping, depending on where they grow. The flowers arise from near the top on the sides of the stems. The best-known species is *M. cavendishii,* which is a prolific bloomer, putting out its nocturnal white flowers from April to September (Photograph 73)  *M. spegazzinii* is conspicuously 3-angled, bluish green spotted with white.

Monvilleas are greenhouse favorites because of their half-erect habit. The plants are best trained to a trellis. They are mostly South American in origin, calling Brazil, Peru, Paraguay, and Argentina their home.

## *Pereskia aculeata*  MILLER
[Syn. *Pereskia pereskia*    (Linn.) Karsten]
*Common Name:* LEMON-VINE

*Pereskia* is a genus of about 20 species, which are considered to be the most primitive forms of the cactus family. Many are shrubs and even trees, but *P. aculeata* (Photograph 74) is definitely a fast-growing vine which looks very much like a *Bougainvillea.* In tropical America this species climbs over walls, rocks, and trees. The whitish flowers appear in large clusters that emit a strong odor of lemon. They are followed by beautiful clusters of yellow berries that are edible. This species has a wide distribution in the West Indies and along the coasts of northern South America.

Another attractive climber is *P. godseffiana,* a sport developed from *P. aculeata,* which has richly colored leaves with purplish undersides.

## *Rhipsalis capilliformis*  WEBER
[Syn. *Rhipsalis gracilis*    N. E. Brown]
*Common Name:* MISTLETOE CACTUS

*Rhipsalis* would hardly be called a cactus as it does not look anything like the usual bizarre spiny plant of the desert. It is an epiphytic or air-loving plant that hugs tree trunks and their branches in tropical forests of the Western Hemisphere. More than 50 species are recognized and they present a diversity of forms. Some, like *R. capilliformis* (Photograph 75), have very slender weak stems that hang in long festoons, while others, like *R. houlletiana,* have flat and thin joints that make the plant resemble a young *Epiphyllum,* and still others, like *R. paradoxa,* have branches in zigzag links. Flowers are rather small, mostly whitish, and the usually globular fruits remind one of mistletoe berries.

## *Schlumbergera gaertneri*    (SCHUMANN) BRITTON & ROSE
[Syn. *Epiphyllopsis gaertneri*    Berger]
*Common Name:* EASTER CACTUS

*Schlumbergera* is a very floriferous cactus inhabiting the rain forests of southern Brazil. It possesses the same growth habit as *Zygocactus* except that it has regular

124

76. SCHLUMBERGERA GAERTNERI    77. SELENICEREUS PTERANTHUS

78. WILCOXIA SCHMOLLII    79. QUISQUALIS INDICA ALBA

rather than zygomorphic flowers. *S. gaertneri* (Photograph 76) is a much-branched epiphyte with elongated, flat, oval joints which hang down from the branches of tropical trees. The starlike, bright scarlet flowers appear at the distal end of the terminal joints, usually in pairs or threes. These are followed by red fruits with winglike angles. The plant is quite handsome and adapts itself to grafting upon *Pereskia* or *Selenicereus* stock.

## *Selenicereus pteranthus*   (LINK & OTTO) BRITTON & ROSE
[Syn. *Cereus nycticallus*   Link]
*Common Name:* NIGHT-BLOOMING CEREUS

*Selenicereus* contains at least 16 species which are all clambering vines with aerial roots. Most of them are vigorous growers and flower freely in cultivation, producing some of the largest blossoms in the cactus family. The range of distribution extends from southern Texas through Mexico and Central America to the northern coasts of South America and to the islands of the Caribbean. *S. pteranthus,* which is probably the species most frequently seen in collections, is characterized by strongly 4-angled stems that are flushed purple. (Photograph 77.) *S. hamatus* is bright green, nearly spineless, and noted for its knobby projections. *S. coniflorus* is often shipped to the United States to be manufactured into homeopathic medicine.

## *Wilcoxia schmollii*   (WEINGART) KNUTH
*Common Name:* LAMB'S-TAIL CACTUS

*Wilcoxia* is a genus of vinelike cacti characterized by clusters of dahlia-like roots. The most desirable species is *W. schmollii* with pencil-thick stems nearly hidden by masses of silky wool and an abundance of flowers of a lovely shade of pink. (Photograph 78.) *W. poselgeri,* the only species native to the United States, is probably the oldest known member of the group, dating from 1853. Its flowers are pinkish-purple and day-blooming, opening and closing for 5 or more successive days. *W. viperina* has densely velvety-puberulent stems and red flowers. The wilcoxias do not do so well on their own roots in cultivation; therefore they are frequently grafted onto stronger stock.

## *Zygocactus truncatus*   (HAWORTH) SCHUMANN
[Syn. *Epiphyllum truncatum*   Haworth]
*Common Name:* CRAB OR THANKSGIVING CACTUS

*Zygocactus* resembles *Schlumbergera* superficially, so is often confused with it. Some specialists in fact, have already united the two genera. The many natural or horticultural variations in both need clarification and until such time we will retain the above name for the plant that bears irregular flowers, blooms earlier, and has joints characterized by sharply notched or toothed margins.

The crab cactus is an excellent house plant and succeeds best in a hanging basket, planted in sphagnum, chopped osmundine, or turfy humus and fed with nutrient solutions. (Color Plate 46.)

80. **CAMPANULA ISOPHYLLA**  81. **CAMPANULA MURALIS**

82. **ABELIA TRIFLORA**  83. **LONICERA HILDEBRANDIANA**

## Campanula isophylla MORETTI
*Common Name:* STAR-OF-BETHLEHEM; ITALIAN BELLFLOWER

Most species of *Campanula* are handsome herbs of common garden cultivation, but a very few, of which *C. isophylla* is typical, have trailing tendencies. This is one that will tumble quantities of starry saucer-shaped white or lavender-blue flowers from the basket or along the bank over which it spreads. (Photograph 80.)

*C. muralis* PORTENSCHLAG has beautiful violet-blue flowers lobed nearly to the base. It is one of a variable group called Adria bellflowers, which are much branched floriferous perennials, usually decumbent with stems from 3 to 8 inches long and very green foliage. (Photograph 81.)

## Canarina canariensis KUNTZE
[Syn. *C. campanula* Lamarck]

*Canarina* species are herbaceous climbers or trailers of tropical Africa, from the Canary Islands to Kenya. They ascend old trees or rocky cliffs by the curling stalks of their ivy-shaped, toothed leaves. On *C. canariensis* the hanging bell-shaped flowers are 1 inch long, 1½ inches wide, and of varying colors, from deep reddish orange through yellowish purple to dull yellow, with red nerves. (Color Plate 51.) Chittenden (22) says that the plant needs greenhouse conditions with perfect drainage for the roots and ample warmth to induce flowering.

In East Africa *C. eminii* and *C. abyssinica* are even handsomer, with 3-inch bell-shaped flowers that are orange flushed with red. They all like wet forests or other damp places (67).

CAPPARIDACEAE—CAPER FAMILY

## Capparis lasiantha R. BROWN
*Common Name:* NIPANG CREEPER

This native climber in northern Queensland reaches 20 feet, bears white and creamy-yellow fragrant flowers in the leaf axils and in terminal clusters. More than half of the 200 species of *Capparis* in the tropics and subtropics are climbing plants that cling to their supports with the aid of recurved stipular spines. Hundley (60) lists 9 species in Burma that are climbers.

*C. micracantha* DC. (Color Plate 48) in the Philippines and throughout Malaysia is often cultivated for the flowers, which are made conspicuous by their many long white stamens. The bright red fruits 2 to 3 inches long contain a transparent sweetish edible pulp. The capers of commerce, commonly used in flavoring, are the unopened flower buds of *C. spinosa* Linn.

## Ritchiea reflexa GILG & BENEDICT

This scrambling or erect shrub from Guinea to Nigeria, with smooth foliage and fragrant greenish-white flowers that are 2 inches long, has been reported introduced to the United States "where it forms a dense trellis vine." (65).

57. MANOTES SPECIOSA

58. TURBINA SHIRENSIS

59. DICHORISANDRA THYRSIFLORA

60. MUTISIA SP. (Peru)

61. SENECIO CONFUSUS

62. NEUROPELTIS SP. (Ivory Coast)

63. JACQUEMONTIA PENTANTHA

64. BONAMIA SEMIDYGNIA

65. IPOMOEA BRACTEATA

66. IPOMOEA HORSFALLIAE

67. IPOMOEA ACUMINATA

68. MARIPA PASSIFLOROIDES

69. IPOMOEA AQUATICA

70. IPOMOEA PALMATA

## *Roydsia fasciculata* KING

This is one of 4 species of *Roydsia* vines in the East Indies, all of them with large, simple leaves, and bearing quantities of 1-inch yellow, fragrant, powderpuff-like flowers in clusters at the branch tips. The flowers consist mostly of stamens, which may number 100 or more.

CAPRIFOLIACEAE—HONEYSUCKLE FAMILY

## *Abelia triflora* R. BROWN

Most kinds of *Abelia* are garden shrubs cultivated for their ornamental flowers, but this species is a scandent shrub in the Himalayas that bears a great profusion of dense ball-like heads of small, white, very fragrant flowers. (Photograph 82.) The persistent feathery sepals form an attractive show after the flowers have fallen.

Bailey (5) says that *A. grandiflora* REHDER, the most commonly cultivated form, is a half-evergreen hybrid between *A. chinensis* and *A. uniflora*. Its long-extended branches that bear dense clusters of pink flowers may be cultivated in the vine manner. (Color Plate 45.)

## *Leycesteria formosa* WALLICH

This vigorous small vine of western China and the Himalayas clambers to 6 feet and bears purplish flowers in whorled spikes. It has been cultivated in California and England. (Color Plate 44.)

## *Linnaea borealis* LINN.

This minute rock-garden trailer known as twin-flower, is an evergreen subshrub that clings to the ground and bear terminal pairs of small funnel-shaped pink flowers with 5 corolla-lobes.

## *Lonicera* LINN.
*Common Name:* HONEYSUCKLE

In this chiefly northern family of about 400 species or ornamental shrubs, the climbers are found almost exclusively in the genus *Lonicera*. Some members of the honeysuckle family have 5 lobes in their flower parts, some have 4; some have flowers classed as "regular"—with all the lobes alike; in some the flowers are "irregular"—the lobes of different shapes.

Honeysuckle flowers are of the irregular type, with 2 lips, one of 3 and one of 2 lobes, at the end of the corolla-tube. The ovary, as in other members of the family, is below the calyx. Most of the 180 species of *Lonicera* are deciduous, though some hold their leaves through winter in the warmer parts of their range. Many are native in North America; others have reached our gardens from Europe and Asia. They are prized for their lovely and abundant flowers that are usually fragrant; also for their freedom from pests, their not-too-rampant growth, and their need of little care.

129

## *L. sempervirens* LINN.
*Common Name:* TRUMPET HONEYSUCKLE

Native throughout the eastern half of the United States from Connecticut southward, this species is popular both as a wild and as a cultivated plant. It is a high climber and, southward, it is evergreen, but in colder areas of England it goes dormant and drops its foliage. It is cultivated for its clustered spikes of brilliant tubular flowers, scarlet without, yellow within. While these are usually about 2 inches long, in certain other species they may be as much as 6 to 7 inches, as in the Burma giant, *L. hildebrandiana* COLL. & HEMSL. (Photograph 83). The fruits are small red berries.

The chief drawbacks of *L. sempervirens* are that the flowers are not fragrant, the stems tend to lose their foliage toward the base and the growth under favorable conditions is too rampant. (Color Plate 47.) A hybrid between this and *L. americana* KOCH (itself a hybrid), known as *L. X Heckrottii* (22), is one of the finest of all garden forms with its fragrant 2-inch, 2 lipped flowers that are purple outside and yellow within. (Color Plate 49). Many other hybrids in this group are offered by nurseries.

*L. flava* SIMS, native from North Carolina to Oklahoma, is particularly fine though rare in cultivation. The flowers are smaller (usually 1¼ inches long), but fragrant and bright yellow or orange-yellow, in June.

The Dutch woodbine (*L. periclymenum* L. var. *belgica* AITON is a twining shrub with smooth leaves that are whitish beneath, and flowers that are pale purple outside.

*L. etrusca* SANTI, from the Mediterranean region, is a vigorous climber, partly evergreen, with fragrant yellowish-white, reddish-tinged, 2-inch flowers in dense clusters.

The Japanese honeysuckle (*L. japonica* THUNBERG) has become naturalized from New York to North Carolina, and is frequently found in woodsy areas, with its fragrant 1½-inch white flowers that change to yellow and are produced all summer. Unfortunately it spreads too easily and becomes a weed. The cultivated form known as Hall's honeysuckle (*L. japonica* var. *halliana* NICHOLS is cultivated in Florida and Puerto Rico. Its pure white 2-inch flowers turn creamy yellow the second day, the plant is evergreen, and the blossoms appear more or less all year. The petals flare near their tips, and one petal is more deeply cut than the others.

CARYOPHYLLACEAE—PINK FAMILY

## *Saponaria ocymoides* LINN.
*Common Name:* SOAPWORT

Central and southern Europe are the home of this trailing, much-branched perennial to 9 inches high. Its leaves are rather covered with small hairs, the light pink flowers with a purplish calyx appear in loose clusters (Photograph 84.) There is a horticultural form with larger flowers of deeper rose, also a white one.

## *Tripterygium regelii*  SPRAGUE & TAKEDA

*Common Name:* THREE-WING-NUT

Most of the climbers in the staff-tree family are distinguished for their fruit rather than their flowers, but an exception is *Tripterygium,* with 2 species of climbing shrubs from Korea and Japan, one of which is often found in California gardens, northward to Vancouver, and occasionally as far east as the Arnold Arboretum near Boston. It has large, alternate leaves, and at the branch tips produces immense clusters of fragrant, small white flowers set off by red stems. These bursts of blossoms in July may sometimes be 18 inches long, and the vine often grows to 12 feet. (Photograph 85.)

CISTACEAE—ROCK-ROSE FAMILY

## *Cistus obtusifolius*  SWEET

*Common Name:* ROCK-ROSE

Pearce (90) says that the rock-roses which are natives of the Mediterranean region, are not entirely hardy in colder areas. *C. lusitanicus decumbens, C. obtusifolius,* and *C. salvifolius prostratus* all have a spreading habit which makes it possible to trail them over a bank or a low wall. The flowers are white with a colored spot at the base of each petal. Although the individual flowers do not last more than a day, they are produced in such a constant succession, especially during sunny weather, that the plants are in continuous bloom during June and July. 'Paladin' (Photograph 86) is one of the many handsome hybrids in the genus.

COMBRETACEAE—COMBRETUM FAMILY

## *Combretum coccineum*  LAMARCK

[Syn. *Poivrea coccinea* DC.]

Some 250 kinds of *Combretum* vines or climbing shrubs have been reported, mostly from Africa, with a few in Asia and tropical America, but only a very few of them are showy in flower, and just 5 species are cultivated in tropical gardens. Three of them are grown in southern Florida. All are big climbers requiring substantial support to which the vines fasten themselves by old leaf petioles that have hardened and become converted into blunt hooks. All of the cultivated *Combretum* species have brilliant red flowers.

The scarlet combretum (*C. coccineum*) from Madagascar is a large climber with very slender stems. (Color Plate 54.) Though in Florida it puts on its floral display in March and April, in hot countries it is almost constantly in bloom. The small bright crimson flowers are borne in profusion in large compact brushlike bunches, contrasting beautifully with the bright green foliage. Firminger (37) calls it "one of the handsomest and most prized ornaments of our Indian gardens."

The showy combretum (*C. grandiflorum* DON) from West Africa is a vigorous woody climber for a heavy trellis. (Color Plate 53.) The young leaves for a foot or more at the vine's growing tips are at first a bright coppery red. The mature leaves are ovate, opposite, and 6 to 10 inches long. From November to June (in Florida) the vine presents a wealth of brilliant red flowers in compact, brushlike, inverted spikes. Individual blossoms are small, ½ inch long and wide, with 4 petals, sheathed at the base with a jet-black, bell-shaped calyx. From the corolla 8 clear yellow anthers protrude. The abundance of flowers compensates for their small size, as there are 25 or more blossoms per stalk and always 4 to 12 stalks on each branch.

*Combretum farinosum* HBK is a Mexican species with its red flowers in spikes of 12 inches or more; it is occasionally seen in south Florida. (Color Plate 52.)

In South Africa the burning bush (*C. microphyllum* KLOTZSCH is a bushy, deciduous climber, its tiny flowers with protruding red stamens in thick mats along the whiplike branches from July to October. Eliovson (32) reported it "spectacular in bloom." (Color Plate 50.)

It is, in fact, a startling sight, according to a letter from G. L. Guy, Curator of the National Museum of Southern Rhodesia, for a low veld of south-central Africa is otherwise almost leafless. It flowers there in spring, before most other species even come into leaf. It is a vigorous climber where there are suitable trees, elsewhere it grows as a scrambling shrub with numerous sprays of slender branches. The bark is gray-brown; the leaves are opposite, petiolate, and usually obovate and paler in color on the undersides. The flowers grow densely on small side branchlets and are of bright scarlet. The fruits have the usual combretaceous four wings and when ripe are pale brown. The vine is known by various names in Africa: flame-of-the-forest, flame-creeper, honey-flower, in addition to numerous vernacular names. It is easily propagated from seed and can also be grown from layers. On a good soil it is a really rampant grower. It should be grown in the sun, in the Northern hemisphere on a southern or western exposure. It will withstand a few degrees of frost. (Color Plate 50.)

In East Africa *C. abbreviatum* ENGLER, according to Jex-Blake (67), is "a splendid indigenous climber, going to the top of tall trees and draping them with its large cymes of brightest scarlet flowers."

*C. paniculatum* VENTENAT is another vigorous climber to the tops of highest forest trees in tropical west Africa. The young shoots have thorns. Flowers are in very striking, huge terminal panicles. The petals and stamens are bright coral-red.

*C. platypterium* HUTCHINSON & DALZIEL is a climbing shrub in Nigeria with large glossy green leaves. It produces long, many-branched inflorescences. The receptacle is a grayish red, with petals yellow to red. The flowers are followed by very attractive 5-winged fruits. (Color Plate 55.)

132

## *Quisqualis indica* LINN.

*Common Name:* RANGOON CREEPER

The Rangoon creeper, so-called, is actually a very large, scandent, deciduous, woody vine indigenous to southeast Asia and tropical west Africa, but cultivated in warm gardens everywhere for its unusual and beautiful flowers. It is particularly attractive through the summer months when it makes the best cover and is heaviest with bloom. (Photograph 79 and Color Plate 56.)

In England and California, which are scarcely warm enough for the climber to grow and bloom normally, it has a disconcerting growth habit that astonished the Dutch botanist Rumphius (George Edward Rumpf) and caused him to give it the strange name of *Quisqualis*—literally, in Latin, *who? what?* He described it:

"The young plant was an upright shrub to 3 feet with few irregular branches and scattered leaves without order. In six months it put forth a runner from the roots which climbed the neighboring trees, throwing out branches in all directions but not twisting about their support. Then the original shrub ceased to grow and perished and the plant looked and acted like a climber."

In warm countries the growth habit of *Quisqualis* is normal for a twining shrubby plant. It has a cylindrical stem, green when young, and is covered with soft brown or golden hairs. The 3- to 5-inch leaves are smooth above except for the nerves, which are hairy; the under surfaces are softly hairy. The leaf petioles are persistent, and after the leaf itself falls, they are transformed into stout curved spines that help the plant climb.

The flowers, produced in hanging clusters, have a 3-inch green calyx tube topped by 5 petals, like a long-tubed *Bouvardia*. The petals are obovate in shape, ½ inch long, rounded at both ends, and are attached to the calyx by a mere point, says Bor (9). The outer surface of the petals is flushed with pink, the inner surface at first a pure white; opening at night, this white turns pink at daybreak, then finally a rich red. As flowers in each cluster open in succession, the resulting effect of the white, pink, and red is charming and unique. The flowers are sweetly scented in the evening.

In India in rich soil Bor reported the vine rapid-growing, rampant, unmanageable, and requiring strong support and frequent pruning, as it becomes very large and blooms throughout the year. It is one of the commonest climbers to be found in Indian gardens. It is frequently grown in Florida but is much less vigorous and overwhelming.

In the botanical garden at Bangalore there grows a white-flowered form of the Rangoon creeper. The flowers stay white. This plant must be propagated vegetatively.

**84. SAPONARIA OCYMOIDES**   **85. TRIPTERYGIUM REGELII**

**86. CISTUS PALADIN**   **87. ERIOCEPHALUS AFRICANUS**

## *Commelina nudiflora* LINN.

*Common Name:* DAYFLOWER

*Commelina* is a genus of 100 species of perennial or annual herbs, more or less succulent, mostly in the tropics, many of them trailing over banks and other plants. They are cultivated for their small handsome flowers and are popular glasshouse plants. *C. nudiflora* is native to the eastern states from New Jersey southward, with ½-inch blue flowers in small clusters, closing at night. Species cultivated in glasshouses include the South African *C. africana* MIRBEL with tawny yellow flowers, the East African *C. latifolia* HOCHSTETTER EX A. RICHARD with brilliant blue flowers, and *C. ensifolia* R. BROWN from Australia, also with blue blossoms. All of these are small creepers, rooting at the nodes, and are useful in baskets.

The dayflower known as "honohono" (*C. diffusa* BURMAN F.), in Hawaii also called wandering Jew, is described by Neal (84) as:

> ". . . a low creeping weed that roots at the joints and has broad, grasslike to ovate leaves. Irregular-shaped, bright blue, paired flowers rise one at a time from a large, folded, leafy bract at the end of the stem, lasting but a day. In Hawaii it is a rapid-growing, succulent plant, covering the ground even in the shade. Honohono is relished by cattle . . . raw or cooked it is sometimes used as food by human beings."

## *Cyanotis kewensis* CLARKE

*Common Name:* PUSSY-EARS

The 40 species of *Cyanotis* scattered through the warm countries of the globe are hairy, creeping perennials like *Tradescantia*. *C. kewensis* from Malaya is a trailer with gray-green woolly leaves and violet-blue, 3-petaled flowers.

## *Dichorisandra aubletiana* SCHULTES F.

The 30 species of *Dichorisandra* in the American tropics are perennial herbs with handsome foliage, often beautifully variegated, and bearing clusters of rich blue flowers. Most of them are erect plants, but *D. aubletiana* in Trinidad is a weak trailer or climbing plant with flowers ½ inch in diameter and 3 inches long, the three petals a lovely deep violet, white at the base, borne in clusters at branch tips.

The blue ginger (*D. thyrsiflora* MIKAN), from Brazil (Color Plate 59), has more or less erect stems to 4 feet with very dark green ornamental leaves. It has beautiful flowers, a rich dark blue, the anthers bright yellow. The thyrse is compact, often 6 to 7 inches long. Chittenden (22) calls it "a very handsome flowering plant." This species is cultivated at Cypress Gardens, Florida, where it reaches 8 feet in height but dies down in winter.

Harry Blossfeld of São Paulo, Brazil, writes:

> "I saw a plant in northern Minas Gerais in thick jungle that had grown through a thicket 20 feet high and had made a canopy of flowers above it.

*Dichorisandra* has rather stiff leaves and it grows side branches arching down first and then bending up again at the tips. The old leaves along the stem and branches rot when the plant approaches blooming. The rotten leaves hang down stiffly and will not drop, thus clasping into the brush to keep the plant in place."

## *Tradescantia blossfeldiana*

While most of the trailing species of *Tradescantia* are grown for their striped and colorful foliage (*see* Chapter X), occasional greenhouse subjects, among them *T. blossfeldiana* from Argentina, have attractive flowers too. (Color Plate 43.) They grow tightly packed in a many-flowered umbell close to the stem of the plant. The 3 rose-colored petals are white at the base. Leaves are leathery, dark green above, purple with long whitish hairs beneath.

COMPOSITAE—SUNFLOWER FAMILY

## *Eriocephalus africanus*  LINN.  ❋ ERNEST E. LORD ❋
*Common Names:* WOOLLY-HEAD; SOUTH AFRICAN ROSEMARY

This is a low-growing evergreen shrub with soft grayish needle-like foliage (often 3-pronged) and small white clustered flowers all summer on numerous side-shoots along the branches. These give place to attractive white fluffy balls. Native to South Africa, it is cultivated in warm temperature climates for its bushy spreading or sprawling habit and pleasing aroma. (Photograph 87.)

## *Hidalgoa wercklei*  HOOKER
*Common Names:* CLIMBING-DAHLIA; TREASURE-VINE

This tender herbaceous vine from Costa Rica is allied to dahlias but climbs by curling its leaf petioles around the nearest support. Its small succulent leaves are deeply cut and toothed. Its 10-rayed flowers are "dazzling orange-scarlet" with a yellow center. It is a tall climber, much branched, and becomes woody at the base. It grows well in southern California but Bailey (4) says it cannot be grown outdoors as far north as Washington.

## *Mikania scandens*  WILLDENOW
*Common Name:* CLIMBING HEMPWEED

This "common weed but a pretty one," according to Bailey (4) is native from New England to Florida and west to Texas, but in Brazil it is cultivated. It is an annual climber with tiny pinkish or white flowers in 2-inch clusters that smell strongly of vanilla. Blossfeld (8) says that *M. speciosa* DC. with pink flowers "is the most attractive for ornamental purposes." Like *M. cordata,* however (Photograph 90), it is not yet well known in cultivation.

88.  MUTISIA COCCINEA       89.  MUTISIA CLEMATIS

90.  MIKANIA CORDATA        91.  SENECIO GREYII

## *Mutisia decurrens* CAVANILLES

Although this and a dozen other species of these showy-flowered vines from the Chilean Andes have been repeatedly introduced into Californian and English gardens and glasshouses over the past 100 years, none seems to have been established successfully. The large and brilliant flowers have drawn the enthusiastic praise of many English gardeners.

Jones (69) in 1937 reported just two plants of *M. clematis* LINN. F. (Photograph 89) growing in the San Francisco area where:

> ". . . the very spectacular flowers excite a great deal of attention. . . . The many-ray flowers make a splash of color 3 inches in diameter in some shade of red, variously described as orange-scarlet or orange-vermilion. Quite as conspicuous as the color are the whitish or gray bracts which line the tube of the flower, growing in four or five rows."

Chittenden (22) wrote that *M. clematis,* an evergreen climber to 20 or 30 feet from Ecuador is the best species of those which have been grown in England.

Bailey (4) reported, for America, that *M. decurrens* with its brilliant orange flowers is "perhaps the best species." Among the other 60 species the flowers range from orange and various reds to satiny pink, pink-and-yellow, pale pink and pale mauve. *M. coccinea* (Photograph 88) is one of the brilliant-flowered ones, its showy clusters in loose, delicate sprays.

On all *Mutisia* species the flowers are long-lasting when cut. The simple or pinnate leaves often end in tendrils which help the plants climb. Some of the leaves are spiny like *Ilex.*

A *Mutisia* species from Peru is shown in Color Plate 60.

## *Othonna capensis* BAILEY
[Syn. *O. crassifolia* Harvey, not Linn.]
*Common Name:* PICKLE-PLANT

The pickle-plant, one of 60 species of *Othonna* in South Africa, is cultivated in glasshouses as a trailer or basket plant. It is a succulent perennial with fleshy stems and tiny pickle-shaped leaves. It bears solitary or small bunches of golden daisy flowers on erect 4-inch stems as long as the sun shines, but on cloudy days they fold.

## *Senecio* LINN.

Climbers are rare in the sunflower family but in the enormous genus *Senecio* (1,200 species—the largest genus of all), are half a dozen excellent vines that are often cultivated in warm gardens. Mostly herbaceous, they tend to creep or trail over other plants, although with opportunity and proper support they will cover fences and climb 30-foot trees.

**92.  SENECIO ANGULATUS**    **93.  SENECIO SCANDENS**

**94.  WEDELIA TRILOBATA**    **95.  ARGYREIA NERVOSA**

## *Senecio confusus* BRITTON

*Common Names:* MEXICAN FLAME-VINE; ORANGE GLOW-VINE; TRAILING GROUNDSEL; MEXICAN DAISY; MEXICAN FIRE-VINE

Commonest in Florida and California is the Mexican flame-vine, a rampant evergreen that covers stumps, waste places, and fences with handsome abandon. The showy orange or orange-red daisy flowers, 1½ inches in diameter, are in abundant clusters produced most of the year, though in greatest profusion in spring and early summer. It is one of Florida's most popular climbers because it knows no pests and it can be kept in check with pruning shears.

*S. angulatus* LINN. F. is a small yellow-flowered vine sometimes cultivated in southern California. (Photograph 91.) It is native to Australia and South Africa. See E. P. Phillips: "Flowering Plants of South Africa," xi: 424.

The tropical African *S. auriculatissimus* BRITTON, according to Bailey (4), is a striking plant and well worthy of more general cultivation on account of the peculiar foliage and bright yellow flowers. The petiolate leaves are transversely oblong or kidney-shaped, 2 to 3-inches across, on slender 2-inch petioles that dilate abruptly at the base into two broad auricles that completely clasp the stem.

*S. chinotegensis* KLATT is often a very striking thing in Central America. It can be weedy, but when it grows up over the trees and is in full flower, it is undeniably attractive.

*S. greyii* HOOKER F., from New Zealand, is a low spreading shrub, often used to cover banks. (Photograph 92.) The young leaves are covered with white tomentum; mature leaves are smooth and shining except at the edges. These and the under sides are densely clad with a soft white tomentum. The yellow ray flowers are in dense clusters.

*S. hoffmanii* KLATT, much like *S. confusus* except that flowers are larger and of grenadine-red or carmine, is often seen in California, and will cover a fence in no time.

*S. macroglossus* DC., called Cape-ivy, with young shoots resembling English ivy, has dark triangular succulent leaves and charming yellow daisy flowers, 2 inches across, on 6-inch stems. The plant prefers to trail, but will climb if tied. It is cultivated in east Africa and Australia.

*S. mikanioides* OTTO, commonly called German-ivy, is a slender, smooth, South African vine, frequently encountered in glasshouses, with dense clusters of small yellow ray flowers.

*S. petitianus* A. RICHARD is a succulent climber to 40 feet in most parts of East Africa, above 3,000 feet. Flowers abundantly after a year of good rains. Flowers are a golden yellow with an orange center produced in dense clusters.

*S. scandens* BUCHANAN-HAMILTON (Photograph 93),, often seen in California, is a hardy Chinese climber to 6 feet or more, with clusters of yellow ray flowers.

*S. tamoides* DC., in South Africa called the canary-creeper or climbing-cineraria, is a semi-evergreen climbing shrub that reaches into trees. It has 5-inch clusters of tiny brillinat yellow daisies which, Eliovson reported, " in autumn are vividly showy, a delightful climber, deservedly popular."

## *Vernonia andersonii*   C. B. CLARKE
[Syn. *V. cuminginana*   Bentham]

Of the thousand species of *Vernonia* scattered throughout the world, most are weedy herbs or shrubs, of little or no horticultural value. This and five other climbing species of *Vernonia* were reported by Hundley (60) from the Burma jungles.

*V. aurantiaca* N. E. BROWN in central Africa, if it has an opportunity, scrambles to the tops of trees and produces quantities of brilliant, deep orange, daisylike flowers. If no trees are available, it remains shrubby .

T. K. Bose writes from Calcutta that in India *V. eleagnaefolia* DC. is a quick-growing evergreen climber with stems pendulous, usually not much branched, whitish when young. The leaves are simple, alternate, lanceolate, broader at the upper portion, irregularly toothed. Flowers are white in small axillary heads. It is a useful and popular climber for screening.

## *Wedelia trilobata*   (LINN.) A. HITCHCOCK

This tropical American creeping herb is prized as a bedding plant in Florida because it can be mowed. (Photograph 94.) Up above the fresh green paired leaves that are 1 to 5 inches long, oval or 3-lobed, and toothed, it has solitary bright yellow 2-inch daisy flowers on 8-inch stems. It is unexcelled as a climber for banks. Five other species in Puerto Rico are described by Britton & Wilson (13).

CONNARACEAE—CONNARUS FAMILY

## *Agelaea obliqua*   (PALISOT DE BEAUVOIS) BAILLON

Irvine (65) called this "a beautiful scrambling shrub or woody climber to 20 feet forming masses on other trees; . . . it is of value as an ornamental plant." The shining, trifoliate leaves have oblique leaflets 3½ by 2½ inches and a larger terminal leaflet up to 5 by 4 inches. The sweet-scented white flowers are rather crowded in foot-long clusters at the branch tips. Irvine reported that another species in Ghana, *A. trifolia* (LAMARCK) GILG, also "is of value as an ornamental plant." It is a scrambling shrub or woody climber to 25 feet or more, with green or creamy-white flowers in ample terminal clusters.

## *Byrsocarpus coccineus*   SCHUMANN & THONNING

This scrambling or climbing shrub, widespread in tropical Africa, was reported by Irvine (65) as "of distinct decorative value with its delicate, young, pink-tinged foliage and white, sweet-scented flowers." The pinnate leaves with 6 to 9 pairs of leaflets, becoming larger near the tips, are reddish-orange and delicate when young, turning light green later; they are about 1 inch long, the tips rounded.

The flowers, January to March, are small, white or pinkish, in clusters in the leaf axils. The yellow or red fruits in June, about ½ inch long, split down one side to release a black seed that is almost surrounded by a large bright yellow aril.

## Manotes longiflora   J. G. BAKER EX OLIVER

This is a scrambling shrub to 20 feet commonly found in secondary forests in Ghana. It has small leaves and bears flowers twice a year, usually August and December, that are hairy, brownish-white or yellowish-pink, with bright pink sepals. They are borne in clusters at the branch tips and in the leaf axils. (Color Plate 57).

## CONVOLVULACEAE—MORNING-GLORY FAMILY

## Argyreia nervosa   (BURMAN F.) BOJER
[Syn. *Argyreia speciosa*   (Linn. f.) Sweet]

*Common Names:* WOOLLY MORNING-GLORY; SILKEN CORD (Cuba); ELEPHANT CREEPER (India)

The woolly morning-glory is a coarse, very heavy Indian climber that needs a great deal of room and a heavy trellis to support it. (Photograph 95.) The smooth, ovate to heart-shaped, dark green leaves are densely covered beneath with silky white hairs. They measure 3 to 12 inches wide and they overlap on the vine so as to provide solid shade.

The same soft, silvery tomentum covers the branches, the leaf stalks, the flower stems and calyx, and even the twining tips of the new growth.

The funnelform flowers 2 to 3 inches long, borne in clusters on 6-inch stems, are rosy-purple inside and white-hairy outside. Flowering begins in May and continues for several months. The brown seedpod clusters are highly decorative but are seldom produced in Florida.

*A. setosa* CHOISY [syn. *Lettsomia setosa* Roxburgh] is one of 30 trailing, climbing, or scandent *Argyreia* species in India—a big, rather coarse climber that is best suited to a boundary fence. It bears dense clusters of pretty rose-colored or purple funnelform flowers that are 1 to 2 inches long, hairy on the outside. The ovate to heart-shaped leaves are 2 to 5 inches long, 1 to 3 inches wide, smooth above and hairy beneath.

## Bonamia pannosa   (R. BROWN) HALLIER F.
[Syn. *Breweria pannosa*   R. Brown]

In northern Queensland two kinds of native trailing vines are found in gardens. *Bonamia pannosa,* that spreads to 8 feet or more, produces velvety dark blue solitary flowers all along the stems. Albert de Lestang wrote from Queensland: "This is a fascinating flower and very showy. It is used here to cover banks or rocks."

**96. CALYSTEGIA SEPIUM    97. CALYSTEGIA SOLDANELLA**

**98. CONVOLVULUS SABATIUS    99. IPOMOEA FISTULOSA**

*B. media* (R. Brown) HALLIER F. [syn. *Breweria media* R. Brown] is smaller, usually to 4 feet, with white solitary flowers in the axils, a profuse ever-bloomer. (Color Plate 64.)

## *Calycobolus heudelotii* (J. G. BAKER EX OLIVER) HEINE
[Syn. *Prevostea heudelotii* (J. G. Baker ex Oliver) Hallier f.]

Irvine (65) reported on this "handsome shrubby climber (liana) to 50 feet or more," from Ghana to the Belgian Congo. It has shining, ovate, acuminate leaves 5½ by 3 inches. From December to March it bears fragrant white flowers, the corolla 1 inch long. These are often crowded in axillary clusters and Irvine called the climber "of decorative value." The outer sepals become much enlarged and striking in the fruit.

## *Calystegia japonica* CHOISY
Common Name: CALIFORNIA ROSE

Many reference books lump *Calystegia* and *Convolvulus* into a single genus, but modern taxonomists insist they very definitely are distinct genera.

The "California rose" comes from Japan. It is an herbaceous perennial twiner to 30 feet, often a weed, growing almost too easily. It produces quantities of bright pink flowers 1 to 2 inches across during the summer. Bailey (5) reported that a sterile double form, the blossoms 2 inches across with narrow wavy petals, is now naturalized from New York to Missouri. The flesh-pink flowers turn to bright rose as they fade. This plant is now known as *Calystegia pubescens* LINDLEY.

*Calystegia sepium* (LINN.) R. BROWN, [syn. *Convolvulus sepium* Linn.], variously known as bindweed, bear-wind, or Rutland beauty is a perennial trailer 3 to 10 feet long in temperate regions. (Photograph 96.) Some varieties have pink flowers striped white. It is a troublesome weed in moist soils.

On the beaches of England and France grows *C. soldanella* (LINN.) R. BROWN [syn. *Convolvulus soldanella* Linn.] with pretty rose or purple flowers and decorative kidney-shaped leaves (Photograph 97). It is a procumbent plant that creeps far but does not twine. Its perennial roots may occasionally submit to transplanting, but Chittenden (22) skipped a description of it because, he said, "It is very difficult to establish successfully."

## *Convolvulus tricolor* LINN.
Common Name: DWARF MORNING-GLORY

Most popular and least aggressive of the half dozen species of *Convolvulus* cultivated in the United States is this sprawling annual, *C. tricolor, with* 1½-inch flowers with blue limb and yellow throat margined with white. It blooms continuously all summer on sunny days.

The Morocco glorybind or Morocco morning-glory, *C. sabatius* VIVIANI [syn. *C. mauritanicus* Boissier] is a twining prostrate plant from North Africa, with strong perennial roots and slender stems. It makes a plant 3 feet across, bearing 1-inch blue or violet-purple flowers with a white tube. (Photograph 98.)

*C. elegantissimus* MILLER, a Mediterranean species with palmately lobed leaves, the lobes very narrow, and pink flowers, is sometimes grown but may become a weed.

## *Hewittia sublobata* (LINN. F.) O. KUNTZE ⚜ BERNARD VERDCOURT ⚜
[Syn. *H. bicolor* (Vahl) Wight & Arnott]

This twining herb with broadly heart-shaped, entire, 3-lobed leaves and bell-shaped white or pale yellowish flowers with dark purple center, is widespread in the tropics, particularly in Africa. It is a poor weedy thing.

## *Ipomoea* LINN. ⚜ BERNARD VERDCOURT ⚜

This genus, containing about 500 species, occurs throughout the tropics and subtropics of both hemispheres. Obviously it is possible to mention only a few here, and there are literally scores of others which, although quite spectacular, have never been cultivated. In some English gardening dictionaries many other species will be found listed, but the majority of these have not been in cultivation for the past century or they were only grown once or twice as curiosities. Many of the species were formerly described in *Convolvulus,* but only the commoner synonyms have been quoted here. The groups *Pharbitis, Calonyction,* and *Quamoclit* are not now considered generically separable, but *Merremia, Opercu-lina,* and *Stictocardia* have been recognized. *Calonyction* and *Quamoclit* are easily recognized by the salver-shaped flowers from which the stamens are exserted and the awnlike appendages from the tops of the sepals. The sweet potato, *Ipomoea batatas* (LINN.) LAMARCK, and jalap, *I. purga* (WENDEROTH) HAYNE, are examples of useful products. Nearly all the species need greenhouse or stove conditions if grown in temperate climates.

    *I. acuminata* (VAHL) ROEMER & SCHULTES [syn. *I. congesta* R. Brown; *I. vahliana* House], blue dawn-flower (Color Plate 67), is a rapidly growing and profusely flowering liane reaching 40 feet, with heart-shaped, entire or 3-lobed leaves. Stalks are many-flowered, the flowers funnel-shaped, blue or bluish-purple with a red tinge, 2 to 3½ inches long. A native of South America it is now grown throughout the tropics and warmer temperate regions. The sepals are very narrow but finely hairy, not bristly, as they are in *I. purpurea,* with which it is frequently confused. It can become too vigorous in the garden.

    *I. leari* PAXTON [syn.: *Pharbitis leari* (Paxton) LINDLEY] is a form with silvery velvety-hairy leaves but it is scarcely specifically distinct. *I. indica* (BURMAN) MERRILL has been suggested as the correct name of this species, but the identity is too uncertain. The name *acuminata* has frequently been mis-applied to *I. nil* and its close relatives.

    *I. alba* LINN. [syn.: *I. bona-nox* Linn.; *Calonyction aculeatum* (Linn.) House; *C. bona-nox* (Linn.) Bojer; *C. speciosum* Choisy], large moonflower, is a mostly hairless, vigorous annual or perennial, 3 to 40 feet long, with heart-shaped, entire or 3-lobed leaves. Stalks are 1 to several-flowered, and the flowers, which are scented, open suddenly in the evening. They are salver-shaped, white or greenish-cream, the tube very slender, 3 to 5 inches long, 1/5 inch

**100.   IPOMOEA PURPUREA**   **101.   IPOMOEA QUAMOCLIT**

**102.   IPOMOEA ALBA**   **103.   IPOMOEA HEDERIFOLIA**

wide, the limb 3 to 6 inches wide. (Photograph 102.) In subtropical climates it will often flower only 6 weeks after planting. For rapid germination the seeds should be nicked or soaked in warm water for several hours. It is an ideal plant for covering unsightly dumps or screens but rather too rampant for temperate greenhouses.

*I. aquatica* FORSKAL [syn. *I. reptans* Auctt.] is a prostrate or floating plant, mostly with thick, semi-succulent stems, rooting at the nodes. Leaves are mostly triangular. Stalks have 1 to 10 flowers which are funnel-shaped, purple or pink or white with a deeper center, 1 to 3 inches long (Photograph 112). It occurs in swampy places throughout the tropics. Several varieties are grown in eastern Asia as vegetables but it is scarcely ever seen as an ornamental. It might be useful to border ponds in rather arid areas. (Color Plate 69.)

*I. bonariensis* HOOKER [syn. wrongly associated with the name *I. ficifolia* Lindley, which is a distinct African plant]. This is a twining plant of South America with deeply 3 to 5-lobed leaves which are covered with hairs. Flowers are narrowly funnel-shaped or almost salver-shaped, the limb spreading and lobed, lilac or pale purple, about 1½ to 2 inches long and wide.

*I. bracteata* CAVANILLES [syn. *Exogonium bracteatum* (Cavanilles) Choisy] is a climbing plant somewhat reminiscent of *Bougainvillea* with woody stems up to several yards long. Leaves are ovate and acuminate. Flowers are in dense hanging clusters, each flower supported by a rounded heart-shaped, folded bract of red, rose, green, or violet, about ¾ to 1½ inches long and wide. Flowers are red or lilac, tubular, about 1¼ inches long; the stamens and style exserted. A native of Mexico. (Color Plate 65.)

*I. cairica* (LINN.) SWEET [syn. *I. palmata* Forskal], railway creeper (Color Plate 70), is a perennial climber which forms dense mats and is now naturalized in most tropical countries but is a native of the Old World. The rootstock is tuberous and stems are hairless but more or less warty when older. Leaves are cut nearly to the base into 5 to 7 elliptic lobes. Stalks are 1 to several-flowered, the flowers more or less funnel-shaped, reddish-purple or purple with a deeper center, 2 to 2½ inches long and wide; seeds with long silky hairs along the edges. An attractive but weedy plant suitable for waste places in warm countries.

*I. carnea* JACQUIN is a woody climber with very finely velvety heart-shaped leaves. Stalks are several-flowered, the corollas narrowly funnel-shaped, pink, 2½ inches long and 3 inches wide. Sepals are very short and broadly rounded. Young buds are silvery-silky.

*I. coccinea* LINN. [syn. *Quamoclit coccinea* (Linn.) Moench], star ipomoea, is very similar to the cardinal's-flower (*I. hederifolia*), described below, and often confused with it, but its fruits curve downward whereas in *I. hederifolia* they are held erect.

*I. fistulosa* MARTIUS EX CHOISY is a large, diffuse or straggling plant with milky juice, closely related to *I. carnea* but more shrubby and with longer leaves. (Photograph 99.) It can be developed into a climber by providing a support and by training it properly. Plants grown in the sun and trained as climbers produce a luxuriance of bloom, while those planted in shade produce more leaves.

*I. funis* CHAMISSO & SCHLECHTENDAHL [syn. *Quamoclit grandiflora* (Llave

147

& Lexarza) G. Don] is a perennial climber with more or less heart-shaped leaves. Stalks are very long, 2 to several-flowered, the flowers salver-shaped, orange or scarlet, 1½ inches long. Sepals are prominently awned. This is essentially a larger version of *I. hederifolia* (below).

*I. grantii* OLIVER is a stout liana up to about 30 feet long with either entire or deeply divided leaves, white beneath but green above and very blistered or bullate. Flowers are funnel-shaped, reddish-purple or crimson, 3 to 4 inches long. This very attractive East African species should be tried in cultivation.

*I. hederacea* JACQUIN [syn. *Pharbitis hederacea* (Jacquin) Choisy] is very similar to *I. nil* with which it is often confused, but it is of American origin and differs in the smaller flowers, 1 to 2 inches long, with rather narrower sepals which are often spreading and recurved at the tips.

*I. hederifolia* LINN. [syn.: *I. angulata* Lamarck; *I. phoenicea* Roxburgh; *Quamoclit angulata* (Lamarck) Bojer], cardinal's-flower, is a slender annual twiner 3 to 16 feet long, native of tropical America but now widespread in the tropics of the Old World and often naturalized. (Photograph 103.) The leaves are simple, hairless, heart-shaped or 3-lobed, 2 to 4 inches long. The brilliant orange or scarlet salver-shaped flowers are borne in long-stalked inflorescences; the tube is about 1 to 1½ inches long and the limb about 1 inch wide, from which the stamens are exserted. This species is good for decorating low fences and it is easily grown from seed.

*I. horsfalliae* HOOKER, Lady Doorly morning-glory or cardinal-creeper (Color Plate 66), a West Indian plant, is perhaps the most popular winter-flowering warmhouse species. It will climb to 20 to 30 feet and bear hundreds of flowers. The leaves are thickish, hairless, 5 to 7-lobed or completely divided into 5 to 7 leaflets. Stalks are many-flowered, the flowers bell-shaped, rose to crimson, 2½ inches long and wide or sometimes smaller. It was first grown by Mrs. Charles Horsfall, an English lady. Var. *briggstii* HOUSE is a freer grower and bloomer with rich magenta-crimson flowers. It will root from cuttings more easily than the typical variety—important since seeds are not easily produced even in Florida; but it is hardy from central Florida southward, the rootstock being able to withstand quite heavy frosts.

For *I. indica,* see *I. acuminata.*

*I. jalapa* (LINN.) PURSH is a slender hairless twining vine from a large woody root with triangular-ovate entire or 3-lobed leaves. Stalks are short, usually 1-flowered, the flowers narrowly funnel-shaped, pink or purple, 2 to 2½ inches long. The roots possess strong purgative properties. Pursh actually had a different species in mind but his combination of Linnaeus's name must be used.

*I. kituiensis* VATKE is a robust scrambler or climber up to 20 feet with heart-shaped or kidney-shaped leaves. Stalks are usually many-flowered, the flowers funnel-shaped, white, cream or yellow with a purple center, 2 to 3¼ inches long. Sepals are long and narrow; seeds are covered with long golden hairs. This native of East Africa is scarcely ever cultivated, but it deserves to be.

*I. hartmannii* VATKE is another rather similar East African species with very bristly stems.

For *I. leari,* see *I. acuminata.*

148

*I. macrorhiza* MICHAUX [syn. *I. jalapa* sensu Pursh] is a perennial trailer or climber to 8 feet with a thick woody root sometimes weighing 30 pounds. Leaves are heart-shaped, entire or lobed, softly hairy. Stalks are 1 to 5-flowered, the flowers salver-shaped, cream or white with a magenta tube, about 3 inches long.

*I. mauritiana* JACQUIN [syn.: *I. paniculata* R. Brown], for long known as *I. digitata* Linn., but it has now been proved that this name refers to a rare plant endemic to Haiti, first discovered by Plumier and not found again until Ekman rediscovered it; nearly every reference to *I. digitata* in literature refers to *I. mauritiana*]. This high-climbing, hairless, tuberous-rooted forest vine occurs in the tropics of both hemispheres. The leaves are large and either entire or 3 to 9 lobed. The small sepals clasp the bell-shaped or funnel-shaped flowers, which are abruptly narrowed right at the base, reddish-purple or pinkish, 2 to 2½ inches long. The seeds have long silky hairs. The plant will not stand frost.

*I. muricata* (LINN.) JACQUIN has flowers similar to those of *I. alba,* but smaller, often purplish, and the expanded part rarely more than 3 inches wide. The stems are usually tuberculate. It is not of much horticultural value.

*I. mutabilis* KER-GAWLER [syn. *Pharbitis mutabilis* (Ker-Gawler) Bojer] is a Mexican species with densely softly hairy stems and entire or 3-lobed leaves which are silvery-gray beneath. Flowers are funnel-shaped, blue with a white tube, 2½ to 3 inches long. Sepals are linear-lanceolate, appressed-silky. The above description is taken from Bailey; from the original plate I would say that it is identical with the *leari* variety of *I. acuminata* and if that is treated as a distinct species then *I. mutabilis* would be its correct name.

*I. nil* (LINN.) ROTH [syn. *Pharbitis nil* (LINN.) Choisy] is an annual or perennial herbaceous twiner with hairy stems and heart-shaped, entire or 3-lobed leaves. Stalks are 1 to several-flowered, the flowers funnel-shaped, pale to bright blue but later often red or reddish-purple with a white tube, 2 to 2½ inches long. The sepals are long drawn out, narrowed at the tips and bristly at the base. The Imperial Japanese morning-glories (*I. imperialis* HORT.) belong here, as does the cultivar 'Scarlet O'Hara' and also cv. *limbata* BAILEY, which has violet-purple flowers margined with white.

*I. pandurata* (LINN.) G. F. W. MEYER, wild sweet-potato, wild potato-vine, or man-of-the-earth, is a perennial climber that attains 12 feet and has very long heavy roots. Leaves are entire, heart-shaped or variously 3-lobed or fiddle-shaped. Stalks are 1 to 5-flowered, the flowers broadly funnel-shaped, white with a dark purple throat. This plant is very hardy and can withstand temperatures of 26° below zero, Fahrenheit, but it can become a most troublesome weed. Native of North America.

*I. pes-caprae* (LINN.) R. BROWN [syn. *I. biloba* Forskal] is a perennial trailer on beaches throughout the tropics; only rarely found inland. (Photograph 104.) The leaves are round or oblong, shortly to deeply notched or lobed at the apex; flowers are funnel-shaped, pink or reddish-purple with a darker center, 1½ to 2 inches long. The vine is of little use save for sand-binding on beaches.

*I. purpurea* (LINN.) ROTH [syn. *Pharbitis purpurea* (Linn.) Voigt] is the common morning-glory. This herbaceous annual twiner has hairy stems and

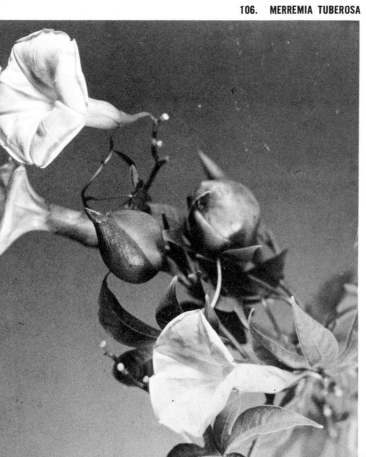

104.  IPOMOEA PES-CAPRAE    105.  IPOMOEA TRICOLOR

106.  MERREMIA TUBEROSA    107.  MERREMIA TUBEROSA

heart-shaped, or 3-lobed entire leaves. (Photograph 100.) Stalks are 1 to few-flowered, the flowers funnel-shaped, purple-blue and reddish white with a very pale or white tube, 2 to 2½ inches long. The sepals are acute, not strongly narrowed above, and have the basal part covered with long bristles, thus distinguishing it from *I. nil* and *I. acuminata* with which it is frequently confused. Although usually stated to be the commonest species in cultivation, in Africa at any rate, it was decidedly inferior to *I. acuminata* and *I. tricolor* and often looked very weedy. Many cultivars, including double forms, are available.

*I. quamoclit* LINN. [syn.: *Quamoclit pinnata* (Desrousseaux) Bojer; *Q. vulgaris* Choisy] is called cypress-vine or Indian-pink. It is an annual twiner, 3 to 6 feet long, hairless, with leaves more or less oblong in outline, divided into 8 to 18 pairs of very narrow segments. Stalks are long, 1 to few-flowered, the flowers salver-shaped, red or white, ¾ to 1½ inches long and ⅜ to ¾ inch wide. Photograph 101.) Being cultivated throughout the world, its origin is doubtful; it often becomes naturalized. It is ideal for covering netting and trellis-work, and although short-lived it produces an abundance of readily propagated seed.

*I. sagittata* POIRET is a twiner of marshes and fields, native to North America and the West Indies. The leaves are strongly arrow-shaped and the flowers narrowly funnel-shaped and purple.

*I. setosa* KER-GAWLER [syn. *I. melanotricha* Brandegee], Brazilian morning-glory, is a very vigorous liana with stems covered with stiff purplish hairs. Leaves are heart-shaped, generally deeply 3-lobed, the middle lobe abruptly narrowed below. Stalks are many-flowered, the flowers salver-shaped, rose-purple, 2 to 4 inches wide.

*I. X sloteri* (HOUSE) VAN OOSTROOM [syn. *Quamoclit sloteri* House] cardinal-vine. This is a hybrid between *I. quamoclit* and *I. coccinea,* first developed by Logan Sloter of Columbus, Ohio, who finally, after 11 years obtained one seed from a hybrid; when planted next year 500 seeds were obtained. It is an annual high-climbing vine with leaves triangular-ovate in outline, divided to beyond the middle into 7 to 15 narrow segments of which the middle one is the longest. Stalks have 1 to 3 crimson, salver-shaped flowers about 2 inches long and 1½ inches wide, from which the stamens are exserted.

*I. ternata* JACQUIN [syn. *I. thomsoniana* Masters; *I. horsfalliae* Hooker var. *alba* Hort.] This is very like *I. horsfalliae,* which may be but a variety, but with 3-leafleted leaves and white, trumpet-shaped flowers 2 inches across.

*I. tricolor* CAVANILLES [syn. *I. rubro-caerulea* Hooker; *Pharbitis rubro-caerulea* (Hooker) Choisy; often quite wrongly called *I. violacea* Linn. and sometimes even confused with *I. acuminata*]. Under the name of 'Heavenly Blue,' this is undoubtedly the most popular of all morning-glories—a perennial but best grown as an annual. An extensive twiner to 20 feet, it will form a rapid covering for walls, pillars, etc. (Photograph 105.) The leaves are hairless, heart-shaped and quite entire; stalks are hollow, 3 to 4-flowered, the flowers funnel-shaped with a white tube; the limb, reddish in bud, turns a perfectly clear azure-blue or purple, 3 to 4 inches long and wide. This is easily distinguished from the other commonly cultivated morning-glories by the small linear sepals. This plant has gained considerable notoriety because of the small amount of LSD contained in the seeds; in Mexico it has long been known as an hallucinogenic plant. Various named varieties are obtainable, including a white one which is not so attractive.

*I. tuba* (SCHLECHTENDAHL.) G. DON [syn. *I. grandiflora* (JACQUIN) Hallier f.; *Calonyction grandiflorum* (Jacquin) Choisy]. Mostly a coastal plant, this occurs throughout the tropics. Flowers are salver-shaped, more or less white, 3 to 4 inches long, opening at night. Though sometimes listed, it is not very successful in cultivation.

*I. tuberculata* KER-GAWLER [syn. *I. dasysperma* Jacquin] is a hairless annual twiner with smooth or tuberculate stems up to 8 feet long and leaves 5 to 9-lobed as in *I. cairica*. Stalks are 1 to 3-flowered, the flowers narrowly funnel-shaped, white or mostly yellow with a purple center, 2 to 4 inches long. This very beautiful African species is seldom seen in cultivation.

## *Jacquemontia pentantha*  (JACQUIN) G. DON
[Syn. *J. violacea* Choisy]

*Jacquemontia* vines of 70 kinds are found mostly in the tropics, with a few in the southeastern United States. The flowers are very much like those of *Ipomoea* and *Convolvulus;* the real differences lie in the stigmas and pollen. The best known species are small climbers with small blue, white or violet flowers, sometimes suggesting the name MINIATURE MORNING-GLORY. (Color Plate 63.)

In Florida gardens the native perennial *J. pentantha* is frequently grown. It is a charming slender climber from the Big Cypress area of southwest Florida, extending rarely to more than 6 feet. It is thick-growing, with small, heart-shaped deep green leaves and many delicate little bell-shaped bright lilac-blue flowers with white centers. They are about 1 inch wide, freely produced most of the year, in loose clusters of 5 to 12, and they look like tiny morning-glories. Like their cousins, these blue flowers begin to close in mid-afternoon, but another bright display will come the next day and almost every day throughout the year—which is something few other plants will do. *Jacquemontia* is a delicate vine with a light, gentle habit of growth well adapted to a small trellis or wrought-iron grillwork, which it enhances rather than hides. It needs a sunny, well-drained location.

A lesser twining annual, *J. tamnifolia* (LINN.) GRISEBACH, grows under cultivation and in waste areas through the southern States. It has ½-inch violet flowers in dense clusters. It is found in gardens in Karachi and is common wild in Africa.

## *Maripa passifloroides*  BENTHAM EX MEISNER  ※ BERNARD VERDCOURT ※
[Syn. *Operculina passifloroides*  (Bentham ex Meisner) Ducke]
*Common Names:* MARACUJA-RANA; LITTLE PASSION-FLOWER

This is a favored species in a genus of about a dozen woody climbers, rarely cultivated even in their native Brazil. It is a large woody liana with thick, simple, oblong-elliptic leaves and bell-shaped, velvety, blue or purple-mauve flowers, mostly shading to white in the center. (Color Plate 68.) Richard Spruce, who

108. MERREMIA DISSECTA     109. MINA LOBATA

110. PORANA PANICULATA     111. PORANA PANICULATA

first collected the plant in 1851, states in his field notes: "This is the first really woody Convolvulus I have found. . . . It is just now the glory of the forest."

A similar species, *M. scandens* AUBLET, with red flowers that give it the name of "brasa" (live coal), also from Amazonia, was reported by Blossfeld (8).

## *Merremia* DENNSTEDT EX HALLIER F.     ☀ BERNARD VERDCOURT ☀

This rather large genus containing about 80 species occurs throughout the tropics of both hemispheres. It is admittedly very close to *Ipomoea* from which it differs essentially in having smooth pollen grains; those of *Ipomoea* are spiny, as can easily be seen under an ordinary hand lens. The flowers of *Merremia* species are more often yellow or white, where as only a few *Ipomoea* such as *I. obscura* (LINN.) KER-GAWLER have truly yellow flowers.

### *Merremia aurea* (KELLOG) O'DONELL

[Syn.: *Ipomoea aurea* Kellogg; *Operculina aurea* (Kellog) House]

This is a slender twiner with large, white, tuberous roots and 5-lobed leaves. Flowers are funnel-shaped with a wide limb, golden-yellow, 2 to 4 inches wide. A native of lower California.

*M. dissecta* (JACQUIN) HALLIER F. [syn. *Ipomoea dissecta* (Jacquin) Pursh; *I. sinuata* Ortega; *Operculina dissecta* (Jacquin) House], noon-flower, is a tuberous-rooted climber, the stems covered with long yellowish hairs. Leaves are palmately 7-lobed, the narrow lobes sinuately cut or toothed. Stalks are 1 or 2-flowered, the flowers bell-shaped, white with a purple center, 1 to 2 inches wide. A native of tropical America; a weed in Florida (Photograph 108.)

*M. hederacea* (BURMAN F.) HALLIER F. [syn. *Ipomoea chryseides* Ker-Gawler] has been included in gardening books but is scarcely a decorative plant, the flowers being minute.

*M. macrocalyx* (RUIZ & PAVON) O'DONELL [syn. *Merremia glabra* (Choisy) Hallier f.] is a rather heavy twiner with 5-leafleted leaves. Stalks are long, 1 to many-flowered, the flowers funnel-shaped, white, about 2 inches long and wide. Fruits and surrounding calyx becoming thinly woody and are sometimes used by flower arrangers in this state. A native of Brazil.

*M. pacifica* VAN OOSTSTROOM is a twiner with broadly heart-shaped leaves. Stalks are about 6-flowered, the flowers funnel-shaped, white with a yellow center, 2 inches long. Native of Fiji and Malaysia.

*M. quinquefolia* (LINN.) HALLIER F. [syn. *Ipomoea quinquefolia* Linn.] is a herbaceous twiner, mostly with hairy stems and palmate leaves of 5 leaflets. Stalks are 1 to 5-flowered, glandular at the tips, the flowers funnel-shaped, pale yellow or whitish, ¾ to 1 inch long. Of tropical American origin, this species has been cultivated in Malaysia and Portuguese East Africa where it has become naturalized. A very rapid grower, it soon covers all other plants.

*M. tridentata* (LINN.) HALLIER F. [syn. *Ipomoea denticulata* R. Brown; *I. filicaulis* (Vahl) Blume] is a perennial trailer or twiner with lanceolate leaves, often lobed, and clasping at the base. Flowers are funnel-shaped, whitish or yellow with a maroon center, mostly about ¾ inch long and wide. In the tropics this is a widespread plant, often listed but scarcely worth cultivating.

*M. tuberosa* (LINN.) RENDLE [syn. *Operculina tuberosa* (Linn.) Meisner; *Ipomoea tuberosa* Linn.], Spanish arbour-vine or wood-rose, is a hairless, perennial, tuberous-rooted climber, rapidly forming extensive masses and rather too vigorous for the better parts of the garden. It will climb right up into the crowns of tall trees. Leaves are palmately 7-lobed, the stalks few to several-flowered, the flowers tubular-funnel-shaped, yellow, 1½ to 2½ inches long and wide. The spreading sepals enlarge in fruit and the whole resembles a wooden flower. (Photographs 106 and 107.) It will grow from seed or cuttings but the latter are difficult to root. In warm climates it flowers after two years.

*M. vitifolia* (BURMAN F.) HALLIER F. [syn. *Ipomoea vitifolia* (Burman f.) Sweet] is a mostly hairy large twiner, 10 to 15 feet long with palmately 5 to 7-lobed leaves, the lobes often toothed. Stalks are 1 to few-flowered, the flowers funnel-shaped, bright yellow, 1½ to 2½ inches long, the limb obtusely lobed. An Asiatic species, sometimes cultivated.

## *Mina lobata* CERVANTES        ⚘ BERNARD VERDCOURT ⚘
[Syn. *Quamoclit lobata* (Cervantes) House; *Ipomoea lobata* (Cervantes) Thellung; *I. versicolor* Meisner]

This species is usually placed in the *Ipomoea* section *Quamoclit,* but it is very distinctive. It is a perennial, hairless twiner, 6 to 10 feet long with entire or 3-lobed leaves. Stalks long, many-flowered, the flowers in short spikes, tubular, red, turning whitish or yellow, ¾ to 1 inch long with the stamens and style much exserted. Sepals are awned. This native of Mexico is a handsome plant for growing on fences in warm climates and is much grown as a greenhouse curiosity in colder areas. (Photograph 109.)

## *Neuropeltis acuminata* (PALISOT DE BEAUVOIS) BENTHAM

Outstanding of the 4 species in tropical Asia and Africa is this climbing shrub, which often becomes a liana of the forest galleries from the Ivory Coast to Gabon. The small white salverform flowers are in spikelike clusters 3 to 12 inches long. The shining leaves, 2 by 4 inches, are velvety beneath. (Color Plate 62.)

## *Operculina* MANSO        ⚘ BERNARD VERDCOURT ⚘

Many species formerly placed in this genus belong to *Merremia* and the group of about 15 species in the tropics is now restricted to those in which the capsule has two layers, the outer splitting around the middle like a lid and the inner bursting irregularly.

## *Operculina turpethum* (LINN.) MANSO
[Syn. *Ipomoea turpethum* (Linn.) R. Brown]

This is a perennial twiner with more or less winged stems and ovate or lanceolate leaves. Stalks are 1 to few-flowered, the flowers broadly funnel-shaped, white, pinkish or yellowish, 1½ or more inches long. The plant is used as a purgative in the Orient and is considered an excellent substitute for jalap. Not very ornamental.

## *Polymeria ambigua*   R. BROWN

This trailing perennial, native to Queensland, reaches 6 feet or more and bears solitary rosy-pink flowers in the leaf-axils. It flowers profusely and is showy. A smaller form, *P. calycina* R. BROWN is a trailer to 18 inches with solitary purple flowers in the axils.

## *Porana paniculata*   ROXBURGH
*Common Names:* CHRISTMAS-VINE; MOUNTAIN CREEPER; HORSETAIL CREEPER; SNOW CREEPER

*Porana* is a twining, clambering, evergreen Indian plant that is grown in Zanzibar, Florida and other warm garden areas for its superabundance of tiny white flowers at the Christmas season. (Photographs 110 and 111.) Much of the year it is an inconspicuous climber with ovate, heart-shaped leaves 3 to 5 inches long, downy above and smooth beneath. In November it loses its anonymity and becomes a profusely decorated white blanket over the tallest trees.

Individual flower sprays are often a foot long and 4 inches across, but these gather into compound clusters up to 4 feet long. The flowers are pure white, ¼ inch across, bell-shaped with a yellowish tube, and sweetly scented. The beauty of the inflorescence lies in the fact that most of the tiny flowers in the cluster are all open at the same time, from top to bottom, so that the climber (and the tree it covers) are bathed in cloudlike masses of minute white bells.

Fine as the Christmas-vine is in the open when in full bloom either in sun or moonlight, it is unsurpassed by any other for interior decoration.

Nehrling (85) likened the fragrance to lilac (*Syringa* species) and often referred to the vine as "Climbing White Lilac."

Unfortunately, the blooming season for the Christmas-vine is rather brief.

## *Rivea hypocrateriformis*   CHOISY
[Syn. *R. ornata*   Aitchison]

This ornamental creeper over rocky slopes in dry areas of Ceylon and into India produces pure white to yellow, sweet-scented flowers, sometimes solitary, sometimes disposed like a spike at the apex of branchlets. The heart-shaped leaves are white-hairy beneath.

The synonym *R. ornata* is one of 5 that are sometimes kept as separate species. This one, commonly called Midnapore-creeper, has roundish heart-shaped leaves that are sometimes hairy beneath. The large white flowers open at sunset and are very fragrant of cloves. Chittenden (22) says that *R. ornata* has a stem that is white and silky and that the leaves have ashy hairs beneath, and the white flowers are silky without.

156

112.  IPOMOEA AQUATICA     113.  CORIS MONSPELIENSIS

114.  CORNUS CANADENSIS     115.  AUBRIETA DELTOIDES

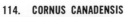

## *Stictocardia* Hallier f.

This small genus of some 12 species throughout the tropics is very similar to *Ipomoea,* but the fruit does not split regularly and there are several other small differences. Several of the African species are very beautiful but scarcely if ever cultivated.

## *Stictocardia beraviensis* (Vatke) Hallier f.    ⚜ Bernard Verdcourt ⚜

This is a strong woody tropical climber with heart-shaped leaves. There are many flowers on very short stalks, the flowers funnel-shaped, 2 to 2¼ inches long, and bright crimson with the base of the tube yellow. (Color Plate 72.) The plant is widespread in tropical Africa and Madagascar, and should be tried more often in cultivation.

    *S. incomta* Hallier f. (Hallier f.) [syn.: *Ipomoea incomta* Hallier f.]. This perennial climber has velvety stems and silvery-velvety heart-shaped leaves. Flowers appear in loose clusters in the axils of the leaves; they are funnel-shaped, pale pink streaked with white, and about 3 inches long. The sepals are densely covered below with curious hairy filamentous outgrowths. A beautiful plant seldom if ever cultivated; a native of Kenya and Tanzania.

    *S. macalusoi* (Mattei) Verdcourt [syn. *Ipomoea macalusoi* Mattei; has been confused with *S. tiliifolia* (Desrousseaux) Hallier f., *e.g.* by Jex-Blake, who gives a splendid plate in his "Gardening in East Africa" (67).] A strong woody twiner or trailer with large, rounded, heart-shaped leaves. The stalks are very short, 1 or 2-flowered, the flowers funnel-shaped, bright scarlet with a paler tube, 2½ to 3 inches long. (Color Plate 71.) This native of coastal dunes in the Somali Republic (southern region) has been cultivated in Kenya and Ceylon. House says that it has been offered in the United States and describes the flowers as orange-colored margined with red.

## *Turbina* Rafinesque    ⚜ Bernard Verdcourt ⚜

A small, probably unnatural genus, very similar in habit and most other characters to *Ipomoea* but differing in having an indehiscent, ovoid-oblong or ellipsoid fruit.

## *Turbina shirensis* (Oliver) Meeuse
[Syn. *Ipomoea shirensis* Oliver]

As a twining shrub this plant rises to 20 feet. Its older stems attain nearly 3 inches in diameter; young shoots are densely, softly tomentose. The leaves are broadly heart-shaped, up to about 5½ inches long and broad, acute at the apex, very densely gray-silky beneath. Inflorescences are many-flowered, the flowers widely funnel-shaped, white, about ¾ inch long. The densely silky-tomentose fruit does not dehisce and contains only 1 seed; the sepals become much enlarged and are twice as long as the fruit. The plant is widely distributed in Mozambique, Malawi, Zambia, Rhodesia and extends into the Transvaal. (Color Plate 58.)

116. IBERIS SEMPERVIRENS 117. LOBULARIA MARITIMA

118. HIBBERTIA VOLUBILIS 119. CALLUNA VULGARIS VAR. COUNTY WICKLOW

## Coris monspeliensis LINN.

This biennial or perennial is the prettiest flowering plant on the beaches in France, growing within a few yards of the sea. (Photograph 113.) It is one of the best plants in that country to withstand not only salt spray but even an occasional inundation. It can ordinarily be grown in light soils, sandy or pebbly. Clusters of rose-violet flowers come in hanging clusters, occasionally quite long, making a magnificent display. Unfortunately, transplanting is difficult. The plant rarely reaches 8 inches in height.

CORNACEAE—DOGWOOD FAMILY

## Cornus canadensis LINN.
*Common Name:* CREEPING DOGWOOD; BUNCHBERRY

Bailey (4) says this is "a handsome plant for half-shady places." (Photograph 114.) Pearce (90) says:

> "This charming little Canadian species is a perennial herb of semi-woody habit. It grows about 6 inches high with many shoots that spring annually from the rootstock at ground level, each growth being terminated by creamy-white bracts that surround a small head of flowers that are followed by bright red berries in autumn. Spreading by underground stems or runners, this *Cornus* is a good plant for the margins of woodland walks or shrub borders, also positions in the rock garden."

## Corokia cotoneaster RAOUL

The tortuous, much interlaced branches of *Corokia* mean that the plant lends itself readily to cultivation as a vine. (Color Plate 82.) Otherwise it is a rounded shrub to 8 feet with thin evergreen leaves. Chittenden (22) says this New Zealand plant in England "is excellent on a cellar wall although occasionally much injured even there in very severe winters." The plant is cherished not only for its ½-inch star-shaped bright yellow flowers borne at the ends of short twigs, but for the bright red roundish fruits.

CRASSULACEAE—ORPINE FAMILY

## Bryophyllum beauverdii A. BERGER

This is a plant of climbing habit with thin wiry stems. Fleshy leaves are awl-shaped. Flowers are about an inch long with white spreading petals. There are several other scandent forms.

71. STICTOCARDIA MACALUSOI

72. STICTOCARDIA BERAVIENSIS

73. HIBBERTIA DENTATA

74. THIBAUDIA SP. (Colombia)

75. EPIGAEA REPENS

76. PENTAPTERYGIUM SERPENS

77. PSAMMISIA SP. (Ecuador)

78. PELARGONIUM PELTATUM

79. PELARGONIUM DOMESTICUM

80. AESCHYNANTHUS SPLENDIDUS

81. AESCHYNANTHUS PULCHRA

82. COROKIA COTONEASTER

83. COLUMNEA BANKSII

84. AESCHYNANTHUS LOBBIANUS

## Aubrieta deltoides   DC.

This plant from Sicily is an attractive, mat-forming perennial with rhomboidal leaves and bright purple flowers, cultivated in rock gardens and in borders particularly in California. It accepts half shade. (Photograph 115.)

## Iberis sempervirens   LINN.                ⚘ ERNEST E. LORD ⚘
*Common Name:* EVERGREEN CANDYTUFT

A low-growing plant, rarely more than 12 inches high, candytuft spreads laterally and becomes bushy. It is a native to Italy and Sicily, and is cultivated in warm frost-free gardens on rockery, walling and the like. (Photograph 116.) White flowers are in flat clusters to 2 inches across but elongate to racemes while seeding; narrow leaves are 1 to 2 inches long. Various named forms are also grown, including double-flowered and variegated-leaved.

## Lobularia maritima   DESVAUX
[Syn.: *Alyssum maritimum* Lamarck;   *Koniga martimia* R. Brown]
*Common Name:* SWEET-ALYSSUM

This common garden edging plant is a creeper though not an actual climber. It has gone wild in many parts of continental United States. (Photograph 117.)

## Matthiola sinuata   R. BROWN

On French beaches in the very windiest places can be found *Matthiola,* growing prostrate on the sands, its stems covered with a whitish down. The rose-lilac flowers are very fragrant and they form clusters up to 20 inches long. A rare green form is known as 'Le d'Yeu.'

## Coccinia adoensis   COGNIAUX

*Coccinia* is a genus of about 30 species in tropical and south Africa. This species is a small tendril climber to 6 feet found in wet savanna areas of East Africa with 3-inch white flowers, yellow inside with pink stripes. The species is variable. The fruit of *C. grandis* LINN. is eaten as a vegetable in India.

CUCURBITACEAE—GOURD FAMILY

## Bryonia laciniosa   LINN.

This vine grows wild as far east as the Philippines, but is rarely cultivated in gardens although found frequently in glasshouses elsewhere in the world. It can be grown from seed satisfactorily. Tuberous roots then put up annual stems. Steiner (106) reports that it grows best in half shade, has much-blistered, rough, cordate, 5 lobed leaves like those of squash. Petals of the creamy-white starlike blossoms display a most striking design: threadlike growths from the inside

161

of the blossoms gracefully entwine in a most interesting pattern. Although hairy within, the blossoms are smooth on the outside. Steiner says the vine is graceful and deserves more interest.

## *Echinocystis lobata* TORREY & GRAY
*Common Name:* WILD CUCUMBER; WILD BALSAM-APPLE

Because it is probably the quickest growing of all vines, Bailey (4) points out that it is therefore useful in hiding unsightly objects or helping slow-growing shrubbery get a start. This climber grows to 15 feet and bears white, foamy panicles of tiny flowers. The fruits are hollow, look a bit like cucumbers. The vine is rarely grown today because of a troublesome virus.

## *Thladiantha dubia* BUNGE

This gourdlike vine from north China produces so many bell-shaped yellow flowers among the large heart-shaped leaves that is often cultivated in gardens. An even more vigorous species, *T. oliveri* COGNIAUX, with larger leaves and more numerous golden flowers, is sometimes grown; it reaches 30 feet.

DILLENIACEAE—DILLENIA FAMILY

## *Hibbertia volubilis* ANDREWS
*Common Names:* TWINING GUINEA-FLOWER; GUINEA GOLD VINE; BUTTON-FLOWER

Probably the finest of 100 species of *Hibbertia* vines in Australia and nearby islands, the Guinea gold vine (Photograph 118) is much planted in California for the handsome, almost succulent leaves and the golden-yellow, solitary, roselike flowers in summer. It withstands temperatures down to 25° Fahrenheit. The blossoms are slightly malodorous.

Jones (69) found it the ideal climber for a focal point in a garden, adorning an iron grill, climbing a wall or a tree, or placed otherwise where not cluttered with miscellaneous plants. It is slow enough not to outgrow its situation and it is one of the few vines that can be on parade all the year. Chittenden (22) reported this a prostrate or twining shrub to 4 feet but in California it often climbs to 30 feet.

Also seen frequently in Australian and Californian gardens, and particularly prized in glasshouses, is the snake-vine or toothed guinea-flower (*H. dentata* R. BROWN). It is an Australian native, mainly herbaceous, woody only at the base, with 2-inch long-lasting yellow flowers amid the coppery foliage. (Color Plate 73.) Harris (51) reported it a trailing plant with slightly toothed leaves and large, short-stalked, bright yellow flowers in spring and summer.

A third species cultivated and nominated by Chittenden for superior quality in England is *H. perfoliata* HUEGEL, a procumbent trailer with bright yellow 1½-inch flowers.

The blossoming season of *Hibbertia* vines often extends for 2 or 3 months and one California grower called them "tops for all flowering vines in our area."

## *Tetracera sarmentosa* VAHL
[Syn. *Delima sarmentosa* Linn.]

※ T. K. BOSE ※

This large evergreen climbing shrub in eastern Asia is one of 40 species. It has a stout woody stem with brownish scaly bark. The leaves are alternate, obovate, leathery, dark green, both surfaces rough, dentate, 5 to 8 inches long, 1 to 1½ inches wide.

At the tips of the branches the vine bears clusters of ¾-inch magnolia-like, white, highly scented flowers with 4 to 6 petals. It is a showy climber with attractive foliage also. It grows well in light shade.

## EPACRIDACEAE—EPACRIS FAMILY

## *Epacris longiflora* CAVANILLES
*Common Name:* FUCHSIA-HEATH

※ ERNEST E. LORD ※

This charming little shrub from New South Wales with slender leafy branches requires support of some kind. The branches are strung with numerous inch-long tubular red flowers tipped with white. This is a good subject for espalier training, with a flowering period almost continuous under temperate climates and with well drained soil.

## *Prionotes cerinthoides* (LABILLARDIERE) R. BROWN
*Common Name:* CLIMBING-HEATH

※ ERNEST E. LORD ※

*P. cerinthoides* is an epiphytic shrub found wild only in the moist temperate forests of western Tasmania and is rarely seen climbing.

The handsome tubular crimson flowers, an inch long, are plentiful on slender stalks along the many thin leafy branches. Not content with their terrestrial habitat, the plants root themselves in the bark of tall trees such as myrtle-beech (*Nothofagus cunninghamii*), sometimes covering the trunks to a height of 30 feet. The plant reminds one of the Himalayan *Pentapterygium serpens* in the heath family.

## ERICACEAE—HEATH FAMILY

※ SIDNEY McDANIEL ※

## *Andromeda polifolia* LINN.
*Common Name:* BOG-ROSEMARY

The bog-rosemary is a native of cold regions of the northern hemisphere, infrequently however occurring as far north as the true Arctic. This handsome plant is sometimes cultivated as a border plant or in rock gardens. It is a low evergreen shrub with erect stems arising from an elongate creeping base. The alternate narrow revolute leaves are often whitened beneath. The tiny but attractive flowers are borne in nodding terminal umbels, the corolla about ¼ to ⅓ inch long, globose-urceolate, and pink or white.

## *Arctostaphylos uva-ursi* (LINN.) SPRENGEL
*Common Name:* BEARBERRY; KINNIKINNICK

The bearberry is native through much of the subarctic and cold temperate regions of the northern hemisphere. It is a trailing shrub with lustrous alternate evergreen leaves about 1 inch long. The white or pinkish urn-shaped flowers are produced in clusters in May and June. The red fruits are dry and mealy and persist through the winter, often buried under the snow, from where they emerge to furnish food for wild birds the next spring. Bearberry is occasionally cultivated as a groundcover for its evergreen leaves and contrasting red fruits.

## *Calluna vulgaris* SALISBURY
*Common Name:* HEATHER

This small evergreen shrub is native in Europe and Asia Minor. It is also naturalized in the northeastern United States in various localities. The bright rosy-pink or white flowers appear abundantly in late summer. Some improved varieties have been tried in gardens where they spread rapidly by underground roots, covering banks and low obstacles. The prostrate form is frequently used in this manner. (Photograph 119.)

## *Dimorphanthera tridens* J. J. SMITH

Most of the 60 species of this genus were described from New Guinea, but a few occur in the Philippines. They are frequently epiphytic and primarily plants of the mountains. This especially attractive species is a profusely flowering plant with large campanulate red flowers. Michael Black, writing in the *Journal of the Royal Horticultural Society* (March, 1966), says of *Dimorphanthera:*

> "They are in general loose growing shrubs with handsome lanceolate or ovate leaves, the inflorescence appearing on the old wood. Generally they preferred to grow terrestrially in shady thickets, often near rivers where the humidity reached 80 per cent. There, the robust exploratory branches thrust their way through the other trees and shrubs, often for more than 20 feet, towards the light."

## *Epigaea repens* LINN.
*Common Name:* TRAILING-ARBUTUS

The trailing-arbutus is probably the best beloved of all the early wild flowers of the eastern United States. (Color Plate 75.) It is native in dry woods from Canada to Florida and west to Wisconsin and Mississippi. Southward, however, it is quite rare and unfortunately seldom seen. It is rarely cultivated except occasionally in glasshouses where an acid soil produces good results. The plant trails on the ground forming patches to 2 feet across. The leaves are alternate, evergreen, and usually have scattered hairs on both surfaces. The salverform flowers are white or pink and ½ inch or more across. They are borne in small clusters appearing March to May and are justly famous for their fragrance.

## *Loiseleuria procumbens*   (LINN.) DESVAUX
*Common Name:* ALPINE-AZALEA

This attractive little plant is often cultivated in alpine gardens. Its natural distribution is circumpolar in Arctic and Boreal regions and it occurs south in North America to New Hampshire. It is a glabrous, prostrate, intricately branched evergreen shrub with small opposite leaves often less than ¼ inch long. Small white or pink campanulate flowers appear in July and August, followed by inconspicuous seed capsules.

## *Macleania cordifolia*   BENTHAM

Among the 40 (more or less) species of *Macleania* occurring as shrubs in mountainous areas from southern Mexico to Peru are a few with long-extended branches that are sometimes cultivated in the vine manner. According to Smith (127) *Macleania pulchra* HOOKER and *M. speciossima* HOOKER, described from horticultural material, are synonymous with *M. cordifolia* BENTHAM. Bailey (4) says of this species: "Branches long and drooping." The plant is native to Ecuador and probably Colombia and has long been cultivated in botanical gardens. The leaves are 1½ to 4 inches long and ovate or ovate-oblong. The flowers are usually in 4 to 19-flowered clusters in the axils of the leaves; the corolla is up to 1½ inches long, cylindric, with a bright scarlet tube, yellow above.

## *Pentapterygium serpens*   KLOTZSCH
[Syn. *Agapetes serpens*   (Wight) Sleumer; *Vaccinium serpens*   Wight]

*Pentapterygium* comprises about 120 species from the Himalayas to the Malay peninsula. Down in tropical Africa this species (Color Plate 76) is a graceful climber with delicate foliage. It produces orange-red hanging-lantern flowers.

## *Phyllodoce empetriformis*   G. DON
*Common Name:* MOUNTAIN-HEATH

The genus *Phyllodoce* consists of about 6 species of evergreen semi-prostrate to ascending heathlike shrubs that produce delicate purple to pink flowers in profusion. Two species, *P. empetriformis* with bell-shaped corollas, native on high rocky slopes from California to Alaska, and *P. caerulea* (LINN.) BABINGTON, with urn-shaped corollas, circumpolar in Arctic regions of the northern hemisphere, are attractive semi-climbers but rarely found in cultivation.

## *Pieris phillyreifolia*   (HOOKER) DC.
*Common Name:* CLIMBING-HEATH

In the Ericaceae there are few climbing plants, but climbing-heath may ascend to 15 feet or more. Characteristically it occurs on pond cypress (*Taxodium ascendens*), but it has been found less frequently on pine and the titi trees (*Cyrilla* species of tropical America). The natural distribution of this species is largely along the Gulf Coast from Georgia to Mississippi and its habitat is around ponds, sloughs, and bays. It may rarely occur as an isolated semi-erect shrub. Usually it climbs by sending leafless stems upward under the outer bark of the supporting tree. Leafy shoots emerge at intervals as the subcorticolous stems increase in length. The attractive white urceolate flowers may appear from January to early March and contrast with the leathery evergreen leaves. *P. phillyreifolia* is rarely cultivated, but the almost midwinter flowers and the general attractive appearance of the plant would make it worth further effort.

## *Psammisia urichiana*   (BRITTON) A. C. SMITH
*Common Name:* WILD-CLOVE

One of about 30 species of *Psammisia* in tropical America, *P. urichiana* is usually a glabrous, epiphytic climber found in the mountain forests of Trinidad, British Guiana, and Venezuela. The somewhat leathery leaves are 6 to 8 inches long, ovate to oblong. Williams (118) says this is a very pretty vine. It has white-tipped, stalked, subcylindric flowers about 1 inch long in bunches on the twigs or in the leaf axils. They somewhat resemble the flowers of cloves but are much handsomer. (Color Plate 77.)

## *Thibaudia*   RUIZ & PAVON

This genus of approximately 40 species in mountainous South America contains a number of scandent or clambering species, some of which would undoubtedly be worthy of cultivation. They are shrubs, frequently epiphytic, with leathery, evergreen, alternate leaves. (Color Plate 74.) The inflorescence is terminal or axillary with few to many stalked flowers. The corolla is subcylindric and commonly red or scarlet. The genus may be distinguished from *Macleania* and *Psammisia* by the smooth or merely slightly granular anther-sacs.

FLACOURTIACEAE—FLACOURTIA FAMILY                    ☀ H. SLEUMER ☀

## *Berberidopsis corallina*   HOOKER F.

The only climber in the Flacourtiaceae is this scandent evergreen shrub to 20 feet. It was originally known from a limited area in the temperate forest of the coastal cordillera of Chile, between Concepcion (Lota) and Valdivia. Apparently in the wild it is now extinct, at least in its northern area south of Lota where reforestation with *Pinus* is in progress. The leaves of the plant are similar to those of *Berberis* or *Ilex,* dark green, a little shiny above, coriaceous, oblong-cordate, spiny-toothed, 2 to 3 by 1 to 1½ inches in size. The flowers are in drooping terminal racemes, globose, crimson, about ½ inch in diameter, consisting of several whorls, the outer ones smaller and sepaloid, the inner ones larger and gradually petaloid.

This plant was introduced to England by Pearce about 1860, and is still cultivated there. It is hardy mainly along the west coast, or elsewhere in protected places. The biggest living specimen of *Berberidopsis* is at White Craggs, Ambleside (West Morland), that part of western England close to the sea. In Cornwall the plant is quite hardy and flowers profusely but never sets fruits. *Berberidopsis* is rarely cultivated outside of Great Britain, except in cool glasshouses.

FLAGELLARIACEAE—FLAGELLARIA FAMILY

## *Flagellaria indica* LINN.

Four species of these climbers are scattered through Asia. Harris (51) says of *F. indica:*

> "This is a tall, slender climber, with elongated leaves 4 to 5 inches long, or longer, and with very numerous, small white flowers borne in clusters in spring. It is a Queensland plant and likes a coastal situation."

FUMARIACEAE—FUMITORY FAMILY

## *Adlumia fungosa* GREENE

*Common Names:* CLIMBING FUMITORY; MOUNTAIN FRINGE; ALLEGHENY-VINE

This popular biennial vine is native from Ontario to Michigan and south to North Carolina. It is delicate, climbing by the slender leaf petioles, bearing ½-inch white or purplish flowers. Bailey (3) reported it "ornamental in both foliage and flowers." It is a plant of moist woodlands, making a shrub the first year, the second year climbing over adjacent shrubs and flowering.

GARRYACEAE—GARRYA FAMILY

## *Garrya elliptica* DOUGLAS

This handsome shrub, native from California to Oregon, is much planted in gardens where it can be protected from frost, particularly the staminate plants which are especially decorative in early spring with their showy pendulous flower clusters up to a foot long. (Photograph 120.) They often bloom in midwinter. In England the plant is much used as a wall shrub on protected south walls or on slopes, and in such locations it is grown in the vine manner to 10 feet or more.

120. GARRYA ELLIPTICA     121. GERANIUM ENDRESSII

122. PELARGONIUM DOMESTICUM     123. PELARGONIUM (L'ELEGANTE)

## *Geranium* LINN.

About 400 species of *Geranium* have been described, mostly in the temperate zones, and among them are a good many trailing herbs that are frequently used as groundcovers.

*G. macrorrhizum* is a surface runner often planted in England and considered one of the most effective all-around groundcover plants in shade or part sun. It produces its pink flowers in spring.

*G. endressii* J. JAY (Photograph 121) is also a useful groundcover, bearing pink flowers for a long period in midsummer.

## *Pelargonium domesticum* BAILEY
*Common Name:* LADY WASHINGTON GERANIUM

This weak plant with trailing, drooping, or climbing succulent stems is useful for dry and warm places like hilly yards in southern California, because it makes a brilliant show of bloom often under most adverse conditions. (Photograph 122.) It loves to cover hillsides, grow over stumps and smother fences with clouds of salmon, pink, lavender, rose, scarlet, or crimson flowers. It is one of 250 descendants of the much confused "geraniums" of South Africa. (Color Plate 79.)

The ivy geranium (*P. peltatum* AITON) is an old window-garden plant with weak stems, often creeping, much planted today in California gardens where it climbs fences and gateways (Photograph 123 and Color Plate 78). It is also excellent as a groundcover plant.

## *Aeschynanthus pulchra* G. DON     ⚜ C. G. G. J. VAN STEENIS ⚜

This is a genus of about 80 species in Indomalaysia and China. All are twining, prostrate-rooting shrubs, with a growth habit similar to that of *Agalmyla* (the next genus treated); very rarely are the plants attached to the soil. Plants have very thin stems, never woody, and many have fleshy leaves.

*A. pulchra* hangs down from tree limbs in thin curtains more than 15 feet high in the Tjibodas mountain forests of Indonesia. (Color Plate 81.) Chittenden (22) says that *Aeschynanthus* species are well worth extensive cultivation, for they have handsome, showy flowers, fine, deep green leaves, and an agreeable fragrance. Other species described as climbing are *A. grandiflora* SPRENGEL, *A. hildebrandtii* HEMSLEY, and *A. javanica* HOOKER (Color Plates 80, 84.)

## *Agalmyla staminea* BLUME     ⚜ C. G. G. J. VAN STEENIS ⚜

*Agalmyla staminea,* the only species, is a root-climbing plant. While sometimes only 2 feet high, it can grow up trees to nearly 20 feet, clinging to them in the primary

124. ASTERANTHERA OVATA    125. COLUMNEA HIRTA

126. LOROPETALUM CHINENSE    127. HYPERICUM CALYCINUM

forest. It does not hang down or trail from tree to tree; its stem can hardly be called woody. The flowers are in axillary clusters, the corolla-limb oblique, 5-lobed, the color scarlet. The plants are native of Borneo, Sumatra, and Indonesia.

## *Asteranthera ovata* (CAVANILLES) HANSTEIN ❦ HAROLD E. MOORE, JR. ❦

*Asteranthera ovata,* a native of the temperate rain-forests of southern Chile, is a vine in nature, climbing to 5 feet or more. The stems are brownish with appressed white hairs and they often root at the nodes. (Photograph 124.) The dark green leaves are opposite, frequently unequal, to 1½ inches long, ¾ inch wide, with pale hairs above and below, ovate-elliptic to nearly round in outline. The base is wedge-shaped, the apex blunt, and the margins are toothed. Flowers are raspberry-red, to 2 3/16 inches long, borne singly or in pairs on bracteate peduncles longer than the leaves. A 5-lobed green calyx surrounds the narrowly funnel-shaped, 2-lipped corolla, inside which are borne 4 stamens with anthers united into a star. The ovary is superior, maturing into a purple and green berry-like capsule to ¾ inch long.

## *Columnea hirta* KLOTZSCH & HANSTEIN

Willis (118) says several of the 200 species of *Columnea* are climbers. This species from Central America (Photograph 125) is an epiphytic scrambler, rooting at the nodes. The stem is densely covered with reddish-brown hairs. Leaves are elliptic, to 2 inches long, 1 inch wide. The flowers are solitary in the leaf axils, the corolla is about 3¼ inches long, vermilion, orange at the base of the lobes, and hairy (22). Other climbers in the genus are *C. hirsuta* SWARTZ, *C. oerstediana* KLOTZSCH EX OERSTED, *C. rutilans* SWARTZ, *and C. scandens* LINN. (Color Plate 83.)

## *Dichrotrichum ternateum* REINWARDT EX DEVRIESE

This Gesneriad has the same curious habit of climbing as *Agalmyla,* but it is more closely related to *Aeschynanthus.* Chittenden (22) says it climbs trees and rocks by means of abundant adventitious roots. The leaves are opposite, unequal, the larger ones heart-shaped. The tubular flowers are crimson, in loose clusters. It is native of the Moluccas and Indonesia. There are 34 other species of *Dichrotrichum* in Malaysia, scattered from Borneo and the Philippines to New Guinea.

## *Mitraria coccinea* CAVANILLES ❦ HAROLD E. MOORE, JR. ❦

*Mitraria coccinea* is native in the temperate rain-forests of southern Chile. It is a branching vine with obscurely 4-angled stems on which are borne shortly petiolate, opposite, delicate green leaves to ¾ inch long. The blades are ovate in outline, acute at the tip, and toothed along the margin. Bright scarlet or orange-red tubular flowers with an oblique limb are pendulous on long stalks that are solitary in the leaf-axils. A green bract enfolds the base of the 5-lobed calyx. Four stamens are present in the corolla-tube, the anthers united in pairs. The superior ovary matures into a rosy-green fleshy capsule ½ inch in diameter and with a persistent elongate style.

## *Sarmienta scandens* (BRANDIS) PERSOON ※ HAROLD E. MOORE, JR. ※

*Sarmienta scandens* is a creeper or climber from the temperate rain-forest of southern Chile. The leaves are thick, small, to 1 inch long, ½ inch wide, elliptic to subglobose in outline and usually 3 to 5-toothed at the apex. Flowers are coral-pink, sharply deflexed on a very short pedicel at the apex of a 2-bracted elongate peduncle that is solitary in the leaf-axil. The calyx is of 5 slender recurving sepals; the corolla is about ¾ inch long, swollen and 5-lobed at the base, suddenly narrowed and then expanded above, subsequently narrowed to a limb of 5 short, rounded, straight lobes. Fertile stamens are 2 in number opposite the lateral lobes. The fruit is an ovoid berry about ⅜ inch long with a persistent elongate style.

## GOODENIACEAE—GOODENIA FAMILY

## *Goodenia auriculata* BENTHAM

*Goodenia* comprises some 80 species of herbs and subshrubs in Australia, of which this is a trailing annual to 20 inches or more in northern Queensland. The sulphur-yellow, loosely arranged flowers are solitary in the leaf-axils.

## HAMAMELIDACEAE—WITCH-HAZEL FAMILY

## *Loropetalum chinense* OLIVER

This evergreen much-branched shrub from China is often grown in California as a trailer on walls, and it is sometimes used in hanging baskets. (Photograph 126.) The branches are brown with a starry down. The feathery flowers in early spring are creamy-white in clusters at the branch tips.

## HYPERICACEAE—HYPERICUM FAMILY

## *Hypericum calycinum* LINN.

*Common Names:* AARONSBEARD; ST. JOHNSWORT

This is an evergreen subshrub a foot or less high with many procumbent or erect 4-angled stems. (Photograph 127.) The plant is stoloniferous, so it is useful as a groundcover. From July to September it displays flowers 3 inches across, solitary or 2 or 3 together. The plant is native to Asia Minor.

Three other species of procumbent habit are in common cultivation in the

**128.  AJUGA REPTANS**   **129.  LAMIUM MACULATUM**

**130.  AKEBIA TRIFOLIATA**   **131.  AKEBIA QUINATA**

United States: *H. buckleii* M. A. CURTIS, *H. olympicum* LINN., and *H. repens* LINN.


LABIATAE—MINT FAMILY


## *Ajuga reptans* LINN.
*Common Name:* CARPET BUGLEWEED

Bailey (3) calls this a "low, dense, fast spreading creeper, excellent for covering shady slopes. (Photograph 128.) A horticultural form with purple leaves is more planted than either the normal blue or white-flowered species. Also a new pink and white variegated one is available.


## *Colquhounia vestita* WALLICH

This is one of two species of Asian climbing shrubs with red and yellow flowers an inch or more long. Stems are woolly. Plants are seldom cultivated.


## *Hemiandra pungens* R. BROWN
*Common Name:* SNAKE-BUSH

Three species are found in western Australia. They are spreading evergreen shrubs, often creeping. The solitary pinkish-mauve flowers have a calyx of which the upper lip is prickly. Flowers are funnel-shaped at the base. The corolla is 2-lipped, the lower lip 2 or 3-lobed, dotted with crimson. The upper lip is 4-lobed.


## *Lamium maculatum* LINN.
*Common Name:* SPOTTED DEADNETTLE

Bailey (4) reports this cultivated species as a half-trailing perennial with purple-red 1-inch flowers in clusters, useful as a climber among rocks. (Photograph 129.) Most kinds of *Lamium* are weeds. The white form of the Deadnettle has been found more satisfactory and desirable in the garden than the red form.


## *Rosmarinus officinalis* LINN. var. *prostratus* Hort
*Common Name:* ROSEMARY

This is a climbing form of a popular garden plant, with light blue, ½-inch flowers. Pearce (90) says: "A very beautiful plant and one that is worthy of wider cultivation and the extra care needed to grow it well."


LARDIZABALACEAE—LARDIZABALA FAMILY


## *Akebia quinata* DECAISNE

This is an exceptionally ornamental vine from Japan requiring full sun; rather fast growing, quickly reaching 12 feet. Foliage is a heavy deep green. Flowers

174

appear in spring, the female ones purplish-brown, about an inch long, the male flowers smaller and rose-purple. (Photograph 131.) Bailey (4) says of this: "The akebias are very ornamental, hardy climbing shrubs of graceful appearance."

Another commonly cultivated species from east Asia, *A. trifoliata* KOIDZUMI, is a vigorous deciduous climber to 40 feet. These flowers are clustered in 3-inch spikes, the numerous male flowers small and lavender (Photograph 130.) the female flowers few, larger, bright royal-purple.

## *Lardizabala biternata* RUIZ & PAVON

Brilmeyer (6) says of this:

> "Here's an interesting novelty for the greenhouse, conservatory or sun-room—a woody, evergreen stem twiner that grows vigorously over California walls and fences, but can be pruned and trained indoors. In late winter and early spring it makes a bold display with drooping clusters of white-petaled flowers set off by contrast with thickish brown-purple sepals. The leaves are neatly divided, fresh green, lustrous and lush."

## *Stauntonia hexaphylla* DECAISNE

A tender evergreen climber from Japan and Korea, this plant has ascending stems to 40 feet or more. (Photograph 132.) In the summer it produces very fragrant greenish-white male flowers and purplish female flowers on separate plants. The leaves are deep bronzy green. This is often cultivated in California and the southeastern states.

LEGUMINOSAE—PEA OR BEAN FAMILY

## *Acacia* LINN.

With close to 500 species in the genus *Acacia,* little attempt will be made here to distinguish them. Most are shrubs or trees, but a number of them are climbers, and the majority are native in Australia and thereabouts. Their leaves bear many paired leaflets; their clustered flowers, in either globes or spikes, are nearly always yellow.

The various common names are differentiated geographically: wattle in Australia, thorn in central Africa, and mimosa in France and the U.S. retail florist trade.

*A. auriculiformis* is one of the 9 climbing species in Burma listed by Hundley (60). Of the genus *Acacia* as a whole, Lord (76) writes this author:

> "In Australia there are no truly climbing Australian species to my knowledge. But *A. aculeatissima* MACBRIDE [syn. *A. tenuifolia* F. Merell] is a familiar little creeping plant here, that works through light grass; of more interest to collectors than 'ornamental.'

175

132. STAUNTONIA HEXAPHYLLA     133. APIOS AMERICANA

134. ANTHYLLIS BARBA-JOVIS     135. ACACIA SP. (IN THE VINE MANNER)

"A remarkable trailing variety of *A. pruinosa* A. Cunningham ex Bentham in a private garden has been under my eye for a number of years; it has no height, all growth strikes out horizontally, then hangs down. It covers densely quite a few square yards. May be called 'Pendula' or 'Horizontalis', if our cultivar authority will accept either. We are trying to propagate it vegetatively, as they do in French Riviera their Acacia hybrids.

"*Acacia iteaphylla* F. Mueller ex Bentham [syn. *A. neriifolia* A. Cunningham ex Bentham] is a shrub of 6 or 8 feet, with beautiful bluish or purplish green soft willow-foliage in very weeping branches. It could lend itself to some such treatment."

The species of *Acacia* grown in California and England do not lend themselves to cultivation in the vine manner, but they can be trained. (Photograph 135.)

## *Afgekia sericea* Craib

Of this Malayan climber, Holttum (54) says: "A strong and quick-growing climber with attractive foliage and large trusses of cream and pink pea-shaped flowers, with pink bracts. Each head continues flowering for several weeks." (Color Plate 94.)

## *Anthyllis barba-jovis* Linn.
Common Names: Jupiter's Beard; Kidney-vetch

This creeping herb, much prized for its straw-colored flowers in cloverlike heads, comes from southern Europe. As a vine to 12 feet or more, it is cultivated in glasshouses for the silky evergreen foliage. (Photograph 134.)

## *Apios americana* Medik.
[Syn. *Apios tuberosa* Moench]
Common Names: Groundnut; Cinnamon-vine; Wild-bean

The groundnut grows in moist places of eastern and midwestern United States and 3 species are found in Asia as small climbing herbs to 3 or 4 feet producing small chocolate-colored flowers in dense heads. (Photograph 133.) The flowers are of a curious construction. Willis (118) says:

"The keel of the flower forms a tube which bends up and rests against a depression in the standard. When liberated by insects, the tension of the keel makes it spring downwards, coiling up more closely, and causing the essential organs to emerge at the apex." In the garden this plant may become a weed.

## *Atylosia reticulata* Bentham
[Syn.: *Dolichos reticulatus* Ait.; *Cajanus reticulatus* F. Mueller]
Common Name: Korlbun

ERNEST E. LORD

A Queensland and north Australian trailer, this tropical climber is clothed in brown velvet, with pale yellow pea-flowers in long-stalked clusters at the leaf-

136.   BAUHINIA ANGUINA      137.   BAUHINIA GLAUCA

138.   BAUHINIA DIPHYLLA      139.   BAUHINIA CUMANENSIS

axils of every branch. The hairy calyx is attractive, also the pod, which is deeply furrowed between the seeds.

## *Bauhinia* Linn.

Some 300 species of *Bauhinia* have been described, mostly shrubs and small trees scattered throughout the tropics, but more than 100 of them are climbers. Many of the lianas in this genus reach to the top of 200-foot forest trees in Malaya where they bring forth some of the most spectacular of flower displays. They are much too big for any garden. Many have stems curiously shaped, flattened or corrugated, twisted by a peculiar mode of growth in thickness. Some species have branches that become tendrils with which to climb.

The genus *Bauhinia* was divided in 1956 by de Wit (160) and about 60 Asian and Australian species, many of them in common cultivation, were transferred to the genus *Phanera*. Several others were put in *Lysiphyllum*. De Wit is the only recent author to accept the genus *Phanera*. He cites as the distribution of the genus: "Tropical Asia, also on the continent. Throughout Malaysia (centered in Borneo)."

This book is for lay readers. They will be less confused if all *Bauhinia* vines are described here under that name; in cases where de Wit has proposed a new name, this is given as a synonym.

## *Bauhinia galpinii* N. E. Brown
*Common Names:* Pride-of-the-cape; Camel's-foot

Best known and most widely planted of the *Bauhinia* vines is *B. galpinii*, which originated at the Cape of Good Hope. (Color Plate 87.) It is now much grown in every tropical country, usually as a shrub to 10 feet. However, with opportunity it becomes scandent and may go to 30 feet. Through the summer and into the fall it bears quantities of very lovely, usually brick-red flowers that look much like oversized nasturtiums. The plants are widely grown in southern California and Florida but almost never as a vine. They are nearly evergreen, and in mild winters will hold their foliage.

The snake-vine (*B. anguina* Roxburgh) has a snakelike stem, climbing over vegetation. There is no beauty in the flowers, but the extremely twisted stems, as they climb, broaden in one direction so that they appear like broad ribbons folding over and over on themselves. These are often called monkey staircase. The Sadhus and Mendicants in India are often seen carrying a walking stick made of this climber; they believe it acts as a charm and keeps off snakes. (Photograph 136.)

*B. Kockiana* Korthals [syn.: *Phanera kockiana* Bentham] is one of the few high climbers in the jungles of southeastern Asia that has been brought into cultivation; it may be found in gardens in Singapore and Hong Kong. (Color Plate 104.) This vine has a compressed stem as if flattened with an iron. It has the typical double leaf composed of twin leaflets, as is common to the genus. These are a glossy green and the flowers are of a brilliant yellow which later turns red.

*B. phoenicea* Heyne [syn. *Phanera phoenicea* Bentham] is a spectacular climber described thus by Kurian (133):

"*Bauhinia phoenicea,* in its natural habitat prefers moist areas. The leaves are bilobed, alternate, measuring 5½ inches long and 5 inches broad. New leaves with beautiful crimson colour appear when the monsoons break and the colour gradually turns green on maturity. Masses of young crimson leaves remain throughout the rainy season, which lasts for over six months. The veins, nine to eleven in number, remain red for a long time. New shoots arising from the base twine around the lofty trees, and spread over the top evidently in search of full sunshine. Branching is profuse and these branches, fully exposed to the sun, give out bunches of bright red flowers measuring more than 3 inches across. The bright red flowers and crimson young leaves brilliantly match with each other and produce striking contrast against the bright green background of the mature leaves. There are from 6 to 9 bunches on short branches and 20 to 25 flowers in an individual inflorescence. The sepals, petals, stamens, pistil and the young branches on which they are borne are all red in colour; the stems are darker, and the flowers brighter. There are 5 petals, fully exposed and stalked. There is no odd petal in shape or colour. The flowers are moderately fragrant. Few pods are set."

*B. esculenta* BURCHELL. Writing from South Africa, Storey (161) said of this species:

"This plant is a runner in open grassveld, with numerous slender vines up to 18 feet long. The vines die back during the winter. The plant bears showy flowers [yellow] in December."

Codd (162) describes it thus:

"*B. esculenta,* the gemsbok-bean or braaiboontje, is a prostrate plant with branches up to 6 feet long radiating from the top of a thick tuberous root. Large bilobed, short-petioled leaves grow at intervals along the branches and occasionally they are reduced to tendrils. There are only two fertile stamens in the flower and the remaining seven or eight are sterile, variously shaped and coloured so that they can hardly be recognized as stamens. The specific epithet *esculenta* (edible) is well chosen because not only is this plant sought out by browsing stock and game, but the tubers and seeds were a staple food for the indigenous people and are even today relished by the farming communities living in the areas where the plants grow. The roasted seeds are said to taste like cashew nuts. *B. esculenta* is found mainly in the sandy country of the northwestern Cape and Bechuanaland but also extends into South West Africa and eastwards into the Transvaal where it has been recorded near Pretoria and Potchefstroom."

This plant (*B. esculenta*) is sometimes known as *Tylosema esculentum* (BURCH) A. SCHREIBER.

*B. glauca* [syn.: *B. corymbosa* ROXBURGH; *Phanera corymbosa* (ROXBURGH)

BENTHAM] is an attractive woody climber from South China, branching from the base. (Photograph 137 and Color Plate 86.) It has been grown successfully in Hawaii and southern California but is rare in Florida, where it has not grown well. The leaves are about 1 by 2 inches, cleft to below the middle. Flowers are to 1 inch across, pale pinkish or rose-colored, or white with pink veins, the petals spreading and nearly all alike, produced in elongated racemes throughout the summer months. The filaments of the stamens are bright red. Hooker in his description of this in the *Botanical Magazine* called it "one of the most beautiful of climbers." In Australia this is called *Bauhinia scandens*.

Some authorities maintain that *B. glauca* and *B. corymbosa* are separate species, the leaves and flowers of *B. glauca* being larger and the stem square. Its distribution is also extended to India.

*B. yunnanensis* FRANCHET. This hardy climber from China is a vigorous plant in Australia. Lord (76) says it has rosy-white flowers striped purple, in droopink clusters, and small pale green leaves.

John Murray in "Gardens of the Sun" wrote of this species when traveling in Borneo:

> "A strong growing species of *Bauhinia* was very showy overrunning the branches of bushes and low trees beside the path, and bearing its pale yellow flowers in large clusters, very profusely. As seen at a distance it has a pleasing effect in the landscape."

*The 5 species that follow are samples of beautiful climbers found in the Malayan jungles.*

## *B. flammifera* RIDLEY

[Syn. *Phanera integrifolia* (Roxburgh) Bentham]

Adult leaves of *B. flammifera* are 4 to 6 inches long, but those near the flower cluster are small, usually 1 inch long. The flowers are in leafy panicles 12 inches long made up of dense, many-flowered racemes 3 to 6 inches long. The petals are yellow, then orange, finally red. Stamens are pink. (Color Plate 85.) Ridley (167) says the vine is common in most of the forests of the center of the Malay peninsula, "very conspicuous and showy."

*B. scortechinii* PRAIN is a large climber in the Malay jungles with smaller leaves, 3½ to 4 inches long, and the flowers fewer, in small clusters. Ridley failed to mention their color.

*B. integrifolia.* Bentham made this identical with Ridley's *B. flammifera* but Ridley disagreed and Bentham calls this *Phanera integrifolia*. At any rate it is a huge climber, the branches, petioles, and clusters of flowers covered with red velvety fuzz. Leaves, unlike those of most *Bauhinia* species, are rough, heart-shaped, entire or retuse at the tip. They are 2 to 2½ inches long and 2½ to 3 inches wide. Ridley (167) says the panicles consist of a few short axillary and terminal racemes 2½ to 5 inches long. Petals, ⅓ inch long, are oblong, rather short-clawed, red-hairy outside.

*B. kingii* PRAIN is a small smooth climber in Malaya with flowers 3 inches long by 2½ inches wide in clusters that may be as much as 6 inches across and up to 18 inches long. The petals are bright red, long-clawed, but small, less than 1 inch long.

*B. finlaysoniana* GRAHAM [syn.: *Phanera finlaysoniana* Bentham]. This is a huge climber to 100 feet or more in the Malayan jungles. Leaves are oblong or ovate, entire, the base slightly heart-shaped, rough. The flowers are in dense clusters, petals white or yellow, ½ inch long and as much across.

*The following climbing species of* Bauhinia *have been introduced into the United States and are more or less in cultivation in Florida and southern California.*

*B. binata* BLANCO [syn. *Lysiphyllum binatum* (Blanco) de Wit]. Dr. David Fairchild brought this from the Moluccas. It is a "vinelike shrub, resembling *B. galpinii* but the new growth possesses coiled tendrils. Leaves completely divided into two separate small, oval leaflets. Flowers white, starlike, to 2 inches across, produced in dense axillary and terminal corymbs from April to June. Stamens 10, white, in age usually becoming red."

There is a vine called *B. diphylla* HAM [syn. *Lysiphyllum diphyllum* (Ham) de Wit] regarding which Firminger (37) wrote: "A very pretty scandent shrub, of stout growth; bears in June and July, middle-sized creamy-white flowers." (Photograph 138.)

J. K. Bose of the Royal Agri-Horticultural Society of India, Calcutta, writes of *B. diphylla:*

> "This large evergreen, much branched climber has a square stem that is green, glabrous, coppery when soft. The leaves are alternate, green, glabrous, two lobes attached near the petiole, each one measuring 1—2 inches in length and ½—1¼ inches in breadth, leathery. The tendrils are strong and flat. The flowers are large, 4-6 on each inflorescence. The sepals are fleshy, green, the undersurface purple. The petals are 5, yellowish-white. They drop off earlier than the sepals. The style is large, red. This is a very quick growing climber. The large and colourful flowers appear in the summer months (April—May). The vine grows well in moist, slightly shady places."

Just to confuse the reader, there is another vine called *Bauhinia diphylla,* this one named by Zollinger. It is a Malaysian species which de Wit says is a synonym of *Lysiphyllum binatum,* described above as *Bauhinia binata.*

*B. cumanensis* HBK. This turtle-vine (Photograph 139.) is native to western Cuba and Trinidad. It was introduced to Florida a half-century ago. The oldest stems become woody, flat and twisted and with turtle-shaped swellings. Leaves are of two types, those cleft to the middle and those on young shoots that are cut nearly to the base. Flowers are white, fragrant, to 1½ inches across, produced in short axillary and terminal elongated racemes from June to October. Stamens are 10. It rarely fruits in Florida.

*B. macrostachya* WALLICH [syn.: *Phanera macrostachya* (Wallich) Bentham]

**140. BAUHINIA FASSOGLENSIS**    **141. BAUHINIA SAIGONENSIS**

**142. CAESALPINIA JAPONICA**    **143. CAMOENSIA MAXIMA**

from India is cultivated in the Orient and was introduced to Cuba and Florida many years ago. Leaves cleft ¼. Flowers yellowish-green, to 1½ inches across, appearing in late summer and fall. Stamens are 7 or 8.

*B. saigonensis* PIERRE EX GAGNEPAIN. This climber was introduced from French Indo-China and has been grown successfully in northern Florida and southern California. (Photograph 140.) It is a delicate but hardy and attractive vine with leaves completely divided into two leaflets. Flowers are pinkish-lavender with red veins, to 1½ inches across, produced in elongated racemes from April to November. Stamens are 3.

*B. fassoglensis* KOTSCHY EX SCHWEINFURTH. This climber is native of central Africa from the Sudan southward to Transvaal. (Photograph 141). The few specimens in south Florida have grown well and they flower profusely but fail to set fruit. It is a scandent shrub, the leaves nearly round in outline and notched only a short distance. Flowers are bright yellow, to 3 inches across, produced in long racemes off and on throughout the year. Stamens are only 2.

*B. hupehana.* This plant is native to central China, has been grown as far north as Gainesville, Florida, under slat shade. Leaves are cleft less than ⅓. Flowers are 1 to 1½ inches across, fragrant, white, usually tinged with pink, produced in elongated corymb-like racemes from March to June. Stamens are 3.

## *Bossiaea cordifera*   BENTHAM EX HOOKER F.

This and a prostrate form known as *B. prostrata* R. BROWN are trailing, semi-climbing plants in the cooler parts of Australia. Both have very small leaves and a yellow flower marked with red. This genus should not be confused with *Bosea,* in the Amaranth family.

## *Brachysema latifolium*   R. BROWN                          ERNEST E. LORD

This is a trailing groundcover with round, dark-green leaves, 1 to 2 inches in diameter, silky-silvery beneath, soon covering an area 3 or 4 feet across. The bright red pea-flowers, an inch long, are on single stems or clustered, and they cover the bush in spring, often also in autumn and winter. This species has only been cultivated in recent years and has attracted considerable attention by its striking beauty of flower and foliage, both on flat ground and on rockwork.

## *Brownea macrophylla*   LINDEN
*Common Name:* ROUGE-PUFF

This species of *Brownea* is one of the most spectacular in flower of all tropical plants. Basically it is a tree to 35 feet with a trunk 8 to 15 inches in diameter. However, it has a viney habit, preferring to rest its branches on other trees. Bailey (3) calls the plant a partially climbing shrub to 18 feet. Pittier's book, "Plants of Colombia and Central America," says of this tree:

> "Flowers 30 to 50 together in large capitate spikes, growing profusely on the surface of the trunk, from base to top, and sometimes on the larger

184

limbs. Flowers fire-red in the axils of the bracts. At blooming time, it is one of the most striking features of the foothill belt in the Sambu Valley. In the semidarkness of the dense tropical forest, its erect stems, entirely covered by the red blossoms, and showing for an instant between the trunks of the larger trees, strike the eye of the traveller almost as would lightning."

## *Butea superba*  Roxburgh
※ J. K. MAHESHWARI ※

*Common Names:* Butea-vine (English); Palas-vel (Marathi); Lata Palasha (Sanskrit); Palas Lata (Hindi)

The genus *Butea* (7 species) was originally proposed by Koenig to accommodate a well-known and striking Indian tree (*B. monosperma* Taubert and *B. monosperma* var. *lutea* Maheshwari). In 1795 and the following years, Roxburgh broadened the scope of Koenig's genus by adding two climbing species, *B. superba* Roxburgh (Color Plate 110) and *B. parviflora* Roxburgh. The latter species is often referred to as *Spatholobus parviflorus* Kuntze, although it resembles *B. superba* both in habit and foliage. It is a large woody climber with stems as thick as a man's leg. The 3 leaflets attain usually a length of 12 to 18 inches and sometimes 20 inches in young plants. The gorgeous flowers are borne in great profusion along the leafless branches. Roxburgh remarks that "when in flower, I do not think the vegetable world offers a more gaudy show."

The flowers are bright orange-scarlet with silvery hairs on the outside. The standard or upper petal is about 1 inch wide and up to 3½ inches long.

The vines are common in the hill forests over a large part of India and extending eastward to Burma. A gum-kino similar to that obtained from *Butea* trees exudes from its stem. The roots and the long branches yield a strong fibre which is made into ropes in central India. The leaves are eaten by cattle. The insects seem to have a particular liking for the seeds, which are all eaten away.

## *Caesalpinia japonica*  Siebold & Zuccarini

Of the 60 species of *Caesalpinia* found in tropical countries around the world, many are climbers although not too frequently seen in gardens. *C. nuga* Ait. is a big climber from India to the Philippines having large clusters of bright yellow flowers. Another Indian species is *C. sepiaria* Roxburgh also with yellow flowers. Both these vines are armed with very large vicious hooks that grasp any available support. Hundley (60) reports 8 species of climbers in Burma.

In gardens the most commonly seen of climbers is *C. japonica* (Photograph 142), which is the hardiest of all and in the United States it is cultivated as far north as Washington, D. C. It is found in England in protected parts and on the French Riviera, though normally as a shrub with handsome canary-yellow flowers and bright-red stamens. To get full sun it frequently becomes scandent and thus be used on a trellis.

*C. bonduc* Roxburgh is a climbing shrub with prickly leaves, bright-yellow flowers, and a short prickly pod. Frequently grown in south Florida and elsewhere through the tropics. *C. vernalis* Champion in China is a tall-climbing, prickly shrub with clustered yellow flowers.

## *Calopogonium orthocarpum* URBAN
*Common Name:* CORDA DE VIOLA

Peter Riedel, experimenting with extra-tropical plants in California 30 years ago, described 3 species of *Calopogonium* in his notes. Of this one he said: "A twining sub-shrubby plant from South and Central America. The one-inch blue sweet-pea-like flowers are followed by small densely hairly pods with nearly rectangular seeds." Regarding *C. mucunoides* DESVAUX Riedel wrote: "A vigorous creeping herbaceous plant . . . with stems 3 to 10 feet long that root at the nodes; it has pale blue flowers in racemes 1 to 4 inches long. In Sumatra it is used as a cover plant in rubber plantations." Regarding *C. brachycarpur* URBAN Riedel says: "A small and often prostrate twining vine with bifoliate leaves and small violet or purple flowers."

※ JOHN D. DWYER ※

## *Camoensia maxima* WELWITSCH EX BENTHAM & HOOKER F.

To try to compare the flowers of the leguminous vine *Camoensia* with those of any other member of the bean family is about as difficult as collecting the flowers in the field. *Camoensia,* with only 2 species, both native to west Africa, is a gigantic woody climber, reputed to have as long a flower as any liana on earth, measuring up to 8 inches. (Photograph 143 and Color Plate 101.)

The blossoms of *C. maxima* hang in a cluster like the fingers of a limp hand; the buds are club-shaped and burst open into a quintet of large unequal clawed petals, the standard being extraordinarily large and round in contrast to the shorter and narrower keel and wing petals.

The flowers resemble those of the genus *Sophora* but the habit, the vegetative organs, and the fruits are quite different. The milky-white petals of *Camoensia* are edged in gold, as if some perfectionist were trying to pay tribute to this magnificent aerial masterpiece.

The leaves are compound, the leaflets spreading like 3 fingers, as in the garden bean. It is the leguminous fruit which gives us a ready clue to the taxonomic status of *Camoensia.* It is widely linear in shape and covered with a fine red-velvet pubescence.

The genus *Camoensia* commemorates the distinguished Portuguese poet Louis Camoens, who accompanied Vasco da Gama on one of his long voyages. This liana surely cannot stand the rigorous climate of Portugal but it has been successfully introduced into southern Florida, Puerto Rico, Trinidad, and Hawaii. Its glorious flowers stand as a living reminder of the sacrifices of a little known botanist and collector, Christian Smith, who was "attached to the unfortunate expedition of Captain Tuckey to the Congo River (Africa)."

## *Camptosema* HOOKER & ARNOTT

Among the 15 kinds of shrubs and climbers in the genus *Camptosema* in Brazil and Argentina there are some that are strikingly beautiful when in flower.

*Camptosema rubicundum* HOOKER & ARNOTT is a tall climber with ruby-red pea-flowers in clusters in the leaf-axils. It is sometimes grown in glasshouses.

*C. grandiflorum* BENTHAM is a large climber, with the new shoots somewhat

144. CANAVALIA ENSIFORMIS  145. CASSIA BICAPSULARIS

146. CENTROSEMA VIRGINIANA  147. CHAMAEFISTULA ANTILLANA

puberulous, later becoming smooth. Leaves are trifoliate, and have rather large oval leaflets with pointed tips. The numerous flowers of vivid red are in pendulous racemes about 10 inches long, from the leaf-axils. These do not spread open very much and they have some similarity to *Erythrina* blossoms. The plant is rare in Brazil and is very subject to a caterpillar pest. But indeed, it is a spectacular beauty. Native name: taape.

## *Canavalia ensiformis* DC.
*Common Names:* JACK-BEAN; CHICKASAW LIMA

Bailey (3) says this is one of a dozen species of widely distributed climbers in warm countries, some of which are cultivated for ornament. The clustered pea flowers are often large and are violet, rose, or white with a bell-shaped 2-lipped calyx. (Photograph 144.)

The Jack-Bean is found in the tropics of both hemispheres, and is grown in the southern states for stock. The pods make passable snap-beans when small. The fully developed pods are up to 14 inches long.

*C. bonariensis* LINDLEY is a twiner in Uruguay and southern Brazil with purple flowers in drooping clusters which exceed the leaves.

*C. obtusifolia* DC. is a prostrate or climbing plant with pink flowers in clusters. It grows in Florida and Texas and southward.

*C. rusiosperma* URBAN is a very tall vine ascending the highest forest trees, according to Bailey.

*C. rosea* DC., in Australia called the Jack-Bean of the Beaches, has large pink pea-flowers and big pods which can be eaten as a vegetable. It flowers from December through the warm weather and withstands harsh conditions.

## *Cassia* LINN.

Most of the 600 kinds of *Cassia* are trees or shrubs. A few of the latter are occasionally scandent.

*C. splendida* VOGEL from Brazil is a shrub in California but in the tropics often grows to 15 feet or more.

*C. bicapsularis* LINN. in Florida (Photograph 145) often is 10 to 15 feet but may go to 75 feet. Near West Palm Beach it has gone wild as a pretty weed on roadside fences for a mile. Apparently speaking of this species, Alfred Russel Wallace, in his book "The Malay Archipelago," wrote: "A few fine climbers were sometimes seen, especially . . . a fine leguminous plant with clusters of large cassia-like flowers of a rich purple color."

## *Centrosema plumieri* BENTHAM

About 45 species of *Centrosema* have been described from tropical America, (Color Plate 96). These are climbers related to *Clitoria,* mostly with showy pea-flowers, but these are often hidden by the foliage. Firminger (37) says *C. plumier,* when cultivated in India for ornament is a heavy climber; in the hot and rainy season it bears "large beautiful pure white pea flowers with a puce spot in the center."

188

*C. virginianum* BENTHAM [syn.: *Bradburya virginiana* (Linn.) Kuntze], commonly called butterfly-pea is a vine of sandy fields and acid soil from Florida west to Texas and north to New Jersey. Its 1-inch pea-flowers often put on a pretty display but the vines seldom exceed 6 feet in height. (Photograph 146.) This species is cultivated also in Australian gardens.

## *Chamaefistula antillana*   BRITTON & ROSE

In its native Puerto Rico this is a vine to 30 feet or more bearing many clusters of dark yellow flowers. (Photograph 147.) Strangely enough, in Florida, it is a small tree bearing its pretty flowers not only among the leaves but in big bunches along the trunk and on larger branches.

## *Chorizema cordatum*   LINDLEY                    ☙ ERNEST E. LORD ☙
*Common Names:* HEART-LEAF; FLAME-PEA

Long cultivated in temperate gardens of Australia for its bright little orange and yellow pea-flowers, this climber ranges over the bush during spring months and often carries a fair amount of bloom in winter. The upper growth tends to climb when given support or when squeezed between neighboring shrubs, where it requires but little space. Or it will run over rockery or trail over a low wall. Heart-shaped leaves usually around an inch in length are rather rough and light green. (Color Plate 100.)

*C. ilicifolium* LABILLARDIERE is similar in general appearance, but its leaves are more holly-like in shape and the scarlet flowers extend from spring into early summer, a good four months. It will not reach the height of *C. cordatum* and is better for trailing over walls or rockery.

*C. varium* BENTHAM in the past has been distinguished from the two preceding species, but it differs little more than by a hairiness of stems and leaf under-surface and is probably not a valid species.

*C. diversifolium* DC. is a small shrub for warm climates, with slender upper growth climbing or twining, in spring gay with clusters of rather small orange-red and yellow pea flowers. Together with *C. cordatum* and *C. ilicifolium* it is a popular and easily grown subject for rock garden or against a low fence or other light supporting structure. The smooth-edged leaves are 1 to 2 inches long, varying in width.

## *Clianthus formosus*   (G. DON) FORD & VICERY          ☙ DOUGLAS ELLIOTT ☙
[Syn.: *C. dampieri* Cunningham]
*Common Names:* GLORY-PEA

Glory-pea is a striking small Australian plant. The flowers, about 3 inches long, are bright scarlet with a big velvety purple-black area on the lower half of the erect standard. (Photograph 148.) The blue-green leaves are covered with long silky hairs. This semi-sprawling subshrub grows in poor sandy soil under fiercely hot sunlight. It is somewhat tricky in cultivation, mainly because it resents any disturbance of its roots. Best results come from seed sown where the plant is to flower. Cover the seed with a sheet of glass. Bailey (4) describes a way of

148. **CLIANTHUS FORMOSUS**  149. **CLIANTHUS PUNICEUS**

150. **CLITORIA TERNATEA**  151. **CORONILLA VARIA**

grafting the barely-germinated seedling of *Clianthus formosus* onto young seedlings of *Colutea arborescens*.

Because of the way British gardeners grow the Parrot's-Bill (*C. puniceus* BANKS & SOLANDER) it has mistakenly been classed as a climber. (Photograph 149.) In its native land it is a true shrub that grows 3 to 6 feet high and has arching branches. In Britain it is too tender to survive in the open, except in rare places, and so British gardeners grow it as they do many other tender (and not-so-tender) plants such as *Magnolia grandiflora* and *Chimonanthus praecox*. They train it up warm sheltered walls. But whereas no one thinks of calling *Magnolia grandiflora* a climber, for some reason gardeners in Britain and the U.S.A. do call this *Clianthus* just that.

Climber or not, it thrives on a wall and that is the best place to display its scarlet beaklike flowers, which in spring hang in heavy clusters under the pinnate leaves. Generally considered one of New Zealand's most attractive shrubs, the parrot's-bill would probably be extinct but for the fact that the Maoris, before the arrival of the white man, cultivated it in their villages. It is now virtually unknown as a wild plant. There are two varieties, a pink and a white. The white comes from seed. Other common names for this are kaka-beak and red kowhai (New Zealand) and lobster-claw (England).

## *Clitoria* LINN.                                    ※ JOHN D. DWYER ※

The common name "butterfly-pea," so often applied to the genus *Clitoria* (legume family) is striking in that the two words bring to mind both the kind of blossom and the characteristic fruit (legume). Several *Clitoria* species are vines and all except one in the genus have compound leaves with 3 leaflets. The striking exception is the best known of the lot horticulturally, the climbing blue-flowered *C. ternatea* LINN. with 5 to 9 leaflets. (Photograph 150.) The flowers of all *Clitoria* are showy though usually solitary in the leaf-axils. The spectacular banner petal, characteristic of the butterfly-like blossoms of the legumes, usually resembles a conch or trumpet and dominates the smaller wing and keel petals. In South America the common name is bejuco de conchitas, or vine of the shells. In all species of *Clitoria* that banner petal seems to produce a rainbow of colors.

The flowers are inverted and thus have a striking form of pollination. When the insect visitor enters, the male pollen sacs and the stigmas of the female organ both touch the hairy shell of the pollinator.

*Clitoria* is a tropical or subtropical genus of some 40 species; perhaps a dozen of those which are climbers are grown horticulturally; one species, *C. mariana* LINN., ranges from Florida to New York State and west to Arizona. Judging from its name of *mariana*, it presumably was described by Carl Linnaeus from a Maryland collection. It is grown in India and Burma.

*Clitoria ternatea*, previously mentioned, is widely cultivated in the warmer climates of the world, being termed the blue pea or the bluebell-vine. The most colorful name is perhaps the zapatico de la reina (Queen's Shoe), referring to the shape of the banner. Linnaeus named the species after the island of Ternate of the Moluccas, a part of Indonesia. Perhaps as he thought of the native island home of this blue-flowered beauty his mind's eye caught the glint of the lovely blue ocean waters as if resembling the blue trumpet of his new *Clitoria*.

*C. arborescens* AITON was described by Hooker as having very woody stems which climb to a great height, and corollas "large, purple and white." This is native to North and South America. Williams (132) calls the flowers pink.

Howard (133), on the other hand, quotes Standley in *Flora of the Panama Canal Zone* on *T. arborescens* listed as *T. portobellensis* BEURLING: "Few plants of the region have such handsome flowers. They are very large and of an exceptionally delicate shade of pink." He then explains the confusion of names. This Panama species has not been tried in cultivation.

## *Coronilla varia*  LINN.
*Common Name:* CROWN-VETCH

A few species of *Coronilla* are grown in glasshouses as ornamentals for their yellow and purple pea-flowers in clusters. (Photograph 151.) Bailey (4) says the Crown-vetch is an herb with stems 2 feet long that tend to be straggling, and ½-inch, pinkish-white flowers in dense clusters from June to October.

Another species from Algeria, *C. viminalis* SALISBURY, a trailing shrub, has flowers that are pale red to white, a red stripe on the banner. This blooms all year in southern California and offers promise as an ornamental.

## *Cytisus battandieri*  MAIRE
*Common Name:* MOROCCAN BROOM

All the brooms are shrubs, but this particular one is frequently found growing in the vine manner. (Photograph 152.) A staff member of the Royal Botanical Gardens at Kew reports that the only broom used for wall and fence culture in England is this vigorous grower, which will quickly cover a large area on the wall and produce quite a handsome display. Of course it has no natural means of attachment and therefore has to be tied to the position or supported by wires. This spokesman adds:

> "There are a number of other small procumbent or semi-prostrate species and hybrids of *Cytisus* which are used on dry walls or rock faces in a rock garden where they are used to cover a given space or area. They include the following: *Cardoini,* FOURNIER, *C. beanii* NICHOLSON, *C. procumbens* VELLOZO."

## *Dalbergia brownei*  SCHINZ

*Dalbergia* comprises some 120 species of tropical plants, most of them trees, but some climbers, a few of which are gigantic lianas. All of them bear bunches of pea-flowers, mostly purple and often not showy. (Photograph 153.) *D. brownei* is a climber native in Jamaica, usually grown on a trellis. When cultivated it grows 6 to 10 feet high and bears clusters of fragrant white flowers. It is a native in Florida too, where it is called *Amerimnon brownei* JACQUIN. The ropelike branches

85. BAUHINIA FLAMMIFERA

86. BAUHINIA CORYMBOSA

87. BAUHINIA GALPINI

88. MACROPSYCHANTHUS LAUTERBACHII

89. STRONGYLODON

90. KENNEDIA COCCINEA

91. KENNEDIA PROSTRATA

92. WAGATEA SPICATA

93. LOTUS BERTHOLETTI

94. AFGEKIA SERICEA

95. LATHYRUS ODORATUS

96. CENTROSEMA PUBESCENS

97. PHASEOLUS ADENANTHUS

98. LATHYRUS SPLENDENS

frequently form almost impenetrable entanglements on the edges of Florida hammocks.

*D. ecastaphyllum* (LINN.) TAUB., according to Standley & Steyermark (105), is a scandent shrub or small tree in thickets along Central American seashores as far south as Venezuela, also in West Africa, bearing fragrant white flowers in short dense clusters. (Photograph 154.)

## *Derris* LOUR.

❀ JOHN D. DWYER ❀

The genus *Derris* has approximately 80 species widely distributed in tropical and subtropical areas; about a dozen and a half of these are climbers or lianas. The leaves are compound; from their axils eye-filling inflorescences arise. The leaflets, usually 5, 7 or 9 in number, present a shiny face to the sun while the blossoms exhibit a wide range of color, with lavender and rose being common. The Brazilian and Guiana *Derris pterocarpus* (DC.) KILLIP (often known as *Deguelia scandens* AUBLET) has yellowish-white flowers.

The generic name *Derris* refers to the pod and literally means "leather covering." The fruits, which defy the literal definition of a legume in not splitting open, contain 1 or 2 flattened seeds, round or kidney-shaped.

*Derris* is a source of a resinous substance, rotenone, derived chiefly from *D. elliptica* (Photograph 155), and in Malaya and South America has long been a native source of fish poison. A small quantity of root placed in a pond stupefies the fish, which may be then gathered up readily by hand. Rotenone is a common constituent in commercial insecticides.

In observing the spectacular racemes of the climbing *Derris* we may forget that the roots hidden in the depths of the soil are conjuring up lethal poisons for fish and flea.

## *Derris scandens* BENTHAM
*Common Names:* JEWEL-VINE; TUBA-ROOT

Among the most spectacular of leguminous vines is this native of Malaya China, and Australia. Its clambering woody stems are bedecked with long racemes of white butterfly-like flowers, each blossom with a characteristic banner, 2 wings and 2 keel petals much as in the larger-flowered sweet-pea.

## *Dioclea glycinoides* HORT.
*Common Name:* SCARLET-WISTERIA

This medium-sized climber has been cultivated in southern California for its bright scarlet 1-inch flowers in clusters, that somewhat resemble those of wisteria. The plant has been confused with *Centrosema* (q.v.) and also with *Campsidium* (q.v.).

The dozen or more species of *Dioclea* in their native Argentina and Brazil are rampant vines bearing quantities of blue, violet, scarlet or white pea flowers in clusters, sometimes an inch long. In their native lands they are seldom cultivated as garden plants although they have attractive flowers, abundantly produced. They are usually regarded as curiosities because of their very large seeds. (Color Plate 102.)

193

152. CYTISUS BATTANDIERI     153. DALBERGIA BROWNEI

154. DALBERGIA ECASTAPHYLLUM     155. DERRIS ELLIPTICA

*D. rufescens* BENTHAM is a liana of very vigorous growth, capable of climbing over several big forest trees, becoming woody and extremely strong. The new shoots are rusty-hairy, as are the flower penduncles. Leaves, on long petioles, are trifoliate, with oval or elliptical leaflets. Flowers hang on long pendulous racemes from the leaf-axils, each blossom ½ inch long, from a brownish calyx. Flowers are whitish with a clear purple blush. They are followed by thick fleshy legumes that become woody and enclose 4 or 5 very large seeds of oval shape and horny surface, with an extremely long hilum girdling the seed to 2/3 of its circumference. This is a spectacular plant in the forest, but it is not cultivated because it grows too big.

## *Dolichos lablab*  LINN.
*Common Name:* HYACINTH-BEAN

Some 60 species of *Dolichos* have been described from warm countries. This one (Photograph 156) is cultivated for its highly ornamental flowers. Brilmeyer (10) says that this stem-twining tropical perennial is best grown as an annual, and describes it thus:

> . . . with 6-inch leaves in triplets and upstanding trusses of fragrant, butterfly-like flowers beginning in midsummer. The flat, beaked seed pods are also decorative. The named variety 'Darkness' has deep purple flowers and purple pods; 'Daylight' flowers are white, the pods lightest green. The vine climbs fast to more than 15 feet."

## *Dumasia villosa*  DC.                    ☘ ERNEST E. LORD ☘
[Syn.: *D. pubescens*  DECAISNE]

This very showy twiner, native to Nepal and northern India, possibly also Ceylon, is occasionally grown in temperate climates or (in Britain) in a cool glasshouse.

The yellow to reddish pea-shaped flowers appear more or less orange in the mass and are borne in racemes to 6 inches long containing up to 40 blooms. Trifoliate leaves may be 2 to 5 inches long on slender stalks.

## *Duparquetia orchidacea*  BAILLON

"This is one of the most beautiful vines in the Ivory Coast," wrote Francis Hallé (50) from Abidjan in French West Africa. It is usually a scandent shrub, wrote Hutchinson & Dalziel (63), but it may be a small tree to 20 feet. It bears showy pink and white, orchid-like flowers in erect, many-flowered clusters at the branch tips. The 5 prominently veined petals are unequal. (Color Plate 99.)

## *Galactia tenuiflora*  WIGHT & ARNOTT          ☘ ERNEST E. LORD ☘

This species is a pink pea-flowered evergreen twining perennial from the hot dry desert of central Australia. Flowers are in small clusters, each about half an inch across; the trifoliate leaves are up to 3 inches long.

156. DOLICHOS LABLAB  157. GENISTA LYDIA

158. GUILANDINA CRISTA  159. HARDENBERGIA COMPTONIANA

Some 50 species of *Galactia* have been recorded throughout the tropics, mostly red and purple-flowered evergreen twiners, but several of them deciduous. Many are found in Central and South America. They are rarely seen in cultivation.

## *Genista lydia* BOISSIER
[Syn.: *G. triangularis* Baumgârten]

*Genista* comprises about 75 species of shrubs, none of them scandent; however, a few are cultivated in the vine manner because of their creeping habit. (Photograph 157.) A spokesman for the Royal Botanical Gardens at Kew says the *Genista* species:

> ". . . are not used as wall shrubs but the procumbent species are used for dry walls or rock garden, and for this, *Genista lydia* is extensively grown and a very handsome subject. Other species used are *G. januensis* VIVIAKI, *G. pilosa* LINN. and *G. saggittalis* LINN."

## *Glycine clandestina* WENDLAND
*Common Name:* TWINING GLYCINE                    ⚜ ERNEST E. LORD ⚜

This is a delicate climber with very fine stems, small trifoliate leaves, and fine-stalked clusters of small pastel-pink pea-flowers. A blue-flowered form is known. It is found throughout Australia and is often grown in gardens, blooming more or less through winter, spring, and summer. The leaves of 3 narrow leaflets are from ½ to 1 inch long.

*G. sericea* BENTHAM of subtropical Australia is similar with rather larger purplish-blue flowers and less extended growth.

About 10 other species of *Glycine* occur in Asia and Africa, most of them twiners. (*Wisteria sinensis* was long known as *Glycine sinensis*.) Best known of all is the important Asian annual *G. max* MERRILL, which produces the soy-bean.

## *Guilandina crista* (LINN) SMALL
*Common Names:* MOLUCCA-BEAN; NICKERNUT; CATS-CLAWS

This shrub with climbing or loosely spreading branches is armed with many scattered sharp recurved prickles, especially on the stem, also on the backs of the leaves (Photograph 158) and on the seed pods which are 2 to 3 inches long. This plant is native to the islands of the Pacific and is sometimes seen in Cuba and in Florida.

## *Hardenbergia comptoniana* BENTHAM
*Common Name:* BLUE CORAL-PEA                    ⚜ ERNEST E. LORD ⚜

A showy, slender-stemmed but vigorous evergreen twiner from western Australia, this climber has lilac-blue pea-flowers in fairly dense racemes, widely cultivated in temperate gardens. (Photograph 159.) The usually narrow-ovate leaves consist mostly of three narrow leaflets, but four or five leaflets, often wider, are not

160. LATHYRUS LATIFOLIUS    161. MILLETTIA MEGASPERMA

162. MILLETTIA RETICULATA    163. PHASEOLUS CARACALLA

infrequent. Flowering period is from midwinter to late spring; two greenish white spots on each flower afford ready identification.

*H. violacea* (SCHNEEVOGT) STEARN [syn.: *H. monophylla* Bentham] is the only other species cultivated; it differs by its simple ovate leaves and generally shorter and lesser growth. An excellent rockery or wall trailer. Flowers are violet-blue; there are white and light pink varieties, also a shrubby form (var. *ovat* BENTHAM.)

## *Hedysarum coronarium* LINN.

⚘ J. K. MAHESHWARI ⚘

*Common Name:* FRENCH-HONEYSUCKLE

The genus *Hedysarum* (275 species) is widely distributed in the north temperate regions of the world. The French-honeysuckle has been planted in India and the United States in flower gardens for ornamental purposes. It is a small perennial or biennial herb with pinnately compound leaves and deep red, fragrant flowers. The plant thrives well on hills and is propagated by seeds or by layering (37). It is also an important fodder and green manure crop in countries bordering the Mediterranean and in parts of Australia.

Several species of *Hedysarum* have been recorded from Tibet (e.g., *H. citrinum* BAKER, *H. obscurum* LINN., *H. falconeri* BAKER, *H. limprichtii* ULBRICH, *H. pseudastragalus* ULBRICH). In Persia, *H. farinosum* PARSA forms a pretty plant with its white-hairy stems and leaves, and racemes of rose-colored flowers.

Bailey (4) says *H. multijugum* MAXIMOWICZ is a Mongolian perennial of angular, straggling growth, 2 to 5 feet high, very showy and worthy of general cultivation, particularly in rockeries. The flowers are violet and purplish-magenta with yellow blotches, in clusters to 18 inches long.

## *Kennedia beckxiana* F. MUELLER

⚘ ERNEST E. LORD ⚘

[Syn.: *Kennedya*]

*Common Name:* SCARLET CORAL-PEA

One of the 15 species of *Kennedia* climbers in Australia, this is a fast-growing evergreen. It has rich scarlet pea-flowers (over 1 inch wide) in pairs with a yellow, dark-margined blotch at the base of the standard petal. It has 3 rounded leaflets, 3 inches long.

*K. rubicunda* VENTENAT from eastern Australia has long been prized in warm gardens for its rapid growth and drought-resistant qualities. It is tolerant of both acid and limestone soils. Flowers are dusky red in racemes, and the rather beanlike, hairy leaflets may be from 2 to 6 inches long, in threes.

The black coral-pea (*Kennedia nigricans* LINDLE.), with its remarkable flowers, is a large and rapid-growing West Australian twiner, black with a yellow blotch on the standard; they are borne in one-sided racemes from midwinter into spring. The runner-beanlike leaves resemble those of *K. rubicunda*. The plant prefers coastal lime soil but has adapted itself to the hot dry inland regions.

The running-postman (*Kennedia prostrata* R. BROWN (Color Plate 91) is an excellent trailing plant to cover rapidly a large area of ground and is native to all Australian states. Its pea-flowers are single or paired along the extended

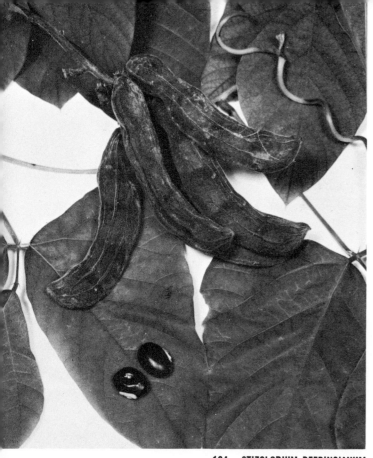

164. STIZOLOBIUM DEERINGIANUM

165. STRONGYLODON LUCIDUS

166. SWAINSONA GALEGIFOLIA

167. VICIA SATIVA

creeping stems, ¾ inch long, and the leaves are of 3 rounded undulate leaflets. This climber is a dazzling blaze of red in early spring.

More refined in appearance and less spreading is *K. eximia* LINDLEY, a splendid rockery or wall trailer (from West Australia), tolerating wet and swampy soils if necessary. Leaves are smaller (under 1 inch), and the clear red flowers are 2/3 of an inch long in small clusters.

By contrast, *K. coccinea* VENTENAT (West Australia), commonly called coral-vine, will quickly cover a vast area of ground, especially after a grass or forest fire. (Color Plate 90.) Long-stalked clusters of ½-inch scarlet pea flowers with a yellow eye are scattered among the giant cloverlike leaves over a long period, resulting in mass displays in winter and spring.

*K. procurrens* BENTHAM, from New South Wales and Queensland, closely resembles *K. coccinea* in character of growth, leaves, and flowers, except that the latter are rich purple. It will thrive in either acid or limestone soils.

## *Lathyrus* LINN.

☀ HOWARD S. IRWIN ☀

The genus *Lathyrus*, the flowering peas or everlasting peas, contains about 100 species of herbaceous tendril-climbers, principally natives of three distinct regions: (1) southern Europe and the mountains of North Africa, (2) temperate South America, and (3) southwestern United States. Nearly all of the presently cultivated species are of the Old World. However, a sizable proportion of the New World species deserve a place in gardens.

The well known annual sweet-pea, generally treated as *L. odoratus* Linn. (Color Plate 95), is in fact derived from numerous forms of that southern European species and another annual, *L. grandiflora*. The tangier pea (*L. tingitanus*) is also an annual with leaves consisting of just one pair of leaflets, and is sometimes cultivated for its pink odorless flowers. This species is sparingly established in southern California and parts of Mexico.

Of the perennial European peas, *L. latifolius*, the perennial pea (Photograph 160), with winged stems and leaves of 2 leaflets, is commonly grown for its red, white, or variously striped and mottled flowers. It is frequently encountered as an escape in fencerows and thickets and on roadside banks. *L. palustris*, a circumboreal species with 3 pairs of leaflets and variable hairiness, occurs in our northern states. The narrowly winged stems bear 2 to 5-flowered racemes of pink to bluish-purple flowers. *L. sylvestris* is a glabrous vine from large rootstocks, bearing one pair of leaflets and red flowers in racemes up to a foot long. *L. pratensis*, occasionally escaped in northeastern North America, differs from all others by its yellow flowers. *L. magellanicus* of Argentina and Chile has purple flowers and one pair of erect leaflets.

The western species of all perennials with 3 or more pairs of leaflets. The most beautiful among them is the well named *L. splendens*, a densely bushy climber, almost shrubby in aspect, which produces a profusion of deep red flowers nearly 1½ inches long. (Color Plate 98.) *L. laetiflorus* is very variable in hairiness and foliage, and bears white flowers with pink veins (rarely all red) in long-stalked racemes. *L. vestitus*, also very variable, has rather short

201

racemes of pale pink or bluish-lavender flowers. All the foregoing are native to southern California. *L. violaceous,* known only in cultivation, but probably derived from one or both of the previous two species, differs from all others of the Southwest by its purple flowers.

Other North American species include *L. venosus,* a leafy perennial mainly of the northern states and Canada, bearing slender racemes of purplish-blue flowers, and *L. japonicus (L. maritimus* in older literature), the familiar beach-pea, a nearly cosmopolitan species of north temperate littoral regions, with glabrous to densely hairy stems and leaves and flowers of red to magenta.

## *Lotus bertholetii* MASFERRER
*Common Names:* WINGED-PEA; CORAL GEM

This small branched slender bush from the Canary Islands is frequently found in glasshouses. (Color Plate 93.) Brilmeyer (10) says of it:

> "Semitropical perennial with branching, trailing stems two feet long or more, foliage like the asparagus-fern but beautifully silvered with light hairs. In spring or early summer it displays clusters of large scarlet, beaked flowers. It will stand light frost."

## *Macropsychanthus lauterbachii* HARMS
*Common Name:* BLUE-MUCUNA

This big vine in the New Guinea jungles has pretty blue petals similar to those of *Mucuna,* but it is not a *Mucuna.* (Color Plate 88.) J. S. Womersley of the Forest Department, Lae, New Guinea, wrote:

> "*Macropsychanthus* is a large liane (or liana) which flowers on the erect inflorescences above the crown of the supporting tree. The blue flowers are sometimes seen fallen on the floor of the forest and lead collectors to envisage a blue flowering vine similar to *Mucuna novo-guineensis.* This is of course not so and *en masse Macropsychanthus* is anything but showy."

In the *Journal of the Royal Horticultural Society* (Nov. 1963) Womersley writes further:

> "For many years casual reports from missionaries, miners and travelers mentioned seeing fallen flowers on the track. Imagination pictured a curtain of blue, comparable with the scarlet shower of the *Mucuna.* . . . Unlike *Mucuna* which has pendulous inflorescences with many flowers opened together, *Macropsychanthus* has erect inflorescences with only a few flowers fully opened at one time. The flower is deep gentian blue, the calyx brown with long rather stiff hairs. Pods are up to 6 inches in length with 3 to 5 seeds.
>
> "There are 2, possibly 3 species [of *Macropsychanthus*] in the New Guinea flora. Plant is usually a very strong liane up to 6 inches or more in

diameter which grows over the high forest trees. Cultivation, except from the largest, well heated glasshouses, would therefore be impracticable. Good growth may be expected in countries enjoying a climate similar to the equatorial tropical low lands. Seed is periodically available from Lae."

## *Mezoneurum kauaiense*  HILLEBRAND

This genus is now more correctly spelled *Mezonevron*. Some species are found in Africa, Madagascar and eastward to Australia and in the Pacific. Hundley (60) lists 6 species in Burma. The plant originally described by Hillebrand is native to Hawaii, where it is a tall shrub to 12 feet with spreading unarmed branches and pinkish-purple flowers. However, many of the other species are armed and a number of them are climbers. Plants are much like *Caesalpinia* except for technical differences.

## *Millettia megasperma*  BENTHAM

Common Name: AUSTRALIAN EVERGREEN-WISTERIA

The genus *Millettia* includes about 40 kinds of showy-flowered climbers that are native to Australia, China, and India, even a few in Africa. Hundley (60) describes 18 of these climbers that are native to Burma. *Millettia* differs from the genus *Wisteria* in having a hard and thick pod which does not open readily. The flowers of the two genera are much the same.

The Australian vine (Photograph 161) is a vigorous tall climber from New South Wales and Queensland; it has glossy deep green pinnate leaves, each leaflet 2 inches long. The flowers are similar to the better known Chinese wisteria but looser in the 5-inch clusters at the ends of the branches. The 6-inch pods are most attractive, thick and woody, covered with dense velvet, and containing large red seeds.

The southern China species, *M. reticulata* BENTHAM (Photograph 162), according to Hui-Lin Li: *Woody Flora of Taiwan,* is:

> ". . . a scandent shrub. Flowers large, red, in terminal erect panicles, 15-20 cm. long and to 20 cm. broad, widespread and common on rocks and trees."

## *Mucuna bennettii*  F. MUELLER

Common Names: BENNETT'S MUCUNA; D'ALBERTIS CREEPER (incorrect); FLAME-OF-THE-FORREST (incorrect); NEW GUINEA CREEPER (incorrect)

This rampant woody climber from the wet forests of Malaysia and the East Indies (Color Plate 103) is one of the world's most beautiful when in bloom. Its brilliant orange-scarlet flowers are borne in large pendent trusses. Holttum (54) calls it one of the most spectacular of all the world's garden plants.

G. A. C. Herklots, botanist-author who lived many years in Hong Kong, wrote that the genus *Mucuna* has been neglected by the horticulturist; he continues:

> "This is a mistake because it contains one of the showiest of the climbing plants of the tropics. *Mucuna* is a Brazilian name for a climbing plant.

Probably the main reason for its unpopularity is that the woody seed pods of many species are densely covered with golden hairs that break off at the slightest touch, penetrating the skin where they cause very unpleasant irritation."

(See *M. pruriens* elsewhere in this book.) (Color Plates 106, 109.)

Unfortunately Bennett's mucuna is cluttered with incorrect common names in the literature. Fairchild (36) insisted on calling this the "D'Albertis Creeper," whereas there really is an entirely different plant which bears the name *M. albertisii* which has whitish-greenish flowers. L. M. D'Albertis, an officer of the Italian Crown, wrote a book about New Guinea, *What I Did and What I Saw,* a century ago in which he described Bennett's mucuna thus:

"There is a plant now in flower that forms the most beautiful ornament of the forest. This plant climbs the highest trees and covers them with its masses of yellowish-red blossoms. Each flower is about 5 inches long and 1 inch wide and the bunches, formed by 18 or 20 of these, are sometimes as much as 2 feet in length."

Continuing his description of the forest, d'Albertis wrote about the plant which subsequently was known as *M. albertisii:*

"Another plant of the same family covers the tops of trees with leaves and masses of flowers. The flowers of this species are rather smaller than those of *M. bennettii* and being of greenish-yellow instead of red, are not so beautiful. I obtained a few specimens which gave Baron von Mueller the opportunity of describing this plant, naming it *M. albertisii.*"

In the Philippines, the common name for Bennett's mucuna is New Guinea creeper. This is incorrect because there is a species *M. novo-guineensis* (Color Plate 105) which also has red flowers, deeper and brighter red than those of *M. bennettii* and more slender, about 3 inches long, and borne in very large clusters. It does not flower as reliably in the open as *M. bennettii.* The author has grown both Bennett's mucuna and the New Guinea mucuna in Florida but both succumbed to nematodes before maturity.

Dr. L. J. Brass of the Archbold Expeditions, of the American Museum of Natural History, wrote of these two climbers:

"No plantsman would ever forget the sight of these magnificent vines in full bloom. They are seen at their best on the edges of the rain forest streams, where they drape the face of the forest, and when they scramble over second growth forests on river banks. The second growth forest of *Macaranga* type has thin peripheral leafage which lets in a lot of light. Seen from the ground in such a situation, the masses of the red flowers of the mucunas fairly glow. I was reminded of this in up-state New York one fall when I looked into the light from the interior of a beech forest and saw the wonderful yellow glow of the leaves against the sun."

※ J. K. MAHESHWARI ※

## *Parochetus communis* BUCHANAN-HAMILTON EX D. DON

*Common Names:* HEMLOCK-PEA; BLUE-OXALIS

The generic name *Parochetus* (*para* = near, *ochetos* = a water-pipe or conduit, a channel) refers to the usual habitat of this pretty herb. The only species, *P. communis*, is widely distributed in India, Burma, Malaysia, Indonesia and tropical Africa. It is usually found in damp situations and grassy fields as a creeping and rooting herb with pale blue or purplish flowers (sometimes almost white) and cloverlike leaves with obcordate leaflets. The sterile specimens remind us of the genus *Oxalis*.

## *Periandra coccinea* BENTHAM

This low climber with clusters of purple pea-flowers is sometimes cultivated in Brazilian gardens. It is one of 8 species found through northern South America.

## *Phaseolus* LINN. ※ HOWARD S. IRWIN ※

More than 175 species, mostly of tropical America, make up the genus *Phaseolus*. They are chiefly herbaceous twiners with trifoliolate leaves that show pronounced sleep movements. In addition to the commercially important kidney bean (*P. vulgaris*) and lima bean (*P. limensis*), a few species are now cultivated for ornament and several others should be taken up horticulturally. Some species are very vigorous, growing 20 feet or more in a single season. All do best in sunny, well-watered positions and seem to be tolerant of a wide range of soils.

The most ornamental species is *P. caracalla*, the corkscrew-flower or snail-vine, a strong climber to 25 feet, with ascending racemes to 1 foot long. (Photograph 163.) The spiraled buds open to reveal curious unsymmetrical flowers 2 inches long, ranging in color from white to pale lavender and fading to yellowish. The keel, instead of resembling a little boat, is coiled and much elongated, hanging off to one side. This species is native to tropical South America, occurring in thickets, forest borders, and river margins. In North America it is cultivated out-of-doors in frost-free areas and elsewhere in greenhouses. Several similar species, also deserving of cultivation, include *P. bertonii* of Paraguay with blue-violet flowers; *P. speciosus,* a white-flowered species of northern South America; *P. spectabilis* of Central America with pale lavender flowers bearing a short once-coiled keel.

Other *Phaseoli* have smaller, more numerous flowers of characteristic sweet-pea form. (Color Plate 97.) The scarlet runner bean (*P. coccineus*) bears red flowers which are followed by equally decorative reddish-purple pods. A Mexican species, another scarlet runner, is much grown in the United States as an ornamental and for the edible pods. *P. glabellus,* a similar red-flowered species of Mexico, is a tender perennial from a deep woody root.

Among other attractive species little grown or not yet known in cultivation are *P. elegans,* a slender vine from Yucatan with purple flowers and slender pointed pods; *P. adenanthus,* widespread in tropical America and introduced in the Old World, variable in foliage characters, but with flowers generally white or purplish-pink splashed with magenta (they are seldom as purple as in Color

Plate 97); *P. sonorensis,* of dry areas in northern and western Mexico, with small hairy leaves and long-stalked racemes of pinkish-purple flowers; *P. strobilophorus,* a handsome Mexican species differing from all others by the large papery bracts surrounding the purple and white flowers; *P. obvallatus,* a downy Mexican vine with numerous small flowers of red or red-violet; *P. glaber,* a smooth Mexican climber also with numerous red flowers; *P. pilosus,* a Costa Rican plant with yellowish hairs and lemon-yellow flowers.

## *Pterolobium nitens*   F. MUELLER

Rare in cultivation, this "handsome woody climber" (Bentham) has glossy green pinnate leaves and small flowers in rusty-hairy racemes. It is native only to Queensland, Australia, but other species occur in tropical Asia. Best known of these is *P. indicum* A. RICHARD [syn.: *Caesalpinia lacerans* Roxburgh], a slender finely downy vine with minute prickles and large dense panicles of small yellow flowers. Native to India and eastward to Indonesia, this is occasionally grown in warm gardens.

## *Rhynchosia*   LOUREIRO

This genus of twining or prostrate climbers comprises about 300 species scattered mostly through tropical America and Africa. Its flowers, in clusters in the leaf-axils, are yellow, the standard petal often darkly lined, ocasionally purple. Chittenden (42) says that few of the species have any special beauty. Three tropical African species, however, are quite ornamental.

R. *buettneri* HARMS is worth cultivating for its long racemes of reddish or purple flowers, turning dark red-brown in drying, and gray-satiny 2-seeded pods, the seeds blue, turning black.

R. *calycina* GUILLAUMIN & PERRETTET is highly decorative with dense racemes of cream-white flowers which turn a dark red-brown when dry, and gray-velvety pods splitting to expose two metallic-blue seeds.

R. *cyanosperma* BENTHAM EX BAKER well deserves a place in the garden for its pretty racemes of bright red or pure white flowers. The roundish, violet-black shining seeds are used as ornaments by the Indian hill people.

## *Sphenostylis stenocarpa*   HARMS
[Syn.: *Vigna ornata*   WELWITSCH]

This is a strong climber, one of 16 species found in West and East Africa and Abyssinia. It is a wide-climbing, moderately stout vine produced from a tuberous root. Its comparatively small pinnate leaves are rather shiny. It bears mauve, pink or purple flowers in small clusters of 5 to 10, rather lax but conspicuous with a corolla an inch long.

## *Stizolobium niveum*   KUNTZE
*Common Name:* VELVET-BEAN

The genus *Stizolobium* is now usually included with *Mucuna,* of which about 120 species have been described. As it is considered here, *Stizolobium* is confined

168. WISTERIA FLORIBUNDA ALBA   169. WISTERIA FLORIBUNDA

170. WISTERIA SINENSIS   171. WISTERIA VENUSTA VIOLACEA

to the dozen species native to the Old World which have been cultivated in the United States mostly for fodder under the general name of velvet-bean. The best known of these is the Florida velvet-bean (*S. deeringianum* HORT.), of unknown origin cultivated for many years in Florida as an ornamental. (Photograph 164). This species, according to Bailey (4), makes a wonderful growth, producing vines to 100 feet long, bearing clusters of large purple pea-shaped flowers. Many other species and varieties are grown in the southern states, some of them with flower clusters 3 feet long. However, the chief value of the genus is as a forage crop because of its heavy growth. The ornamental species have smooth pods up to 4 or 5 inches long. The pasture weed, known as cowage or cowitch (*S. pruriens* MEDICUS, now known as *Mucuna pruriens* DC.) is so called because the pod is covered with stinging hairs. (Color Plate 106.)

## *Strongylodon macrobotrys* A. GRAY
※ MONA LISA STEINER ※

*Common Names:* JADE-VINE; BAYOU (Negrito); BAYABAK (Tagalog)

One of the most unusual-colored vines is the jade-vine with long trusses of brilliant blue-green flowers, a color found nowhere else in blossoms. Although discovered in 1854, it has only recently been cultivated successfully in tropical countries. The genus *Strongylodon* comprises about 22 species, dispersed over Madagascar, tropical Asia, to islands of the Pacific, but only the jade-vine is of horticultural importance. (Color Plate 89.)

It is a very large woody creeper with twisted stems, growing in damp forested ravines along streams at low and medium altitudes in Luzon and Mindoro, Philippine Islands. The individual flowers are 3 to 4 inches long, half-moon-shaped, crowded along unusually long flowering stems. One raceme may be up to 5 feet long. Leaves are trifoliate, dark green and glossy. Even the fruits are extraordinary, ovoid to globose, often as large as the head of a child, remaining closed. 8 to 10 large seeds are formed in a fruit, but they have been found unusually short-lived, viable for 1 or 2 weeks only.

*S. caeruleus* MERRILL, amethyst-vine, is another endemic woody vine of northern Luzon, Philippines, found in forests at low and medium altitudes. The trifoliate glossy leaves are similar, but the flowers are purplish-blue, less striking than those of the jade-vine. The flowering racemes stand out horizontally, are 6 to 10 inches long; the individual flowers are only 2 to 3 inches long, much narrower than those of the jade-vine, and only slightly curved. The plant is still rare in cultivation.

*S. lucidus* (FORSTER F.) SEEMANN, called the pink strongylodon (Photograph 165) is another vigorous, woody, tropical climber with branching inflorescences, erect or horizontal. This is found in Ceylon, the Philippine Islands, Fiji, and Hawaii. The coral-pink flowers are only 1½ to 2 inches long, crowded along the branching flower stems. A few plants are cultivated in Manila.

## *Swainsona galegifolia* R. BROWN
※ DOUGLAS ELLIOTT ※

A number of plants are called subshrubs, which means they come halfway between true shrubs and herbaceous perennials. Many of them need a severe after-flowering pruning to keep them tidy and vigorous. *Swainsona galegifolia* is one of these. (Photograph 166.) It sends up several shoots from ground-level and by the time they reach their full height of 3 to 4 feet they are so wobbly they need some kind of support; and so the plant is included among the climbers. My guess is that in its native home in Australia it grows through small scrub that holds it up off the ground and protects it from storms.

The plant looks like a perennial sweet-pea. The leaves are pinnate and the flowers (about ½ inch long) are in clusters of 6 to 12 on 8-inch stems that come out from the joints between the leaves and stem.

If you raise it from seed you should get a mixture of colors—pink, red, terra-cotta, and pure white. The pure white is popular with florists.

In mild districts the flowers appear almost continuously.

## *Ticanto nuga*  (LINN.) MEDICUS

This is a tough woody vine from the East Indies with greatly elongated stems. It bears clusters of bright yellow flowers. It is cultivated to some extent in south Florida and is locally naturalized.

## *Vicia cracca*  LINN.

*Common Name:* VETCH

Of the 150 species found in the temperate zone everywhere, including many in the United States, only three are ordinarily cultivated for ornament. Mostly the plants are grown for soil improvement rather than for the flowers.

*V. cracca* is a medium-sized perennial climber bearing clusters of purplish pea flowers about ½ inch long. *V. gerardii* GAUD. is a hardy annual with small violet flowers in short clusters; native of southern Europe. *V. fulgens* BATTANDIER, sometimes called scarlet vetch, is an annual climber of 3 to 5 feet bearing small clusters of red or nearly scarlet flowers with a purple stripe. It is a native of northern Africa and is cultivated in this country only along the Gulf or in southern California.

*V. sativa* LINN., known as common vetch, spring vetch, or tare, is a variable annual or biennial creeping plant not surviving northern winters. (Photograph 167.) It is grown as a cover crop and for green manuring. The flowers of some forms are larger than the usual 1 inch, and may be white or scarlet. Although native of Europe and Asia, the plants are naturalized in the United States.

## *Vigna*  SAVI

✻ J. K. MAHESHWARI ✻

The genus *Vigna* (215 species) is represented throughout tropical and sub-tropical regions. It is separable from *Phaseolus* only by the keel petals which are not spirally twisted, though often incurved.

*V. cylindrica* (LINN.) SKEELS [syn.: *V. catjang* Walpers], the cowpea of Queensland, is cultivated for its pods, which are eaten like French beans, and for its seeds ("catjang"), the edible pigeon-pea.

*V. capensis* WALPERS (Indian sweet-pea) is very common at Mahabaleshwar, near Bombay, India. About the middle of the rainy season, this is one of the commonest flowering plants. The flowers very nearly resemble those of the sweet-pea of gardens, but they have no perceptible scent.

In South India a very pretty climber with pink flowers is found in grasslands in Wynaad, Coimbatore and Pulney Hills (*V. wightii* BEDDOME). It is known there as the Wynaad sweet-pea.

Three species of *Vigna* are known in the United States, which Bailey (5) says are probably all forms of one. The asparagus-bean, also called yard-long-bean (*V. sesquipedalis* FRUWIRTH), is a strong annual climber with purplish flowers an inch long, 2 or 3 together opening in the early morning, closing flat by noon, then soon falling. The pod often lies on the ground, measuring 1 to 3 feet long and mostly less than 1/3 inch wide, thick fleshy, soft, and somewhat inflated or flabby, shrinking when dried.

*V. sinensis* SAVI, commonly called cowpea, is like the preceding except that the pod is only 8 to 12 inches long, not flabby or inflated when green. These are both allied to *V. cylindrica*. The cowpea in northern Queensland is a climber to 10 feet with yellow or purplish pea flowers in clusters in the leaf-axils.

*V. vexillata* A. RICHARD in Australia is a medium-sized scrambler with large pale mauve or purple pea flowers much like sweet-peas without any odor. It withstands strong sea winds and drought.

*Vigna* is separated only by technical characters from *Dolichos* (q.v.).

## *Wagatea spicata* DALZIEL

⚜ T. K. BOSE ⚜

This huge evergreen climber in northwest India sometimes reaches the tops of trees 60 to 70 feet high. (Color Plate 92.) The stem is woody, very thorny throughout, and may attain a diameter of a foot or so. The leaves are bipinnate, the leaflets ovate-elliptic, 1 to 1½ inches long, ½ inch wide. The upper surface is glossy green, the lower surface hairy. The flowers are reddish-orange, pea-shaped, borne on stout spines a foot or more long during February and March.

*W. spicata* is one of the largest of climbers, spreading in all directions. It is rarely grown in home gardens but mostly found in large public parks. It becomes very difficult to control in the limited space of a pergola or wall and it will quickly encroach upon the nearest tree.

## *Wisteria floribunda* DC.

*Common Name:* JAPANESE WISTERIA

The genus *Wisteria* comprises about 10 species native to southeastern Asia and southeastern United States. Bailey (4) says these attractive large climbers with pea-shaped flowers are the noblest of the woody vines for temperate regions and that the Japanese species (Photographs 168 and 169) is one of the best and commonest in cultivation in the United States. (Color Plate 107.) It is a deciduous shrub with twining branches, at least when young, bears hanging clusters of violet or violet-blue flowers about ¾ inch long in clusters 1½ feet long. Var. *macrobotrys,* Bailey says, has flower racemes 2 to 3 feet long. These have reached 6 feet long in Japan. Chittenden (22) says this is best planted

**172. ASPARAGUS PLUMOSUS**

**173. LOASA VULCANICA**

**174. FAGRAEA SP.**

**175. NICODEMIA MADAGASCARIENSIS X MARGARET PIKE**

where its long racemes can be allowed to fall their full length freely. A kind of cage is sometimes constructed for it.

The Chinese species (*W. sinensis* SWEET) is considered a better climber, reaching 100 feet with trunks up to 5 feet in girth. (Photograph 170.) The flowers are mauve or deep lilac, 1 inch long in racemes 8 to 12 inches long, opening simultaneously. Chittenden (22) calls this the "noblest hardy climber ever introduced".

The silky wisteria (*W. venusta* REHDER & WILSON) is another Chinese vine often cultivated in the United States, this one to 30 feet, with flower clusters 6 inches or less long. (Photograph 171.)

Two *Wisteria* vines are native to the United States. *W. frutescens* POIRET is found from Virginia to Florida and westward to Texas. It is a climber to 40 feet, the trunk sometimes several inches in diameter, the lilac-purple flowers ½ to ¾ inch long in clusters about 3 or 4 inches long. *W. macrostachya* NUTTALL is a slender climber to 30 feet native from Tennessee to Texas. It bears lilac-purple or light blue flowers ¾ inch long in clusters a foot or more long.

## *Aloe ciliaris* HAWORTH
*Common Name:* CLIMBING ALOE

This is a climbing species of these famous succulent plants, with fleshy, spiny-edged leaves about 6 inches long. The 1-inch bright red flowers are clustered in 6-inch spikes. Sparingly cultivated in California, this plant will climb to 10 feet if it is supported by a trellis. More frequently it is allowed to sprawl on the ground where the flower spikes always stand straight up. (Color Plate 116.)

## *Arthropodium cirrhatum* R. BROWN

This liliaceous plant spreads its 3-foot leaves along the ground, and bears 1-inch white flowers in a cluster 1 foot across. It is a New Zealand species, one of a dozen species, mostly Australian.

## *Asparagus falcatus* LINN.

*Asparagus* comprises some 300 species of plants, usually vines, mostly in dry places between Siberia and South Africa. One (*A. officianalis* LINN. var. *altilis* LINN.) with inconspicuous flowers is everywhere grown for food. Many others are grown as ornamental plants. On all of them the leaves are reduced to scales, with little green shoots in the axils, usually in tufts.

*A. falcatus* is a spreading woody vine to 40 feet, much branched above. It bears white sweet-scented flowers in loose clusters to 3 inches long.

*A. crispus* LAMARCK is a weak climber to 6 feet with small white fragrant flowers.

176. SCHIZANDRA PROPINQUA    177. HETEROPTERIS BEECHYANA

178. HETEROPTERIS PURPUREA    179. TRISTELLATEIA AUSTRALASICA

*A. sprengeri* REGEL, a common scrambler, has branches to 6 feet long and bears fragrant pinkish flowers in loose clusters to 3 inches long.

*A. plumosus* BAKER is the asparagus-fern or fern asparagus commonly cultivated by florists to be cut in strands of decoration. (Photograph 172.) Its tiny whitish flowers are inconspicuous.

*A. asparagoides* WIGHT is the smilax of florists. It is a tall, much branched smooth vine with greenish-white inconspicuous flowers. What botanists call smilax is a very different plant; see the genus *Smilax,* the greenbrier, in Chapter X.

## *Gloriosa superba* LINN.
Common Name: GLORY-LILY

※ WYNDHAM HAYWARD ※

The tropical vines have no more beautiful and arresting members than are found in the genus *Gloriosa,* one species of which, the well known *G. superba,* goes back to the sixteenth century and is found today growing naturalized in old Florida gardens from early introductions.

The even showier and better known *G. rothschildiana* O'BRIEN, introduced 60 years ago from East Africa, is similarly found in old Florida plantings or as an escape from nearby gardens, thus showing its excellent adaptability to the Florida subtropical climate.

*Gloriosa superba,* so named by Linnaeus, is a late summer and fall-blooming vine or trailer that climbs along hedges, shrubs and even wire fences with equal facility. The stems are green and slender, with long, oval leaves ending in a tendril or curled point, called a "clasper" in the old books, by which it "climbs" or rather holds to whatever object is in its way and suitable in size for its purpose. The vine grows 6 to 10 foot tall (or long) and may have from 2 to 3 to 20 or more blooms.

*G. rothschildiana* has larger flowers, 6 to 8 inches across when wide spread. The color is a brilliant scarlet and gold, the entire flower deepening to a rich crimson at maturity. The petals expand like a true lily, and actually recurve at full bloom. The petals of *G. superba* are orange and yellow, the color deepening with age. They are attractively crisped, while those of *G. rothschildiana* are more widely wavy at the edges.

Other species worth growing are *Gloriosa plantii,* a South African form close to the older *G. virescens,* also *G. carsonii* and a rare clear yellow named *G. greeneae* (Color Plate 114) after Wilhelmina F. Greene, who retrieved it from a Trinidad garden where it had been brought from Africa. The exact botanical status of *G. greeneae* is still undetermined, but it seems close to *G. carsonii.*

*G. supreba* was first known from the Far East where it was encountered by Dutch botanists. It is found in upper India and Africa, although the exact relationships of the Nepalese and African forms are uncertain. A curious thing is that the chromosome complement of all known *Gloriosa* species has been found to be a 2n = 22, which might indicate that Dr. John Hutchinson was correct in his idea that all forms of *Gloriosa* are merely variants of one widely spread species.

The *Gloriosa* grows from a "bulb" or more correctly a tuber, which remains dormant in the ground between growths. *G. superba* and *G. carsonii* make only

214

a single growth in a year, where as *G. rothschildiana* and *G. plantii* will bloom like gladiolus whenever the tuber is ripe for growth. In fact, *G. rothschildiana* can be had in bloom 3 times a year.

Growth in winter even in Florida requires protection from frosts. The tuber will live over the winter outdoors with a good mulch anywhere the ground does not freeze deep enough to damage them, even as far north on the Atlantic Coast as Norfolk, Virginia, but every few years a freeze will wipe them out in such extreme locations. Hence they are better dug and stored like dahlia tubers in the fall after flowering.

The bulbs are most oddly shaped, like the letter "L" or "V", in mature specimens, although the young bulbs may be round or oblong. There is an eye at the end of each arm of the tuber, and gardeners usually break the "bulb" into two, before planting, if the second arm is large enough to grow well.

Large tubers will bloom in 6 to 8 weeks in the North in a warm sunny garden bed if well sprouted and planted carefully outside in mid-May.

## *Littonia modesta*   HOOKER

This tuberous-rooted climbing lily from South Africa climbs by tendril-tipped leaves, like *Gloriosa,* but has more clambering stems. It bears brilliant orange flowers over a longer period in summer; the plant is well branched and will climb to 4 feet or more, according to Brilmeyer (10). (Color Plate 115.)

## *Sandersonia aurantiaca*   HOOKER

This half-erect shrub from Natal, related to *Gloriosa,* is scarcely a climber but does creep from its tuberous base. It produces very showy urn-shaped orange flowers in the leaf-axils. It is usually seen as a greenhouse plant.

## *Thysanotus patersonii*   R. BROWN      ⚜ T. R. N. LOTHIAN ⚜
*Common Name:* CLIMBING FRINGED LILY

There are approximately 30 Australian species of *Thysanotus* and at least one extends to South China and the Philippines. (Color Plate 117.) In addition to being called fringed lilies, they are also known as "fringed violets."

The climbing fringed lily has a tuberous rootstock, somewhat oblong, and usually white in color. The radical leaves are thin and narrow and disappear very rapidly as the thin twining light green stem quickly elongates. At intervals this has small bracts which act as leaves. The stem, often reaching 18 to 24 inches high, is slender, twining and branched, but if it lacks support then it is prostrate. Normally it scrambles over other plants.

The flowers are a bright purplish blue, solitary at the ends of branchlets, and usually there are 2 to 4 on each short lateral branch. The flowers are approximately ½ inch in diameter, the sepals are lanceolate in shape, the petals are ovate-lanceolate and heavily fringed. The flowers rarely last more than a day, but numerous buds provide a continuing supply.

The plant is very attractive; it is rarely grown, mainly because of scarcity of supplies, but will survive in moist sandly loam to which organic matter has been added.

## *Tricyrtis*  WALLICH

Chittenden (22) says this is a genus of 9 or 10 perennial lilies with shortly creeping rhizomes, that are native to Taiwan and Japan and extend to the Himalayas. The arching stems bear rather large but few flowers that are bell-shaped, often spotted within. (Color Plate 118.)

## *Hugonia planchonii*  HOOKER F.

Irvine (65) says this is a climbing shrub or tree fairly common in the forests of Ghana, "well worth cultivating for its beautiful yellow flowers."

## *Blumenbachia chuquitensis*  HOOKER F.

The stinging hairs on most kinds of *Blumenbachia* prevent cultivation in glass-houses, though their unusual and pretty flowers make them excellent trailers. In their native South America they are perennials but in cultivation elsewhere they are usually treated as tender annuals. *B. chuquitensis* has 2-inch brick-red flowers that are yellow within and tipped yellow without. *B. insignis* SCHRADER has white petals.

## *Loasa*  ADANSON

This is a genus close to 100 species of annual or perennial herbs, decumbent or twisting, all of them covered with stinging hairs. They range from Mexico south-ward and are found chiefly in the mountains of Chile and Peru. Flowers are generally yellow and face downward; occasionally they are white or red; they are usually solitary but may be clustered and often quite showy. The plants are much more widely cultivated abroad than in the United States. Chittenden (32) de-scribes 9 species. Firminger (37) says of the species cultivated in India that "the flowers are often more curious than beautiful." (Photograph 173.)

Also in the Loasaceae are the genera *Mentzelia, Eucnida,* and *Caiophora,* mostly herbs from the Andes, "frequently twining," according to Willis (122). While *L. vulcanica* is not recognized as a climber, under glasshouse conditions it may show the twining habit of the genus.

216

## *Centropogon lucyanus* SCHOENLAND IN ENGLER & PRANTL

More than 100 species of these shrubs have been described from tropical America but are seen in this country only in glasshouses. A few of them, like *C. lucyanus,* are scandent. Stems of this plant normally are 1 to 2 feet long and in the sunlight may climb much higher. Clusters of rose-colored flowers are produced at the tips of the branches in midwinter.

## *Lobelia quadrangularis* R. BROWN

The genus *Lobelia* contains 300 or more species scattered all over the world, mostly tropical and subtropical although there are many temperate-zone forms in the United States. *L. quadrangularis* is a creeper in northern Queensland. De LeStang says this native grows to 5 feet in height with purplish-blue solitary flowers ever-blooming profusely. It is a trailing plant, often cultivated.

## *Fagraea* THUNBERG ☙ ELIANE NORMAN ☙

This genus of about 35 species of woody climbers or trees is found in Malaysia, southern China, Formosa and many southwest Pacific isles. Some species are known to be in cultivation but mostly in botanical gardens of that area.

*F. auriculata* JACK [syn.: *F. imperialis* Miquel] is an epiphytic climber with thickly coriaceous, entire leaves, auriculate at the base, 5 to 20 inches long by 2 to 10 inches broad. Flowers are solitary or in 2 to 7-flowered cymes. The funnel-shaped corolla is white, up to 10 inches long and 10 inches across. (Photograph 174.) Fruits are oblong-ellipsoid 3 to 5 inches long, grayish white, the seeds embedded in orange pulp. The flowers, which bloom throughout the year, are pollinated by insects and birds and the seeds are dispersed by birds and ants.

*F. berteriana* A. GRAY EX BENTHAM is usually a tree to 45 feet high but sometimes an epiphyte or a scrambling shrub. The leaves are entire, coriaceous, elliptic or oblong, 3 to 5 inches long by 2 to 4 inches broad. Flowers are very fragrant, about half the size of the above species, often used for leis. Fruits are ellipsoid to globular, 1 to 2 inches in diameter, orange to red.

## *Gardneria nutans* SIEBOLD & ZUCCARINI

This genus is made up of 5 species found growing in southeast and east Asia. This species is known from Japan where it is called "horai-kadura" and Korea where it is known as "eishu-kadzura." It is a vine with thick oblong to lanceolate leaves, 2 to 4 inches long and 1 to 2 inches broad. The flowers have 5 petals and occur singly or in pairs, the corolla rotate, yellowish-white, about ¼ inch long, densely pubescent inside. Berries are about ¼ inch in diameter.

## *Gelsemium sempervirens*   (LINN) AITON F.

*Common Names:* CAROLINA YELLOW JESSAMINE; CAROLINA WILD WOODVINE, EVENING TRUMPET

*Gelsemium* is a genus of 3 species, one in southeastern Asia, the other two in southeastern United States, extending to Mexico and Guatemala.

The Carolina yellow jessamine has opposite lanceolate or ovate-lanceolate leaves, 1 to 4 inches long; it bears bright yellow, sweet-smelling flowers in clusters of 1 to 6 blossoms, in the axils of the leaves. (Color Plate 112.) Individual blossoms are funnel-shaped, 1 to 1½ inches wide, with 5 lobes. Seed capsules are 2-valved, flattened, and somewhat less than 1 inch long. This climber, a favorite through the southern states, blooms from February to April, and is used as a porch, trellis, or bank cover. All parts of the plant are poisonous to eat, owing to the presence of several alkaloids.

## *Nicodemia madagascariensis*   (LINN) PARKER

This small genus of 6 species apparently is restricted to Madagascar and the Mascarene Island. It is often merged with *Buddleia* but it differs from that genus in that its fruit is a berry rather than a capsule. (Photograph 175.) A straggling shrub to 10 feet, it is occasionally cultivated in Florida and California gardens; it can be trained on wire. The ever-lengthening stems have no tendrils, but they wrap themselves around any available support. Bailey (4) says that as a shrub it may reach 20 feet. The leaves on the long stems are ovate-oblong or ovate-lanceolate, up to 5 inches long and 2 inches broad. They are dark green on the upper surface, but densely silvery-white-woolly on the underside and on the stems. The orange flowers are borne in large terminal panicles, on lateral cymes; individual blossoms are densely woolly outside and approximately 1 inch long. The small round fruits are at first white, but turn purple-blue when they ripen. The plant flowers in winter.

## *Usteria guinensis*   WILLDENOW

This monotypic genus from west tropical Africa comprises climbing or twining lianas about 30 feet high with opposite shining leaves with purplish midrib. The leaves are entire, orbicular to oblong-elliptic 2½ inches long and 1 to 3 inches broad. The flowers are arranged in a much branched cyme; the calyx is made up of 4 sepals, one lobe much larger than the others. The corolla is lilac or white, sometimes with splotches of yellow, ½ to ¾ inch long, with one solitary exserted stamen.

MAGNOLIACEAE—MAGNOLIA FAMILY                                      ※ J. M. FOGG, JR. ※

## *Kadsura*   JUSSIEU

Although most members of the magnolia family are trees, two genera (*Kadsura* and *Schisandra*) are vines or twining shrubs. Some botanists place these in a separate family, the Schisandraceae. *Kadsura* (not to be confused with the gatsura-tree, *Cercidiphyllum*) is a genus of evergreen twining shrubs with alternate entire or dentate leaves. The white or pinkish flowers, borne on slender stalks, are about 2 inches in diameter with 9 to 15 tepals (sepals and petals which are not differentiated). Even more showy than the flowers are the large globose heads of scarlet berries which render these plants handsome in the autumn. About 10 species of *Kadsura* are indigenous to the tropical and subtropical regions of southeastern Asia.

*K. japonica* LINN., a native of Korea and Japan, is the one most frequently seen in cultivation. It is evergreen in mild climates, climbs to about 10 feet, and bears small yellowish-white flowers.

## *Schisandra* MICHAUX
[Syn.: *Echizandra* DC.]

Eastern North America is the home of several members of this genus of a dozen or more species of deciduous or evergreen, somewhat aromatic, twining shrubs. Others are native to Asia. The small unisexual flowers, which have 7 to 12 tepals (undifferentiated sepals and petals), vary from white through pink to red and from yellowish to orange. The female flowers develop into clusters of red berries, borne in drooping racemes.

The following species are in cultivation:

*S. chinensis* BAILLON. Northeastern Asia and Japan. Flowers white; fruit scarlet.

*S. coccinea* MICHAUX. South Carolina to Texas. Flowers crimson; fruit scarlet.

*S. grandiflora* HOOKER F. & THOMSON. China. Flowers pinkish; fruit scarlet.

*S. henryi* CLARKE. China. Flowers white; fruit red.

*S. sphenanthera* REHDER & WILSON. China. Flowers orange, fruit red.

*S. propinqua* HOOKER F. & THOMSON. Chinese species with pale yellow flowers. (Photograph 176.)

MALPIGHIACEAE—MALPIGHIA FAMILY                    ❋ ELIZABETH McCLINTOCK ❋

## *Banisteria laevifolia* JUSSIEU

This is a large climbing shrub with opposite leaves and rather slender dark brown stems and branches. The leaves are variable in shape, mostly ovate and entire and 4 inches long, but they vary in width from 2 to 5 inches, and they are covered when young with silvery-white, silky hairs which become shaggy and dark colored in age.

The yellow flowers are about ½ inch across and are borne in terminal panicles which are showy and attractive. The winged fruits are reddish. Brazil and Paraguay.

**180. STIGMAPHYLLUM CILIATUM**    **181. STIGMAPHYLLUM PERIPLOCAEFOLIUM**

**182. ABUTILON CYNTHIA PIKE**    **183. ABUTILON VITIFOLIUM ALBUM**

## *Acridocarpus alternifolius*   (SCHUMANN & THONNING) NIEDENZU

West tropical Africa is the home of three species of scrambling or climbing shrubs with alternate leaves, very decorative and worth cultivating for their showy yellow flowers and pinkish or reddish winged fruits, or samaras.

    *A. alternifolius* has narrowly oblong leaves up to 7 inches long and 2 inches wide with few flowers in a subcorymbose inflorescence. The samaras are nearly 1½ inches long and about ½ inch wide. From Sierra Leone to Nigeria.

    *A. natalitius* A. JUSSIEU, has oblong, linear or linear-lanceolate leaves, up to 4 inches long and 1½ inches wide, and flowers in terminal racemes to 6 inches or more long. Its samaras are mostly to 1¼ inches long and ¾ inches wide (163). Mozambique.

    *A. smeathmanii* (DECANDOLLE) GUILLAUMIN & PERRIER has obovate-lanceolate leaves to 5 inches long and 2 inches wide and numerous flowers in terminal panicles. Samaras are up to 2 inches long and ½ inch wide. Sierra Leone to Cameroons.

## *Heteropteris leona*   (CAVANILLES) EXELL
[Syn.: *Banisteria leona*   CAVANILLES]

This genus of woody climbers is found mostly in the American tropics, with the exception of *H. leona* in west tropical Africa. This has twigs with conspicuous lenticels and opposite, leathery, oblong-elliptic leaves to 8 inches long and 3 inches wide. The yellow flowers are in terminal and axillary, rusty-tomentose panicles about 4 inches long. The reddish samaras have 1 to 3 wings, each about 1 inch long. The plant is decorative both in flower and in fruit (165). It is native in west tropical Africa, in mangrove swamps on the coast and inland in Nigeria.

    *H. beecheyana* JUSSIEU is a large vine with oblong to oval leaves from 1 to 2½ inches long which are glabrous above and tomentose beneath and nearly sessile. (Color Plate 111.) The numerous small pink flowers appear in panicles in the late fall and are followed by pinkish-rose samaras which persist for weeks and are more showy than the flowers. Widely distributed from Mexico to Bolivia (166) and sparingly grown in Florida. (Photograph 177.)

    *H. purpurea* HBK is a low climbing shrub from the West Indies to Venezuela, with few purple flowers in clusters followed by 1-inch fruits having half-obovate-oblique wings. (Photograph 178.)

## *Hiptage benghalensis*   LINN.
[Syn.: *H. madablota*   GAERTNER]

This tall evergreen climber is cultivated in tropical countries for its attractive fragrant flowers. Its opposite, ovate leaves, to 6 inches long, are 2 to 3 times as long as broad and when young are covered with pink or reddish short hairs. The flowers are pinkish to white, about 1 inch across, and occur in axillary and terminal racemes. The samaras are 3-winged, dark reddish when fresh, shiny brown when dry. Widely distributed over India, Ceylon, southern China, Taiwan, and Malaysia. Sparingly grown in Florida.

221

## *Schwannia elegans*  A. JUSSIEU

This is one of 5 species of climbing shrubs in Brazil bearing red flowers in clusters at the tips of the branches. Leaves are softly and densely hairy beneath, and even the flowers are hairy. (Color Plate 108.)

## *Sphedamnocarpus pruriens*  SZYSZYLOWICZ

This is a climber with silky hairs on the reddish stems and on the leaves. It is closely related to *Acridocarpus* and was once included in this genus. The opposite leaves are grayish-green, ovate-oblong, 1 to 4 inches long and strongly mucronate. The yellow flowers, about 1½ inches across, occur in subcorymbose terminal clusters; their petal margins are undulate and crisped. The fruit has two broad wings much like a maple and it is the maple-like fruit which is the basis of the generic name, taken from two Greek words: *sphedamnos,* maple, and *karpos,* fruit. South Africa.

## *Stigmaphyllum*  JUSSIEU

This genus of tropical American climbers features flowers that have broad, somewhat leaflike stigmas. The generic name is taken from two Greek words meaning stigma and leaf and alludes to the expanded and flattened stigmas. Another distinguishing character of *Stigmaphyllum* is the presence of two glands near the upper part of the petiole on each leaf. Two species are cultivated in warm areas for their attractive yellow flowers. Sometimes but not originally spelled *Stigmatophyllon.*

S. *ciliatum* (LAMARCK) JUSSIEU is a slender twiner with ovate-cordate leaves to 3 inches long and sometimes nearly as broad. (Photograph 180.) The venation is palmate from the base of the leaf blade and the margins are ciliate with glandular hairs. The flowers, about 1 inch across, are arranged in umbel-like clusters of 3 to 6, and the petals are fringed. The broad samaras are about 1 inch long. Uruguay, Brazil.

S. *periplocifolium* (DESFONTAINES) JUSSIEU [syn.: S. *lingulatum* (Poiret) Small] is a scandent shrub with elliptic-oblong or lanceolate leaves to 5 inches long having pinnate venation and entire margins. The flowers, about ¾ inch across, are arranged in more or less elongate racemes which are sometimes shortened into subumbellate clusters. (Photograph 181.) West Indies. Both these vines are grown in Florida gardens.

## *Tristellateia australasiae*  A. RICHARD
[Syn.: *T. australis*  A. RICHARD]

This climbing shrub has prominent lenticels on the stems and opposite or whorled leaves which are ovate or ovate-oblong, 2 to 4 inches long, glabrous, and with entire margins. The star-shaped yellow flowers are in terminal racemes about 6 inches long, each flower about 1 inch across. (Photograph 179.) The fruit is 3-parted and each part is further divided into several radiating wings. Widely distributed from the Philippine Islands and Taiwan to the Malaysian region.

184. CALLIRHOE INVOLUCRATA    185. SIDA FALLAX

186. MARCGRAVIA SP.    187. DRAWING (MARCGRAVIA SP.)

The generic name, made up of two Greek words, *tri,* three, and *stella,* star, alludes to the three star-like parts of the fruit.

## MALVACEAE—MALLOW FAMILY

### *Abutilon megapotamicum*  ST. HILAIRE & NAUDIN
*Common Name:* FLOWERING-MAPLE

*Abutilon* includes a number of favorite garden plants with bright red or yellow, mostly drooping, mallow-shaped flowers. (Photograph 182.) Some are herbaceous, some woody, mostly shrubby, but a few make excellent plants for rockeries or baskets. Brilmeyer (10) says this species is a dangler, and a long one at that. She continues:

> "The stems are slender and wiry; crisp leaves of bright green are brilliantly splashed with gold, in variety *variegatum* the pendent flowers are curiously shaped like brick-colored lanterns on a bright yellow base, with protruding brown or purple centers. An outstanding hanging-basket plant. Outdoors it will cascade from the top of a wall or from the edge of a window box."

*A. vitifolium* PRESL, a handsome blue-flowered species, known also in a white form (Photograph 183), is an erect rather than a dangling shrub; it can undoubtedly be trained against a wall.

### *Callirhoë involucrata*  A. GRAY

A dozen species of *Callirhoë,* all native of North America, are perennial herbs producing showy poppy-like flowers. *C. involucrata* (Photograph 184) is a procumbent perennial with rather hairy stems that never get more than 6 inches high. Flowers are crimson or cherry-red, nearly 2 inches across in loose clusters. *C. papaver* A. GRAY is also a perennial, decumbent or oftentimes ascending, the stem about 3 feet long. It is found in very dry, sandy places.

### *Hibiscus rostellatus*  GUILLAUMIN & PERROTTET

This plant from tropical Africa will grow erect but usually it is a slim climber to 10 feet or more. Its stems have small recurved spines (Color Plate 128). The typical hibiscus flowers are a bright golden-yellow with a large maroon eye.

*H. rhodopetalus* F. MUELLER EX BENTHAM, of northern Queensland, is a prostrate plant bearing striking rich pink flowers with a hint of orange, 3 or 4 inches across in the wild and up to 5 inches in the garden. The blossoms last only one day but are produced in abundance through the growing season. The plant grows from a carrot-like tuber.

99. DUPARQUETIA ORCHIDACEA

100. CHORIZEMA ACICULARE

101. CAMOENSIA MAXIMA

102. DIOCLEA REFLEXA

103. MUCUNA BENNETTII

104. BAUHINIA KOCKIANA

105. MUCUNA NOVO-GUINEENSIS

106. MUCUNA PRURIENS

107. WISTERIA SINENSIS

108. SCHWANNIA ELEGANS

109. MUCUNA BRACHYCARPA

110. BUTEA SUPERBA

111. HETEROPTERIS BEECHYANA

112. GELSEMIUM SEMPERVIRENS

## *Sida fallax* WALPERS

*Common Name:* ILIMA

In many parts of Hawaii from sea level to an altitude of 2,000 feet are found various forms of ilima plants, from about 4 feet high to nearly prostrate. (Photograph 185.) Some are cultivated for their bright flowers, which range from yellow to rich orange to dull red. They are about an inch across, 5-parted, solitary or 2 or 3 together near the branch tips. The flowers are often used in making leis. The form known as ilima-ku-kahakai is low, creeping along rocks.

MARCGRAVIACEAE—MARCGRAVIA FAMILY

## *Marcgravia* LINN.

The genus *Marcgravia* lends its name to the family which includes 5 genera of climbing shrubs in tropical America, often epiphytic. They have 2 kinds of leaves and usually small flowers surrounded by bracts that are enlarged and transformed into brightly colored nectaries. Probably most common in cultivation is *Norantea*.

There are 55 species of *Marcgravia* extending up into the West Indies. Willis (118) says:

> "They are climbing epiphytic shrubs, with two kinds of shoots—vegetative, with two-ranked sessile leaves and clasping roots; and flowering shoots with stalked leaves, spirally arranged, and ending in a cymose umbel of flowers. Central flowers are abortive and their bracts are transformed into pocketlike colored nectaries with stalks. The fertile flowers stand upside down, the inflorescence being pendulous. Hummingbirds visit the inflorescence and have been observed to sip nectar from the nectaries, but there appears to be no direct evidence of pollination by their means. Some species are certainly self-fertilized."

As shown by Photograph 186 and the accompanying drawing, young leaves on the tree are small. They fasten adventitious roots to the trunk of the tree. The adult leaves hang on the long aerial branches that terminate in the flowers. *Ficus repens* and *Hedera helix* (q.v.) have a little of the same form.

## *Norantea brasiliensis* CHOISY

[Syn.: *N. guianensis* AUBLET]

*Common Name:* RED-HOT-POKER

This is a stunning vine of the Trinidad forests. Some 35 species occur in the West Indies and northern South America, in growth habit much like Philodendron, climbing by roots attached to any support. (Color Plate 120.) This plant, like *Marcgravia,* has 2 kinds of leaves. Flower clusters appear at the tips of lateral branches hanging out from the trunk of the tree. The true flowers are small, violet in color, but the petal-like bracts which surround them are bright

188. HETEROCENTRON ELEGANS

189. TIBOUCHINA URVILLEANA

190. METROSIDEROS FULGENS AURATA

191. METROSIDEROS CARMINEA

scarlet. This is the showy part of the inflorescence. Sometimes these clusters of bracts are 6-inch spikes scattered along the stem of the branch.

## *Souroubea guianensis* AUBLET

The leaves of this species are up to 15 inches long and 2 to 4 inches wide, unequal-sided, smooth and thick. The veins are invisible above and conspicuous beneath. The yellow flowers are tiny, widely scattered along the branch, but they are surrounded by bright red 3-lobed bracts that are about ¾ inch long, 2 of the lobes spreading, the middle one club-shaped-tubular. Various species of *Souroubea* spread from Trinidad west to Amazonia and northward through Central America. Dr. L. O. Williams of the Field Museum of Natural History, Chicago, wrote:

> "I saw a *Souroubea* in the tops of the trees in Amazonian Peru which turned the crowns of these trees into a mass of red. We sent an Indian up and got some. I don't know what the species is; it is probably new."

MELASTOMATACEAE—MELASTOMA FAMILY                    ☀ JOHN J. WURDACK ☀

Although many species of the *Melastomataceae* were cultivated as greenhouse plants in Europe in the 19th century, the members of this very large tropical family are presently neglected; the group has scarcely been sampled, though there are innumerable wild kinds of probable horticultural merit. The family characters are the opposite leaves with several strongly developed longitudinal veins, the separate petals (ranging in color from various shades of red-purple to orange and yellow, as well as white), and the stamens with appendages of various forms and placement on the anther connectives.

Among the vining species cited by Chittenden (22) is *Clidemia blepharodes* DC. [syn.: *Adelobotrys lindenii*], a native of southeastern Brazil, with small reddish floral bracts and small white to pinkish petals, not particularly of horticultural distinction and probably not cultivated at present.

Several of the true species of *Adelobotrys,* ranging from Central America (and Jamaica) to Bolivia, would be well worth cultivating; these are usually vines with shiny coriaceous leaves and white to pinkish-white flowers in panicles. Perhaps the most widespread species is *A. adscendens* (SWARTZ) TRIANA, found in Central America, Jamaica, and western tropical South America; it climbs up tree trunks from 5 to 25 feet.

## *Blakea* P. BROWNE

This tropical American genus, with about 85 described species, includes trees, shrubs, and woody vines, sometimes epiphytic; several species are recorded as having been cultivated in Europe in the 19th century. *Blakea trinervia* LINN. (148) of Jamaica is a woody vine or shrub 10 to 14 feet or longer, with shiny

192. ABRONIA UMBELLATA    193. ABELIOPHYLLUM DISTICHUM

194. JASMINUM CV. ANN CLEMENTS    195. JASMINUM FLUMINENSE

leaves 3 to 4 inches long; the flowers arise from the upper leaf-axils, are bracted at the base, and have 6 pink petals about 1½ inches long. (Color Plate 125.)

*B. gracilis* HEMSLEY (149) of Nicaragua, Costa Rica, and Panama, is a much-branched vine or shrub 4 to 13 feet tall, but flowering when much smaller in cultivation; the flowers are 2 to 2½ inches across, with 6 pale pink petals. The related genus *Topobea,* with about 57 species described from tropical America, is similar to *Blakea,* but with linear rather than short thick anthers; apparently none of the vining species of *Topobea* has been cultivated, but should merit consideration.

## *Heterocentron elegans* (SCHLECHTENDAHL) KUNTZE
[Syn.: *Schizocentron elegans; Heeria elegans*]

*Common Name:* SPANISH SHAWL

This is the most commonly cultivated vining melastome, an elegant creeper usually grown as a basket plant or sometimes as a groundcover of shady spots in southern California. (Photograph 188.) The species is native to southern Mexico and Guatemala. The flowering time in temperate-climate greenhouses is usually during the spring months. The leaves are dark green, glossy, and about ½ inch long; the flowers are solitary on short branchlets and about 1 inch across, with 4 pink petals.

## *Kendrickia walkeri* (GARDNER) HOOKER F.

This Old World vine or epiphytic shrub has solitary or subumbellate bright rose flowers 2½ inches across. Concerning this showy plant, T. B. Worthington writes:

> "It grows around 6000 feet elevation and covers the canopy of several 100-foot trees, a magnificent sight if one is lucky enough to get a look at it from somewhere above. At 2000 feet here [Kandy], I have kept it alive a year or more but never got it to grow. Trimen says it grows down to 2000 feet and climbs precisely like ivy, a very lovely ornament to the lower montane jungles."

*Kendrickia* apparently has not been cultivated in Europe or the New World.

## *Medinilla* GAUDICH

Many of the 450-odd species of the Old World genus *Medinilla* are vines, sometimes epiphytic. Two Fijian species are especially ornamental, although neither has as yet been cultivated in the Western World:

*M. waterhousei* SEEMANN is a high-climbing woody liane with numerous short inflorescences drooping from the upper branchlets. (Color Plate 124.) The brilliant red bracts and pedicels contrast vividly with the 4 white petals which are about 1 inch long. The vine, known only from mountain crests of Taveuni and Vanua Levu, was named for a hospitable missionary, Rev. J. Waterhouse. It is often considered as perhaps the most beautiful indigenous plant of the Fiji archipelago. The species is the "tangimauthia" of Fijian legend; it also has vernacular names of "tekiteki vuina" and "moceawa"; a color photograph was published as the frontispiece of Parham's *Plants of the Fiji Islands* (1964).

*M. spectabilis* A. C. SMITH is closely related to *M. waterhousei* and was described as new to science only in 1967 (150). In his description Smith wrote:

> "To find another spectacular *Medinilla* near the lake of Taveuni was a delightful surprise, the more so as the second species is nearly, if not quite, as exquisite as the tangimauthia."

*M. spectabilis* (Color Plate 123) has magenta or pink inflorescences, with pale pink petals about ¾ inch long. Both these Fijian species, as well as numerous others in the genus, would be distinct adornments to a garden of exotic vines.

## *Monochaetum myrtoideum*   (BONPLAND) NAUDIN

This genus comprises 50 species of evergreen shrubs of western tropical America, many of them scandent, often cultivated in glasshouses for their few-flowered clusters of rosy-purple to violet blossoms up to 2½ inches across. *M. myrtoideum* is a Columbian species with bright pink flowers.

## *Oxyspora paniculata*   DC.

This has been grown in Europe and is a native of northern India, Nepal, and Assam. From Smith's description (151), the species is a subscandent shrub 3 to 5 feet tall, with long weak branches and bright rose flowers about 1 inch across, the drooping panicles often a foot long.

## *Tibouchina*   AUBLET

Several species of *Tibouchina* are weakly climbing shrubs or vining groundcovers. Even the well known *T. urvilleana* (DC.) COGNIAUX (Photograph 189) is sometimes trained on walls although it is more commonly an erect shrub; *T. organensis* COGNIAUX is similarly grown on greenhouse walls in Europe.

> *Editor's Note:* T. urvilleona with its handsome royal purple flowers, is the correct name for a scandent shrub known in the United States for many years by nurserymen under the incorrect name of T. *"semidecandra"* and also by two really antique generic names, *Pleroma* and *Lasiandra*. In Brazilian wilds there is a species *T. semidecandra* but it is not in cultivation. For a synopsis of the plants in this New World genus that are commonly cultivated, and an explanation of the confusion of names, see *Baileya* 15:1-6. 1967).

*T. laxa* (DESR.) COGNIAUX has been cultivated in Europe (152) and is a subscandent shrub 3 to 8 feet long, with deep violet flowers 2 to 2½ inches across; it is native to middle elevations (7,000 to 10,000 feet) in the Andes of Ecuador and northern Peru. *T. mariae* WURDACK, from northern Peru, is similar in habit and flowers. (Color Plate 126.) Both species would grow well where summers are not overly warm, but are not winter-hardy in temperate climates.

One species, *T. chironioides* (GRIESBACH) COGNIAUX, native to the very moist elevations (2,300 to 4,200 feet) of Dominica, West Indies, is a beautiful groundcover with a habit similar to that of *Heterocentron elegans*. The branches are up to 3 feet long and the very narrow leaves about ½ inch long; the bright pink flowers are about 1 inch across and usually solitary on short branchlets.

MENISPERMACEAE—MOONSEED FAMILY

## *Menispermum canadense* LINN.
*Common Name:* MOONSEED

This hardy, attractive, woody vine, native from Canada to Georgia and west to Arkansas, can hardly be ignored in a "flowering vine" book; the blossoms are tiny and not showy, but they come in clusters big enough to be noticed and loved. (Color Plate 127.) It represents one of the largest families of climbers, the Menispermaceae, in which occur 65 genera and some 350 species, many planted as ornamentals. The family is allied to the Lardizabalaceae.

## *Tinospora* MIERS ⁂ DONALD G. RHODES ⁂

*Tinospora* is a genus comprising some 40 species in tropical Africa, southeastern Asia, and Australia. The plants are most commonly encountered in the Indo-malaysian region. The membranous or rarely arched leaves are often deciduous and are usually smooth, borne on slender petioles. The membranous bark is often much split and in some species long aerial roots develop. Flowers are usually yellowish and although small they are frequently moderately showy. *T. smilacina* Myers, from northern Queensland, was reported by de LeStang as a climber to 15 feet. It bears clusters of greenish-white flowers along the branches.

## *Sinomenium acutum* REHDER & WILSON

Pearce (90) says this is a vigorous, twining, woody climber; it has variously shaped leaves sometimes deeply lobed, and at times heart-shaped, often intermediate between them. It is a striking plant that bears during the summer small yellow flowers that are followed in autumn by round blue-black berries if both male and female vines are present.

MYRTACEAE—MYRTLE FAMILY

## *Feijoa sellowiana* BERG

This small fruit tree from southern Brazil is not a vine but may be trained in the vine manner. Its glossy evergreen leaves are silvery-gray beneath. Flowers

1 to 1½ inches across have petals that are white and fuzzy outside, purplish within. In the center the style and mass of stamens are dark red. Named varieties are cultivated in California for their fruit. Regarding this tree, Harry Blossfeld, plantsman of São Paulo, Brazil, wrote:

> "*Feijoa* is decidedly not a climber. It grows however on stormy cliffs in southern Brazil, near the ocean, and the sea winds keep the shrub down, close to the cliff, where it grows prostrate and might be taken for a climber."

## *Metrosideros carminea*  W. R. B. OLIVER ※ DOUGLAS ELLIOTT ※
*Common Name:* AKAKURA

Climbers are rare in the myrtle family. In fact, the only ones I know are *Metrosideros* with 5 climbing species in New Zealand. They cling to wood and rock by means of aerial roots (like ivy).

Two are outstanding ornamentals, *M. carminea* (Photograph 191) and *M. fulgens* (Photograph 190).

*M. carminea* is generally considered New Zealand's most beautiful climber. (Color Plate 129.) In the garden it forms a thickset plant which in its juvenile stage clings flat against its support; as it matures (after 3 or 4 years) it sends out branches in much the same way as the mature ivy, and if grown on a low tree stump, it looks like a shrub. Or it will clothe a concrete power pole over 25 feet high. In spring it covers itself in a smother of bright carmine flowers in which the main feature is the stamens. The leaves are small and round.

The rata-vine or aka (*M. fulgens* SOL. EX GAERTNER) is a good garden plant. It has bigger leaves and flowers than akakura. The stamens are about an inch long and the type species is orange-scarlet. A variety called *aurata* is yellow. The rata-vine flowers in late summer and early winter. Less spectacular are the species with small white flowers which, except for the color, closely resemble akakura. (Also see Photograph 4.)

## *Micromyrtus ciliata* (not *ciliatus*)  (SM.) DRUCE ※ ERNEST E. LORD ※
[Syn.: *M. microphylla*  (SIEBOLD) BENTHAM; *Baeckea plicata* F.v.M.]

From the temperate regions of Victoria and South Australia comes this attractive low-growing evergreen shrub, now popular in gardens, with strong horizontal growth (in its normal form) extending several feet over the surrounding ground or rockwork. This growth does not root from branches. The plant is useful also for growing in a large garden urn or vase. Leaves are minute (2mm.); numerous tiny buds in spring are red, opening to masses of small white 5-petaled flowers which, after petal-fall, display the red calyces for several weeks. The changes in apparent flower color are intriguing, at times red and white in mixture.

This is not truly a vine but is often so used because of its flat growth habit.

## *Nolana paradoxa* LINDLEY
[Syn.: *N. atriplicifolia* D. DON]

*Nolana* comprises three score species of trailing, succulent, perennial herbs from Chile and Peru, of which a few are cultivated in borders, rocky hillsides and baskets. *N. paradoxa* is a seaside creeper in Peru. It bears "exceedingly beautiful" (37) 2-inch flowers on 3-inch stems, "much like those of *Convolvulus minor,* bright blue," above a white zone that skirts the yellow throat.

NYCTAGINACEAE—FOUR O'CLOCK FAMILY

## *Abronia* JUSSIEU                                    R. E. HOLTTUM
*Common Name:* SAND-VERBENA

Verbena-like inflorescences, each with a whorl of bracts at its base, give *Abronia* its common name. The flowers on these herbaceous trailing plants are fragrant and either yellow, pink, or white. There are 30 species in North America, mostly in the West, in open sandy places. (Photograph 192 and Color Plate 132.) A few are cultivated, particularly *A. fragrans* (night-blooming and white), *A. latifolia* (yellow), and *A. umbellata* (pink). In Britain they are treated as annuals.

## *Bougainvillea* COMMERSON EX JUSSIEU MUT. CHOISY        R. E. HOLTTUM

Bougainvillea plants are strong bushy shrubs or woody climbers that provide brilliant massed color for gardens in tropics and subtropics. Little is recorded about their early cultivation in South America where they are native. Several varieties of *B. spectabilis* and *B. glabra* were named in cultivation in Europe in the 19th century, and from Europe were distributed to tropical Asia. Chance hybrids between cultivars of the two species began to appear after 1900; in 1910 *B. peruviana* X *glabra* ('Mrs. Butt') was brought into cultivation at Trinidad and after 1920 rapidly spread to other parts of the world. In 1917 the first controlled crossings were made by Harland at St. Vincent; later, hybrid seedlings were raised in many places. Since 1930 bud-variations (and later seedlings) from X *buttiana* have added to the color range.

The leaves of Bougainvillea are alternate and bear axillary thorns. Toward the ends of the branches there is a transition from thorn to inflorescence. The flowers, which are without petals, are in groups of 3, each one attached to a large colorful bract. The calyx is tubular and has a small star-shaped limb, or tip. The several stamens, of varying lengths, are within the tube. The ovary, also surrounded by the calyx-tube, forms a small dry fruit containing a single ovule. The bract to which the flower is attached becomes a wing for wind-dispersal.

While to gardeners most Bougainvilleas are known as vines, in Rio de Janeiro there is a street tree, *B. "arborescens"* (Photograph 3 and Color Plate 144). Given the right opportunity, this too would undoubtedly have a tendency to climb.

Of the score of known species, three, with large colored bracts, and their hybrids are in cultivation; they were first known to European botanists through the collections of Commerson at Rio de Janeiro during de Bougainville's voyage of 1766-1769. (Color Plates 130, 131, 133, and 134-147).

## DISTINCTIONS BETWEEN SPECIES

Flower-tube very slender, little constricted in the middle, hairless; leaves with a very broad base, surfaces quite smooth...................................*B. peruviana*

Flower-tube distinctly swollen in basal part, more or less hairy; leaves ovate to elliptic, more or less hairy:

Hairs on flower-tube short (to 1/5mm.) and curved upwards; leaves widest in middle, smooth to touch but with short hairs as flower-tube; flowering when leafy in warm wet season (continuously in wet tropics) ........................................................................................*B. glabra*

Hairs on flower-tube to 1 mm. long, straight and spreading; leaves somewhat ovate (widest below middle), softly hairy to touch; flowering mainly in cool dry season, often when leafless........................*B. spectabilis*

*B. peruviana* Humboldt & Bonpland ('Ecuador Pink'; 'Lady Hudson'). Native in Ecuador, Peru, and Colombia. Inflorescences crowded near ends of branches; bracts delicate pale magenta-pink, crinkled; flowering in response to dry weather; much less vigorous than its offspring X *buttiana,* but with an elegance of its own. First recorded in cultivation at Trinidad in 1920; no distinct cultivars known.

*B. glabra* Choisy [syn.: *B. splendens*]. Species described in 1849 from northern Brazil; first records of cultivation in 1860 (in Britain and Mauritius), introduced to India soon afterwards. Inflorescences borne all along smaller branches; bracts not crisped, usually with green veins, changing little in color with age. Several cultivars, of unrecorded origin, exist:

cv. 'Sanderiana'. Bracts rather small (30 by 18 mm. at flowering) with distinctly acute tips, medium purple; very free-flowering. Exhibited and named in London 1894 (FCC); probably the best-known cultivar of *B. glabra.*

cv. 'Cypheri.' Bracts at flowering 45 x 29 mm. apex blunt, a fresh bright medium purple, slightly redder when old. Named and exhibited at Shrewsbury in 1897; a very fine cultivar.

cv. 'Formosa' (a form of *B. glabra* var. *brachycarpa*). Bracts to 35 by 23 mm. at flowering, elliptic with a short abrupt tip, light mauve; flower-tube much swollen and angled; old bracts persistent. Named and exhibited in London, 1904; very handsome when in full flower but old bracts unsightly.

cv. 'Magnifica' (also *magnifica* var. *traillii*). Bracts a little smaller

234

than in cv. 'Cypheri' but a deeper color. Named in Australia in 1893, said to have been brought from the Seychelles; probably the finest cultivar of *B. glabra*.

*White-bract cultivars.* There have been more than one; they have been too little compared and described.

*B. spectabilis* Willd. Though having the habit of *B. glabra,* in most varieties it is more vigorous, attaining a very large size and flowering best when climbing high on a tree. The first *Bougainvillea* plants grown in Europe were of this species, flowering at Paris from 1835 or earlier. It is not known whether the original cultivar still exists; it had rather deep purple bracts. Among the most important cultivars and varieties of *B. spectabilis* now being grown are the following:

cv. 'Speciosa' (*B. speciosa*). Bracts at flowering 55 x 37 mm., ovate, hairy, the apex slightly rounded, a fine purple, changing little with age. Described 1849; figured from plants grown in Britain 1854.

cv. 'Thomasii'. Habit and size of bracts about as in cv. 'Speciosa', but bracts a fine bright carmine-pink. Grown by Mr. Thomas near Brisbane, Queensland, from 1905; probably the finest cultivar of *B. spectabilis.*

var. *lateritia* (*B. lateritia*). Bracts when young red-purple, at flowering brick-red, fading to orange; hairs on flower-tube spreading as in typical *B. spectabilis* but (in cases observed) only ½ mm. long. Named and exhibited at London in 1865. There are several cultivars (not clearly distinguished) having these characters, with bracts of varying size; they have been important as parents of *glabra—spectabilis* hybrids, contributing much to the color-range now available.

## DISCUSSION OF HYBRIDS

*B. spectabilis* X *B. glabra* hybrids. Grex name: Spectoglabra. These are intermediate between the two parents in hairiness of flower-tube; they show a large range of size and color in bracts, and of color-change from young to old bracts, also in relationship between climate and flowering. Probably the first of these hybrids developed by natural crossing at Teneriffe from about 1900; the first to be named and cultivated outside the Canaries was 'Rosa Catalina' (FCC, London, 1909). Color-change is usually from purplish to less purple (to red, pink, or orange); this is the reverse of the change in X *buttiana*.

In the 1930's hybrids of this group were raised in the West Indies, at Calcutta by S. Percy-Lancaster, in Queensland by W. F. Turley, and doubtless elsewhere; they have been inadequately recorded. Some are very large and vigorous, approaching *B. spectabilis* in habit. Good cultivars are 'Turley's Special', 'Mrs. Lancaster', 'Aida', 'Jubilee', 'Mrs. Fraser', 'Maharajah of Mysore', and 'Mrs. H. C. Buck'. 'Mary Palmer' originated in India as a bud-sport from 'Mrs. H. C. Buck' after drastic pruning of a very large plant; the young shoots bore bracts from very pale pink to creamy white, or sometimes partly purple (patented in the U.S.A. as 'Surprise'). 'Ardeni' is a recent S. African cultivar, a fine tomato-red. 'Margaret Bacon' and 'Barbara Karst' were raised in Florida by J. E. Hendry; I have not seen descriptions of any other cultivars named in Florida, some of which appear to duplicate names used elsewhere. 'Afterglow' (Florida) belongs to this group.

*B. X buttiana* (*B. peruviana X glabra*). First recorded at Trinidad, 1910, from a plant brought by Mrs. R. V. Butt from a garden in Cartagena, named 'Mrs. Butt' by R. O. Williams; introduced to Florida from Trinidad by E. N. Reasoner in 1913 and sold by him from 1917 as 'Crimson Lake'; a similar form was produced later by controlled cross of *B. peruviana* in Peru by S. C. Harland. Bracts in close bunches at ends of branches, crisped (not flat), crimson when young, fading and turning to mauve when old; leaves with a very broad base and slender tip, those of sucker shoots very large (to 18 x 14 cm.). Flowering in response to dry weather but not leafless.

In cultivation, 'Mrs. Butt' has produced bud-sports with bracts of lighter color; and seedlings have been raised, first in Kenya and Natal (some being back-crosses with *B. glabra*). I do not know of a hybrid involving also *B. spectabilis*, but probably such have been produced in Kenya, where 'Mary Palmer' (probably also other Spectoglabra hybrids) has been grown together with X *buttiana* varieties. Cultivars in this group include these:

cv. 'Scarlet Queen' (India from 1920) differs from 'Mrs. Butt' in having flowers that appear as if their tips had been cut off.

cv. 'Mrs. McLean' (syn.: 'Orange King'). A bud-sport from 'Mrs. Butt', originating at Trinidad, 1931; young bracts orange, old ones pale mauve.

cv. 'Louis Wathen'. A bud-sport from 'Scarlet Queen', Madras, 1932; color as 'Mrs. McLean', flower-tubes imperfect.

cv. 'Doña Luz Magsaysay'. Origin Manila, brick-red to salmon-pink.

## SEEDLINGS FROM X BUTTIANA

'Killie Campbell', raised by W. Poulton in Natal, now very popular in South Africa; bracts a fine bright red, fading to mauve. 'Poulton's Special', bracts larger and lighter in hue than 'Killie Campbell', a very fine cultivar. 'Brilliant,' large bracts, good under glass at Kew. 'Hensbergii,' grown at Pretoria, similar to 'Mrs. Butt' but bracts larger. 'Crimson Jewel', grown in Pretoria, origin U.S.A., deep crimson with little change when old. 'Golden Glow', reported from Jamaica in 1949, young bracts yellow, later pale orange, finally pale carmine.

## "DOUBLE" CULTIVARS OF X BUTTIANA
## OR ITS OFFSPRING

Several of these have originated recently, by bud-variation, in the Philippines (in one case after drastic pruning of an old plant); Dr. J. V. Pancho, College of Agriculture, Laguna, has described and named them. Instead of one flower at the base of each primary bract, there is a little shoot bearing a variable number of smaller bracts of the same color, with or without rudimentary flowers on some of them; color is said to be maintained longer than in cultivars with normal bracts. Three such cultivars have been patented in the U.S.A.: 'Carmencita', 'Doubloon', 'Manila Magic Red'; all have also other (earlier) names in the Philippines. A more recent "double" cultivar has almost white bracts.

## INFLUENCE OF CLIMATE ON FLOWERING AND ON COLOR

Some cultivars will only flower well in a strongly seasonal climate, and conversely. Color of bracts, even in the same cultivar, can vary considerably under different climatic conditions, and is generally more intense in drier climates with cloudless skies than in ever-wet equatorial regions; perhaps night temperature also has some influence. A variety of outstanding value in one climate may be of little use in another.

## INTERNATIONAL REGISTRATION OF CULTIVAR NAMES

The Division of Horticulture of the Indian Agricultural Research Institute, New Delhi 12, India, has been appointed International Registration Authority for the record of cultivar names in *Bougainvillea*. Growers who wish to name new cultivars are requested to communicate with the Authority.

## CULTURE

For an account of cultural methods in southern England, see article "Bougainvilleas" by A. L. Poulton and J. Walker in *Park Administration,* Vol. 32, No. 8 (August 1967).

EDITOR'S NOTE: Concerning Color Plate 133 (*Bougainvillea glabra*), photographed in Rio de Janeiro, Dr. Holttum wrote:

"I have never seen a *Bougainvillea glabra* so completely covered with flowers and with so little foliage evident. The picture looks to me more like *B. spectabilis;* but it does not tell me enough to be sure. *B. spectabilis* flowers, almost leafless, in dry season (I have seen it so at Brisbane in Queensland). *B. glabra* flowers when fully leafy in the warmer, wetter part of the year at Brisbane, and continuously in the wet climate of Singapore (where *spectabilis* flowers little). Apart from this difference in behaviour, the easiest diagnostic character is the hairs on the flower-tube and on the leaves. *B. spectabilis* has spreading soft hairs on the flower-tube, and *glabra* has very short curved ones which are not easy to see without a lens. Of course there are now many hybrids between the two species, some more like one parent, some more like the other, and the plant in the picture could be a hybrid."

❊ ERIC V. GOLBY ❊

# HISTORY OF BOUGAINVILLEA IN FLORIDA

The history of *Bougainvillea* in Florida dates back to 1881 when Pliny Reasoner, a farm boy from Princeton, Illinois, arrived at Manatee, Florida, to run a nursery he had bought by mail. His younger brother, Egbert, followed two years later. He corresponded all over the world, with botanical gardens and others, in an effort to import plants and seeds suitable for Florida cultivation, conducting this effort 15 years prior to the establishment of the Plant Introduction Bureau of the U.S.D.A. Pliny died in 1886; Egbert died in 1927. His son, Norman Anderson, established Reasoner's Tropical Nurseries in Bradenton in the early '30's as a family enterprise. His son, Egbert Samuel ("Bud") Reasoner, has headed the organization since 1957. This writer has been with the Reasoners 20 years as Horticulturist. Facts in this paper are derived primarily from talks with the participants or their descendants.

The first *Bougainvillea* grown in Florida was a purple called "splendens" brought in 1885 by Pliny from Havana, where it was being grown in gardens. The first *Bougainvillea* offered for sale by the Reasoner Brothers (Royal Palm Nurseries) of Oneco was in 1887. This was a mauve purple named *B. glabra,* grown from plants obtained from Henry A. Dreer Co. of Philadelphia. James E. Hendry of the Everglades Nursery, Fort Myers, reported that his grandmother Frierson had grown the ancestor of his stock plant of *glabra* from a cutting brought from Brazil by a sea captain in 1875.

I now feel reasonably sure that *glabra* was Jim Hendry's ancestral plant. This is the one we in recent years have called *B. brasiliensis,* and from which *sanderiana* most likely arose as a mutation or as a seedling.

Pliny's letters and catalog description name it *B. spectabilis,* but refer to it as a growing purple, and rich green foliage, and these were grown from cuttings without the benefit of glasshouse or bottom heat in the earlier days, and the plant was a free and mass bloomer. None of this fits the *B. spectabilis* that we know today with its rank growth, hairy stems and leaves, and shy once-yearly blooming. It was just a mistaken name because of the unavailability of reference material. I think that as soon as Egbert could track it down, he used the correct one, *B. glabra,* in 1898.

EDITOR'S NOTE: Because of the occasional conflicts in nomenclature and dates, the Editor has asked Dr. R. E. Holttum to offer comments on Mr. Golby's record. The indented paragraphs which follow were written by Dr. Holttum after he had read this report.

> *B. glabra* var. *sanderiana.* This name originated in 1894, when the firm of F. Sander & Co., St. Albans [England] exhibited a plant at the Royal Horticultural Society and won a First Class Certificate. As regards origin, the only information they gave was that it came "from an old English garden." Of course it must originally have come from the Americas; but the same *sanderiana* was not in use for the variety until 1904. (A plant was sent by Sanders to Singapore in 1894, so I know my information about it is authentic.)

"*B. splendens*" was a name used in 1861 for a plant exhibited in London, of unrecorded origin. The name has no botanical status. The variety was illustrated the following year, and in my judgment is a variety of *B. glabra,* notably the first to be cultivated in Europe.

Egbert's triumph came with the first good dark red; this was known in the British tropics as 'Mrs. Butt'. This was purchased at the close of the Columbian Exposition in Chicago in 1893 when Egbert bought all the *Bougainvillea* in the South American exhibit and had them sent to Oneco. None of them was labeled. When the red plant bloomed it was named 'Crimson Lake' for the dye color, and under this name it was shipped by Reasoner's nursery all over the country. It became the best type with open growth and was well adapted to shearing to keep in shrub form. It is now rarely propagated in Florida, having been superceded by 'Barbara Karst' with its bushier habit.

When thousands of plants are produced over a period of years, sports or mutations are apt to occur. 'Afterglow', an orange variety, whose bracts turn dusty rose as they age, was the first well known sport of 'Crimson Lake'; it occasionally reverts. Later, at the Royal Palm Nurseries, an orange-yellow mutation occurred. Unfortunately a few got mixed in with a lot of 'Crimson Lake'. Another mutation of 'Crimson Lake' was a purplish rose-pink named 'Helen Coppinger'.

'Crimson Lake' was first offered to the public in the 1916 Reasoner catalog. To acquire sufficient plants to offer for sale at that time, the original plant would have had to be in the greenhouse several years. Norman said the introduction was in 1912-1913, which was prior to receiving 'Mrs. Butt' from Trinidad. Mrs. R. V. Butt brought her specimen from Cartagena to Trinidad in 1910; this was its first introduction to cultivation in the West Indies. There is no question but what 'Mrs. Butt' was the original name of the plant. Egbert just gave it a descriptive name where the label was lost and it stuck in this country. In the former British colonies this is still known as 'Mrs. Butt' or "*buttiana*".

Because bougainvilleas that bloom in the shade are lighter in color, there is some variation in descriptions of the same plant. Bougainvillea plants offered by German greenhouses in 5-inch pots as house plants and grown by the thousands are all shade-grown and they vary greatly in color from the species.

At the close of the Pan-American Exposition in Buffalo in 1901, Reasoner also obtained several other unnamed bougainvilleas. He gave these names. A beautiful soft sweet-pea-pink was 'Panama Pink'. There is no other with the same lovely light pink color. The bracts were slightly smaller than average, the growth was usually thin and vining, and the plants seemed to be a seasonal rather than a frequent bloomer. Our nursery discontinued growing it in 1957.

"Panama Pink" must have been *B. peruviana.*—E.

Another received at that time was called 'Rosa-catalina'. This was darker than 'Panama Pink' and outdoors was a lavender pink. It was a free bloomer and in the greenhouse a lighter shade. It was difficult to propagate by cuttings and propagation was abandoned in the late '30's.

The first recorded use of this name in England, 'Rosa-Catalina', was in 1909 when Col. Petre exhibited a plant for which he was awarded a F.C.C. by the Royal Horticultural Society (135). It was introduced from Las Palmas, Grand Canary, and perhaps the name originated there. Another record (136) has the name originating in Santa Catalina, Canary Islands. Dr. G. V. Perez, Teneriffe, writing in *Revue Horticole* in 1913, thought 'Rosa-Catalina' was a sport (bud-variation) from *B. spectabilis* var. *lateritia*. His plant of *lateritia* had sported; but later he said he had seedlings from this plant which he was sure were hybrids due to cross-pollination, and there are other records of intermediates between *B. glabra* and *lateritia* occurring in the Canaries about that time.

Another was *"B. brasiliensis"*. This was a rich violet with dark shiny foliage, not hairy. This is a massive bloomer, not too difficult to propagate. It can be "bushed" like *glabra sanderiana,* and may be its parent. People find its color not easy to use, so its sale is not large. This could be the one Jim Hendry's grandmother brought in.

*"Brasiliensis"* as a species name has no status, and it has been used in different senses; I have not been able to find the origin of the name. Dr. Perez (137) stated that the name *"brasiliensis"* had been used for *lateritia*.

Another that may have been brought in direct from Brazil was *"refulgens"*. This was a royal purple of reddish hue, a rank grower with hairy leaves of the *"spectabilis"* group. Its color is against it today, and it was discontinued in the 30's. Another old purple was 'Chrisman', no longer grown.

The name *"refulgens"* originated with William Bull's Catalogue of 1887, with only a very vague description that is not regarded as having botanical status as a binomial. It had brilliant purple bracts and hairy leaves. I do not doubt that it was a form of *B. spectabilis*. A plant of this name was introduced from Kew to Singapore in 1889, and I do not doubt it was part of Bull's original. It has never flowered in Singapore from that day to this, and so is a variety which needs a cool dry season (such as never happens in Singapore) to induce it to bloom. What I regard as typical *"spectabilis"* does flower a little in Singapore, now and then, being best on a plant that has been allowed to climb high on a tree (one such plant killed a tree, and I had to cut down both.)

On his honeymoon in Jamaica in 1896, Egbert Reasoner brought back from Hope Gardens, *lateritia,* a beautiful orange-brick-red of the *"spectabilis"* group with hairy leaves. It is a seasonal bloomer that covers itself in a mass. It does not root from cuttings (typical of the *"spectabilis"* group) so it is always air-

113. ARTHROPODIUM CIRRHATUM

114. GLORIOSA GREENEAE

115. LITTONIA MODESTA

116. ALOE CILIARIS

117. THYSANOTUS PATERSONII

118. TRICYRTIS SP.

119. GLORIOSA ROTHSCHILDIANA

120. MONOCHAETUM MYRTOIDEUM

121. MEDINILLA SPECTABILIS

122. PSITTACANTHUS ROBUSTUS

123. TIBOUCHINA MARIAE

124. MEDINILLA WATERHOUSEII

125. BLAKEA TRINERVIA

126. NORANTEA GUIANENSIS

127. MENISPERMUM CANADENSE

128. HIBISCUS ROSTELLATUS

129. METROSIDEROS CARMINEA

130. BOUGAINVILLEA X SPECTOGLABRA
MARGARET BACON

131. BOUGAINVILLEA SPECTABILIS
(Cypress Gardens)

132. ABRONIA VILLOSA

133. BOUGAINVILLEA GLABRA (?)
(Rio de Janeiro)

134. BOUGAINVILLEA 'BRILLIANT'
at Kew

135. BOUGAINVILLEA X SPECTOGLABRA
'MARY PALMER'

136. SPECTABILIS
'THOMASII' (orig. plant)

137. B. 'KILLIE CAMPBELL'
in So. Africa

138. B. GLABRA (white cultivar)

139. BOUGAINVILLEA X BUTTIANA
at Kew

140. BOUGAINVILLEA X BUTTIANA
(pink cultivar) at Kew

layered. This does not permit mass production and it will always be scarce. Also, its massive size precludes growing it as a shrub. The original plant was chopped down in the remains of the old "A" greenhouse at the Royal Palm Nurseries five years ago with a trunk as big as Jackie Gleason's waist. Thousands of people still remember the glorious sight when it was in bloom; it brought people from all over Florida.

A plant named *B. lateritia* was exhibited to the Royal Horticultural Society in London in 1865 (138). When publishing an illustration of it (139) Lemaire reduced it to the status of a variety of *B. spectabilis* and it was so treated by Heimerl. It agrees with *"spectabilis"* in everything except bract-color. I also treat it as a variety of *B. spectabilis;* or rather, it probably should represent a series of cultivars, as evidently there are varieties with orange bracts of different sizes (I had a specimen of one from Trinidad which was much larger than the one we had in Singapore). So far as I know, the name *lateritia* originated with the exhibition of the plant in 1865.—

Later Egbert imported *"rosea"*, a hairy-leaved rich medium-pink from Hope Gardens. We still propagate this by air-layers.

'Rosea'. This is not a valid species name; the plant was probably a pink variety of *B. spectabilis*.—

Also from Hope Gardens came *B. spectabilis*. This is a rich royal purple. One flower and bracts fill a tea cup. It is a tremendously rank grower, going to the tops of tall trees. Once established, it grows long stems of great size. In Brazil, Mr. Reasoner was told, the natives were able to climb old vines, using the huge thorns as rungs of a ladder. We believe this is the true species *spectabilis*. Many authors seem to have *spectabilis* and *brasiliensis* transposed; others with *glabra*. My feeling is that hairy-leaved ones belong to *spectabilis,* and the glabrous ones belong in *brasiliensis,* including *glabra sanderiana*. We gave up *spectabilis* 5 years ago. There are 2 double-canopied rows of 300 feet in Hope Gardens of varieties that I doubt have been brought to Florida.

Reverting to the "vining" character, in my experience *B. spectabilis* is always a very strong climber; the only ones I have seen without support simply grew into dense thickets on sprawling branches.

The varieties of *B. glabra* mostly grow into bushes which can be kept as such by trimming and by giving the main stem some support when young; they vary in their "vining" capabilities.

Where Norman got the white 'Elizabeth Doxey', I do not know, but it was after his father died in 1926. This white is not a robust grower; thin and vining, and cuttings root poorly. Its foliage is narrower and more acute at the tip and is always a lighter shade of green. It opens greenish-white and becomes creamy-white. It does not show up well against Florida's many white homes. A California nursery has trademarked one 'Jamaica White'. This appears with only slight experience (none in the ground) to be different from 'Elizabeth Doxey' (which is also called 'Madonna' and 'White Cloud'.) Its leaves appear broader and the flowers whiter, in cool weather occasionally flushed pink.

In 1927 Jim Hendry cut open a bougainvillea flower to find out why seed was never set. He tried a knife to cut open the tube of the flower, found it difficult, so used a single-edged safety-razor blade. His first cross was with pollen of 'Rosa-Catalina' on *lateritia*. He sealed the cuts with small pieces of adhesive tape (because scotch tape had not been invented). His previous use of wax destroyed the flower. Ten seeds were set, and two excellent new bougainvilleas were produced. A rich lavender and rose-pink, he named 'Margaret Bacon' for his niece in Oyster Bay, New York. A darker purple-pink he named 'Daniel Bacon' for her husband. Both of these are hairy-leaved types, and are not easily grown from cuttings. 'Daniel Bacon' is rarely seen any more, 'Margaret' only occasionally. When found, "rosea" is a prettier pink. Realizing the need for a bush-type red, he made many other crosses, using mainly 'Crimson Lake'. Most of these were discarded. One seemed to be the answer—a good red of bushy growth that flowered all along the stem. This he named 'Barbara Karst' for his married daughter. He told me he thought *glabra sanderiana* was the other parent, but he kept no records. He made several crosses using *glabra sanderiana* but none of the others was bushy as he had hoped. He had now found no need to seal the cut in the tube. Since the early 40's 'Barbara Karst' has been the predominant variety in Florida, California, and south Texas. It would be hard to find a plant of 'Crimson Lake' for sale in a nursery today.

From this same group of seedlings he obtained one which he called 'Crimson Lake Jr.' It was dwarf and of compact growth, but had terminal flowering and smaller than average bracts and foliage. It never was a great success, and was not as free blooming as 'Barbara Karst.'

Later he produced his favorite, 'Betty Hendry', named for his daughter-in-law. This is an excellent one. Growth is more slender, prostrate or dwarf, and flowers are cerise-red, very freely produced and in long sprays along the stem. This is also used in urns and planters where some of the branches cascade down gracefully.

The darkest maroon red was 'Susan Hendry', named for his granddaughter. This was a robust vine type with huge bracts and large leaves. It is grown somewhat in Ft. Myers. The variety 'San Diego', put out by a California nursery several years ago, is similar, but *not* identical—we have grown both side by side. 'San Diego' has a lighter tone of red on opening. His 'Hendry #61' is a bush-type, purplish-pink that we liked, but the Florida trade didn't seem to accept. The California nursery trademarked a softer pink as 'Rose Queen'. I think it is identical to 'Rosa-Catalina'.

Another Hendry seedling we like is 'Helen Johnson'. It is the same red as 'Crimson Lake' on a very compact plant with thin stems. We think it ought to sell when it is better known. Note that the two "Bacons" were hairy-leaved and all these others are glabrous except 'Susan', which has wine-red new shoots that develop a few hairs.

From somewhere on the east coast, 'Lateritia Jr.' was produced. It has the same color, as var. *Lateritia,* but smaller bracts and foliage, and is slightly bushy. But it never went over big because it was inferior to its parent.

Mike Fascell of Coral Way Gardens, Miami, brought out a lovely soft lavender called 'Easter Parade'. It has the same foliage and compact growth as *glabra sanderiana* and is most likely a mutation of it. 'Easter Parade' replaced one called 'Wilson's Orchid' because the spent bracts drop off cleanly, instead of browning and remaining on the plant and spoiling the appearance. Another similar lavender was 'Lewis' Lavender Seedling' by Lewis Nursery on Military Trail, Lake Worth. 'Easter Parade' has a bit of pink in its lavender and is the best one of the three.

About 10 years ago we obtained from California a nice light orange variety changing to mauve, named 'Hugh Evans' (not trademarked). This is a free-blooming one that does very well in pots and urns for forcing. A year ago, we ordered one from California trademarked 'Blondie'. When it bloomed it was identical to 'Hugh Evans' though it had been described as light yellow. A letter of complaint brought the reply that all bougainvilleas in California are mixed up.

Bert Kraft, Fort Lauderdale, in 1965, put a trademarked two-tone pink-cerise bushy type with vibrant color called 'Jamaica Pink' on the market. It is a good one.

The records of the plants exhibited at the Royal Horticultural Society in London are the principal records of new cultivars of *Bougainvillea* brought into cultivation in Britain, as of other kinds of plants. These records have been well kept, and they are my principal source of information about plants brought into cultivation and named in this country. The same varieties may well have had other, possibly older, names in the Americas, but I know of no place where they have similarly been recorded.

*The United States Department of Agriculture in 1968 distributed to its official experimenters 8 varieties of* Bougainvillea *that had been obtained from the Park Department, Nairobi, Kenya, in 1963. Here is the list of introductions:*

P.I. 292972 *Bougainvillea.* 'Isabel Greensmith'. Bracts erect, orange-red changing to red. Free-flowering. Leaves medium, dark green, ovate with acute apex. Spines small. Vigorous grower.

P.I. 292973 *Bougainvillea.* 'Killie Campbell'. Bracts thin, red. Free-flowering. Leaves long, ovate, somewhat waxy with wavy margins. Spines many, stout and long. A vigorous grower. South Africa. (This plant, also 'Brilliant' and 'Poultonii' (see below) originated with Poulton in Natal. They are seedlings from 'Mrs. Butt' or one of its varieties.)

P.I. 292974 *Bougainvillea.* 'Mrs. Butt'. Bracts are pinkish-red. Leaves medium, ovate. Spines are small and slightly curved. (This does not seem to be the original by that name.)

P.I. 292977 *Bougainvillea.* 'Poultonii'. Bracts are small, slightly purplish-pink, somewhat wavy along the margin. Leaves are ovate and medium in size. Spines small, thin, and straight. Compact habit.

196. JASMINUM MULTIFLORUM     197. JASMINUM DICHOTOMUM

198. JASMINUM OFFICINALE      199. JASMINUM SAMBAC "GRAND DUKE"

P.I. 292979 *Bougainvillea*. 'Brilliant'. Bracts are medium size, spreading, brilliant red, fading to magenta. A heavy bloomer. Leaves are long. Spines are stout and long.

P.I. 292980 *Bougainvillea*. 'Lady Mary Baring'. Bracts are small, yellow with greenish veins. Blooms are borne in large trusses toward the ends of the branches. Leaves large, ovate. Spines straight.

P.I. 292981 *Bougainvillea*. 'Orange'. Bracts are large bright orange changing to pink. Leaves are ovate. Spines medium length, straight. A good showy variety.

P.I. 292982 *Bougainvillea*. 'Sweetheart'. Bracts red. Leaves large, ovate, medium green. Spines are large and straight.

## *Pisonia* Linn.

R. E. HOLTTUM

This is a genus of about 35 species, mostly small trees, pantropic but mainly in the Americas; named for Willem Piso (born in Amsterdam, 1611), a pioneer of tropical medicine who traveled in the West Indies and Brazil.

*Pisonia aculeata* Linn. is a strong woody climber, pantropic in distribution; like *Bougainvillea* in its thorns but with opposite leaves and very small flowers borne in much-branched inflorescences, male and female flowers on different plants; the small fruits covered with persistent glandular perianth-tube.

Oleaceae—Olive Family

## *Abeliophyllum distichum* Nakai

PETER S. GREEN

*Common Name:* White-forsythia

This native of Korea is scarcely a vine; it is usually grown as a shrub. (Photograph 193.) It can, however, send out long shoots which tend to arch, scramble and hang down. It is hardy and deciduous, with opposite leaves, blooms in early spring, before the leaves appear, and, in a good sunny position, produces masses of white, slightly fragrant flowers shaped like those of a miniature forsythia— hence the misleading "common" name which has been coined for it. The buds, in short racemes in the axils of the leaves, are produced in late summer and autumn, and borne in a more or less exposed condition throughout the winter; as a result they may be killed by very severe frost. Fruit, which is not commonly produced—the species is self-incompatible and heterostylous—is flattened, rounded and surrounded by a wing.

In some plants the flowers are flushed pink in the bud and careful selection and breeding might perhaps lead to new forms with this color intensified.

## *Forsythia suspensa* (Thunberg) Vahl

PETER S. GREEN

*Common Name:* Forsythia, Golden-bell

The genus *Forsythia* contains 6 or 7 species of hardy, deciduous shrubs but of these only *F. suspensa* approaches inclusion in this book on vines, because of its long and arching, scrambling, pendulous or trailing shoots that can be trained. Cherished for its abundance of golden-yellow flowers in early spring, before the leaves appear, it is characterized by long shoots which can be trained like a vine up walls, trellises or house fronts, even to 30 or more feet. It is a vigorous grower with opposite leaves which are usually simple and broadly lanceolate but may be trisect or even trifoliate on strong growth. The 4-lobed flowers, about 1½ inches across, hang down and are borne in clusters along the growth of the previous year. The fruit, which is a capsule, is not often seen, as individual plants are self-sterile and both a long and a short-styled plant are required for pollination.

Where the winters are severe the buds may be killed by frost, but this species, like other forsythias, is a widely popular plant, growing well in urban conditions. Pruning, as a shrub, should be aimed at removing the oldest branches and encouraging new growth; too often one sees plants clipped into shape, thus removing the young growth upon which the next year's flowers are borne.

*Forsythia suspensa* is one of the parents of the most widely grown forsythia, the hybrid *F. intermedia* (25). (Color Plate 162.)

Two varieties are best known: *F. suspensa* var. *sieboldii,* the original variety introduced to the West in 1833, producing the longest branches and therefore the most suitable one for training as a vine, and var. *fortunei,* with a generally more upright growth and slightly larger flowers. Among other well-known variants are *atrocaulis* with young shoots tinged with a purplish coloration (the cultivar 'Nymans' Variety' is a form of this), and cv. 'Pallida' whose yellow flowers are slightly lighted in color. Less well-known and inferior are cv. 'Variegata' with leaves variegated with yellow and cv. 'Decipiens' with flowers borne singly.

## *Jasminum*  LINN.

✻ R. D. DICKEY ✻

*Common Names:* JASMINE; JESSAMINE

*Jasminum* is a genus of more than 200 species found in tropical and subtropical countries around the world. They range in growth habit from drooping or weeping to erect or scandent shrubs and to vigorous climbing vines. Leaves are simple or compound, and are usually opposite though they are alternate in a few species. The white, yellow, red or pink flowers are usually borne in terminal cymes or clusters, though they are solitary in a few species. (Color Plate 126.)

Certain white-flowered, sweet-scented jasmines have been widely known for centuries, so much so that several unrelated plants with sweet-scented flowers are called "jasmines" or "jessamines." A few species have, for many years, been used in perfume making and to scent tea.

Though most kinds of jasmine are subtropical or tropical in their cold temperature tolerance, there are a few species such as *J. beesianum, J. nudiflorum, J. floridum* and *J. grandiflorum* which will stand several degrees of frost.

There is some confusion in the nomenclature of *Jasminum* so that the correct name is not always applied to a species. Because of this there are several species that are now being distributed under incorrect names in Florida and elsewhere.

Space permits discussion of only a few of the more important jasmine species in cultivation. For those interested in detailed taxonomic information on the genus *Jasminum,* the works of Green (121, 122, 123) and Kobuski (124) are suggested.

*J. beesianum* FORREST & DIELS, rosy jasmine, is a hardy member of the genus that comes from southwestern China. It is a low climber growing up to 8 feet, with slender grooved stems. The leaves are simple, opposite, ovate-lanceolate to lanceolate, to 2 inches long and sharp pointed. The small, fragrant, pink to deep rose flowers are ½ to ¾ inch across, and are produced 1 to 3 at the branch terminals. This plant will tolerate winter temperatures experienced along the east coast of the United States as far north as Washington, D. C. However, it does not flower satisfactorily as far south as Florida.

*J. stephanense* LEMAIRE is of interest because it originated as a cross between *J. beesianum* and *J. officinale.* This plant has leaves that are simple or with 3 to 5 leaflets. The flowers are fragrant, pale pink and about ½ inch across.

*J. dichotomum* VAHL, Gold Coast Jasmine. This jasmine from Africa was introduced into Florida several years ago by Dr. David Fairchild. It is a vigorous-climbing, woody vine with simple, large, dark green leaves which are usually opposite but may be single or in whorls of three. The small, fragrant flowers are produced in much-branched, tight terminal clusters at intervals throughout the year. Unopened flower buds are tinted red on the outside, but open flowers are pure white on the inside. (Photograph 197.) This species fruits freely in southern Florida, but has not become a weed plant in this locality. The plant is tender but can be grown in areas subject to only a few degrees of frost.

*J. fluminense* VELLOZO. Although a native of Africa, this plant was first described from Brazil where it was introduced by the Portuguese. (Photograph 195.) It had become established in the trade in Florida, California, and elsewhere under the erroneous botanical name of *J. azoricum* LINN. and the common name of Azores jasmine. The plant fruits freely in the West Indies, in southern Florida and on the Keys, and as a result, has become a troublesome weed pest in these areas.

This jasmine is a strong growing woody vine that will climb over its support to considerable heights. The opposite, compound leaves consist of 3 dark green leaflets and the center leaflet is larger and has a longer leaf-stalk. The stems and petioles are strongly pubescent. The small, very fragrant flowers, about 1 inch across, are borne in loose clusters at the ends of side branches that develop from buds in leaf-axils along the older stems. The flowers are produced at frequent intervals throughout the year. This plant is tender and can be grown in areas subject to only a few degrees of frost.

*J. multiflorum* ANDREWS [syn.: *J. pubescens* Willdenow; *J. gracillimum* Hooker f.]. Furry jasmine; downy jasmine; star jasmine; pinwheel jasmine. This native of India, Burma, China, and Malaysia (Photograph 196) is widely grown in tropical countries of the world and is probably the one most planted in Florida and California. The plant is a strong-growing woody vine which will climb to a height of 20 feet or more by scrambling over its support. It is also a good bank plant or groundcover, but it is more commonly grown as a shrub. Its dark green foliage is dense and the young leaves and stems are quite hairy or pubescent. The leaves are simple, opposite, acute, rounded or slightly heart-shaped at the

200. JASMINUM VOLUBILE 201. JASMINUM NITIDUM

202. JASMINUM NUDIFLORUM 203. JASMINUM REX

base, and 1 to 3 inches long. The pure white star-shaped flowers, about an inch across, are borne in few to many-flowered clusters at the tips of short side branches. The flowers may be odorless or fragrant; the calyx teeth are about ½ inch long and covered with spreading yellow hairs. Flowers are present throughout most of the year, but are produced in greatest abundance during the summer and fall months. Temperatures below about 25°F. will usually severely injure the plant, but it comes back quickly from the roots and will bloom again in the fall.

The plant described in the literature as *Jasminum gracillimum* HOOKER F. is so similar to *J. multiflorum* that it seems to be no more than a clone of this species.

*J. nitidum* SKAN, a native of the Admiralty Islands, is known in the trade under the erroneous botanical names of *J. amplexicaule* G. DON, *J. undulatum* KER and *J. ilicifolium* HORT., and is usually sold in Florida under the latter name. It is now grown throughout the world in climatically adapted areas, and is especially popular in Florida, California, and Hawaii. (Photograph 201.)

This plant is a strong-growing woody vine which climbs by scrambling over its support, but it is usually trained and used as a shrub. The simple leaves are opposite, glossy, dark green, ovate-lanceolate, and from 2 to 4 inches long. The very fragrant flowers, in evidence during most of the year, are produced in few to many-flowered clusters at the tips of side branches that develop from leaf-axils along the old stem. The buds are tinted pink on the outside but the flowers are white when open and are about 1½ inches across. The calyx-teeth are prominently sharp-pointed and stand at right angles to the tube as the flowers mature. This jasmine is climatically adapted to temperatures experienced in the southern half of peninsular Florida.

The jasmine grown in California under the name of *J. magnificum* LINGELSHEIM, the angel-wing jasmine, is apparently only a form of *J. nitidum*.

*J. nudiflorum* LINDLEY, winter jasmine, is the hardiest member of the genus, a native of western China, and one of the best known and most widely used of the jasmines in the West. (Photograph 202.) The winter jasmine is grown extensively in Britain and from New York southward in the United States. This plant is a deciduous, almost erect shrub to 15 feet in height with slender, 4-angled, drooping branches. The compound leaves are borne opposite and are composed of 3 oblong or ovate leaflets which are ½ to 1 inch long. The bright yellow, solitary flowers, which are borne in leaf-axils on bare shoots during the winter and early spring, are ¾ to 1 inch wide with narrow green bracts at their base. In the United States winter jasmine is strictly a shrub although in England it is cultivated in the vine manner.

A variety with leaves variegated with yellow has arisen in nature and has been called 'aureum.'

*J. officinale* LINN. [syn.: *J. affine* Royle ex Lindley], poet's jasmine or white jasmine, is native to an area extending from Iran to China, has been in cultivation for centuries, and is probably the best known of all. (Photograph 198.) It is a deciduous to semi-evergreen climbing shrub with long weak stems that scramble over its support up to 30 feet. The degree of leaf fall seems to be influenced

204. JASMINUM GRANDIFLORUM  205. VANILLA PLANIFOLIA

206. VANILLA PLANIFOLIA 207. VANILLA PLANIFOLIA

by day length and severity of the winter. The compound, opposite leaves have from 3 to 9 leaflets, which are elliptic to ovate-acuminate and 2½ inches long. The fragrant white flowers, from ¾ to 1 inch across, are borne at branch terminals in loose clusters. The calyx teeth are linear, prominent, and from ¼ to ½ inch long. In warmer areas flowers are borne throughout the year, but flowering is inhibited during winter months in the colder areas. This species is the hardiest of the white-flowered jasmines; it will stand the cold temperatures experienced throughout Florida and, according to Green (122), it can endure the winter temperatures of Britain.

*J. officinale grandiflorum* (LINN.) KOBUSKI, from southern Asia, has been variously called the Italian, Catalonian, Royal or Spanish jasmine. Opinions vary as to the correct botanical name of this plant since some have considered it as only a variety of *J. officinale,* while others have made it a separate species. Because of variations in seedling populations of other jasmines, it does not seem that the differences between *J. officinale* and variety *grandiflorum* are any greater than would be expected in seedling populations of any species. (Photograph 204.) The flowers of this jasmine have been used for centuries in making perfume, and it has been grown commercially in southern Europe for many years.

In general, variety *grandiflorum* is similar to *J. officinale,* but the foliage is not as dense, the leaves have from 7 to 11 leaflets, the flowers are very fragrant, about 1½ inches across, and tinted red on the outside, and it will stand less cold than *J. officinale.*

*Jasminum polyanthum* FRANCHET, a native of China, is similar in general characteristics to *J. officinale* but is much less well known. It is grown in California and in greenhouses in Europe but has not become popular in Florida and Hawaii. Green (121) states that it will grow in the open in south and southwest England. This plant is a vigorous-growing woody vine which climbs by scrambling over its support to a height of several feet. The compound, opposite leaves have from 5 to 7 leaflets with the end one being much larger than the others. The small, very fragrant flowers, white on the inside and reddish on the outside, are produced in clusters of 20 to 30. They are most abundant in late winter and spring in greenhouses and in the spring and early summer on plants growing in the open.

*J. rex* DUNN, king's jasmine. This native of Siam is the largest-flowered jasmine in cultivation. (Photograph 203.) Though the large white flowers, which are produced in abundance, would seem to have insured its popularity, thus far it has not been widely planted—perhaps because the flowers are not fragrant. Green (123) has suggested that "there is an open field for hybridization experiments and it may be possible by cross-pollination to introduce scent from some other species such as *J. multiflorum, J. sambac,* or, especially *J. nitidum.*" Paul Swedroe of Fort Lauderdale, Florida, has reportedly made crosses between *J. rex* and *J. nitidum* and one of the resulting hybrids has been named 'Ann Clements'. (Photograph 194.)

This vigorous, scandent shrub has simple, opposite, smooth, leaves which are 3 to 5 inches long. The large, non-fragrant, pure white flowers are borne in profusion in large terminal cymes. The flowers have 9 broad overlapping

208.   FREYCINETIA ARBOREA   209.   FREYCINETIA BANKSII

210.   PLATYSTEMON CALIFORNICUS   211.   PERIPLOCA GRAECA

petals and are about 2 inches in diameter. The king's jasmine is tropical in origin and will stand little frost.

*J. sambac* AITON, Arabian jasmine, a native of India, which may be grown as a low climbing vine. It has been widely planted in tropical areas of the world, is the jasmine most planted in India, and is the national flower of the Philippines. Scent is extracted from the flowers to make perfume, the Chinese use it for flavoring tea, and in Hawaii the flowers are used in making leis.

The simple leaves, borne opposite or in threes, are elliptic or broadly ovate in shape, dark green, from 1½ to 3½ inches long, and prominently veined. The fragrant, pure white flowers, from 1½ to 2 inches across, may be single, semi-double or double, and are borne at branch terminals and in leaf-axils immediately below the terminals. There are 2 clones of this species commonly grown, 'Grand Duke' (Photograph 199) or 'Grand Duke of Tuscany', which is double-flowered, and 'Maid of Orleans', which usually has semi-double flowers. This plant is slightly hardier than the furry jasmine (*J. multiflorum*), enduring about 25° Fahrenheit.

*J. volubile* JACQUIN [syn.: *J. gracile* Andrews], Australian or wax jasmine, is known in the trade, especially in Florida, under the erroneous botanical name of *J. simplicifolium* FORSTER F. It is a scandent shrub similar in growth habit to *J. nitidum,* but is not quite so vigorous, particularly in its climbing habit. The simple, opposite, dark green leaves are shorter and comparatively wider than those of *J. nitidum.* The pure white, fragrant flowers, from ¾ to 1 inch across, are borne in clusters at the branch terminals in the spring. They also appear at irregular intervals during the rest of the year, but seldom in any quantity unless the plant is grown in full sun. (Photograph 200.) The calyx-lobes are very short and inconspicuous.

There is a variegated form of wax jasmine, seen occasionally in Florida, that has blotches of lighter green and/or cream-color on its leaves. It is otherwise identical with the species.

The wax jasmine will tolerate temperatures similar to those experienced in the warmer areas of central Florida and in the southern part of the state.

ONAGRACEAE—EVENING-PRIMROSE FAMILY

## *Fuchsia magellanica*  LAMARCK

Of the 50 or more different kinds of *Fuchsia,* besides the many varieties, only one or two species could be called climbers. Hoyt (58) particularly recommended *F. magellanica,* a blue-flowered form with red calyx from Peru and Chile.

> "A charming little plant for hanging baskets, window boxes or rock-work. Small heart-shaped leaves on slender stalks, and pretty orange flowers tipped with purple and green, followed by large red berries. It is the only *Fuchsia* known with erect flowers, all others being suspended."

## *Zauschneria californica* PRESL

*Common Names:* CALIFORNIA-FUCHSIA; HUMMINGBIRD'S TRUMPET; BALSAMEA

This trailing plant with bright red fuchsia-like flowers is usually seen as a trailer in a rockery or occasionally in a hanging basket. It climbs if opportunity offers. (Color Plate 163.)

ORCHIDACEAE—ORCHID FAMILY            ⚘ DAVID FAIRBURN ⚘

## *Vanilla* MILLER

*Common Name:* VANILLA-VINE

In the great family of orchids there is a wide variation in growth habits of the 20,000 or more species scattered throughout the world. Many orchids grow on the ground or on rocks. Others prefer to live high up in the trees. Some have definite climbing habits, attaching themselves to tree trunks, poles, stakes, or walls and often attain a height of 20 feet or more.

But for lush, rampant growth, the vanilla orchid is in a class all by itself. Here we have a real climber (Photograph 207) with vining characteristics which, under ideal conditions, may reach a length of 200 feet.

Vanilla is not outstanding as an ornamental, but it is of real economic value. It is the source of vanilla extract, several million pounds of which are used every year to flavor ice cream, candy, food, tobacco, liquors, and soaps. The vanilla extract (vanillin) is obtained from the seed pods or "beans." To produce the beans commercially, the inconspicuous yellow or green flowers (Photograph 205), about 2 inches across, are pollinated by hand, as natural pollination by insects is rarely accomplished. Five to six months after the flowers are pollinated, when the beans are about 20 cm. (8 inches) in length and still not ripe (Photograph 206), they are picked, dried, and cured. This curing process consists of killing the beans by exposure to direct sunlight, heating in an oven, or treatment with hot water. They are then dried in the sun about 2 hours every day for 3 weeks, and finally placed in a sweating box for several months until the vanilla aroma develops.

There are over 50 species of *Vanilla* native to tropical countries of the world, but only 3, *V. planifolia* Andrews, (Photographs 205, 206, 207.) *V. pompona* Schiede, and *V. tahitensis* J. W. MOORE, are of commercial importance. Of these 3 species, *V. planifolia* is by far the most important from the standpoint of quantity produced, quality of the beans and market value. According to data compiled by the Federal Experiment Station of Puerto Rico, most of the vanilla is produced in Madagascar, Mexico, French Oceania, Réunion, Dominica, Indonesia, French West Indies, Seychelles Islands, and Puerto Rico.

Vanilla, native of the tropics, requires a warm moist environment with light shade for maximum growth, flowering and bean production. Here in Florida it flowers during the winter months or the dry season. It has been noted that a vanilla vine that is permitted to grow straight up on a tree seldom flowers freely

3 BRACTS:
THE TRINITY

THE 10 APOSTLES

THE CORONA:
HALO OR CROWN
OF THORNS

5 SEPALS

5 PETALS

3 NAILS:
3 STIGMAS

5 HAMMERS
OR 5 WOUNDS:
5 STAMENS

SCOURGES:
AXILLARY
TENDRILS

LEAVES:
HANDS OF THE
PERSECUTORS

**212. ADENIA SP.**

**213. LEGEND OF THE PASSION FLOWER**

**214. PASSIFLORA SANGUINOLENTA**

**215. PASSIFLORA ANTIOQUIENSIS**

or produces beans. Training the vine to bend downward, twisting and curving of the stems, and pruning off several inches of the growing tips stimulate the development of flowers and beans.

Vanilla plants thrive in a slightly acid, well-drained soil of average fertility. A thick fibrous mulch over the soil is beneficial to the roots. Prolonged drought during the active growing season should be avoided. Vanilla is also allergic to frost. Consequently, at McKee Jungle Gardens, Vero Beach, Florida, where a cold front in winter may bring an occasional frost, we grow our vanilla vines in greenhouses. Here they make rapid growth in about 50% shade and flower abundantly during the winter months. Under favorable conditions these vines will grow up to 40 feet long from established cuttings in 3 years.

Vanilla vines are really interesting. Try one sometime. Add flavor to your orchid collection.

PANDANACEAE—SCREWPINE FAMILY

## *Freycinetia arborea* GAUDICHOT
*Common Names:* IEIE; CLIMBING SCREWPINE

Sixty or more species of *Freycinetia* are found from Ceylon eastward through Polynesia to Hawaii. They are mostly slender climbing shrubs with flowers much like those of *Pandanus,* the screwpine. That is, they consist of tightly packed male and female cones surrounded by rosettes of bracts and then by long slender pointed leaves. These floral bracts are fleshy and usually brightly colored.

One species that is prominent in Hawaii but known nowhere else is *F. arborea,* the "ieie" (Photograph 208). Otto Degener, writing in "Plants of Hawaii National Park," said of this unusual climber:

"*Freycinetia* is common throughout the Hawaiian Islands in the forest, especially at lower elevations.

"The ieie is very conspicuous along the highway from Hilo to Kilauea Crater during the summer when it is in bloom. Some plants climb the trees and reach their very tops, the main stem gripping the trunks with its slender aerial roots while the branches curve out into the sun. Other individuals trail on the ground in great masses, forming impenetrable jungles.

"The woody, yellow stems of the ieie are about one inch in diameter and ringed with the scars of fallen leaves. They produce numerous, long, adventitious air-roots of almost uniform thickness throughout, which not only gain nourishment for the plant but enable it to hold on to its support. The stems branch every few feet to produce terminal clusters of slender, shiny, green leaves. These are pointed at their ends and spiny along their edges and on the lower side of the midrib. . . .

"The special method that the ieie has devised to insure cross pollination is so unusual as to be worthy of more detailed discussion.

141. BOUGAINVILLEA 'MANILA MAGIC RED'
(double)

142. BOUGAINVILLEA X BUTTIANA VARIETIES ON
FENCE, WITH JACARANDA. PRETORIA

143. B. 'PANAMA PINK'
(B. peruviana ?)

144. B. 'ARBORESCENS'
(Rio de Janeiro)

145. B. 'DOUBLOON' (Double cultivar)

146. BOUGAINVILLEA X SPECTOGLABRA
'AFTERGLOW'

147. BOUGAINVILLEA X SPECTOGLABRA
'EASTER PARADE'

148. ANTIGONON LEPTOPUS

149. PASSIFLORA INCARNATA

150. ANTIGONON LEPTOPUS ALBA

151. PASSIFLORA FOETIDA VAR. HISPIDA

152. PASSIFLORA QUADRANGULARIS

153. PASSIFLORA CIRRHIFLORA
(French Guiana)

154. PASSIFLORA MIXTA
(Ecuador)

"At flowering time the ends of certain branches of the ieie develop about a dozen bright, orange-red leaves called bracts. These are fleshy and slightly sweet near the base. Within them stand three brilliant cones, or inflorescences. Each is composed of hundreds of flower clusters, each cluster consisting of about six united flowers of which nothing remains excepting their pistils firmly grown together. On entirely different individuals, similar showy bracts occur, also containing cones. These, instead of bearing pistils, bear only stamens that shed pollen. The ieie has thus prevented all possibility of self-pollination by bearing its two sexes on two separate kinds of plants. . . .

"In viewing the matured flowering branches growing there, one will find them almost invariably mutilated—most of the fragrant, colored, fleshy bracts have disappeared. They have been eaten by rats which, in their quest for food, climb from flowering branch to flowering branch. In eating the fleshy bracts, the whiskers and fur of the rodent are covered with pollen, some of which undoubtedly rubs off on the stigmas of female plants visited later. The ieie is the only plant in the Hawaiian Islands and one of the very few in the entire world that uses mammals to effect pollination. Some of its relatives are pollinated by the flying fox, a kind of fruit-eating bat, that enjoys the bracts."

*F. banksii* Cunningham, sometimes used as a glasshouse pillar plant, with sphagnum supplied for it to cling to, has succulent white flower bases. (Photograph 209.) Both these and the fruits are eaten in New Zealand, where the plant is native. Leaves are 2 to 3 feet long, slender, spiny, and arching.

PAPAVERACEAE—POPPY FAMILY

## *Platystemon californicus*  BENTHAM
*Common Name:* CREAM-CUPS

This delicate California annual has creeping stems that give it a trailing habit. Beautiful little snowdrop-like flowers of pale yellow are borne amid the ash-green foliage. (Photograph 210.) The plants are attached to the soil by such fragile stems and roots that they can be transplanted only with difficulty; they should therefore be grown from seed.

PASSIFLORACEAE—PASSION-FLOWER FAMILY

## *Adenia lobata*  (JACQUIN) ENGLER

More than 100 species of *Adenia* vines, from Africa to Indomalaysia, have been described, most of them not ornamental. (Photograph 212.) Irvine (65) says

257

the present species is a tall woody climber with flexible green stems and a long tough tendril. In July and August it bears yellow bell-shaped, sweet-scented flowers which attract bees. The inflorescence is usually provided with a terminal spiral tendril.

Some of the *Adenia* plants are of peculiar habit. *A. venenata* FORSKAL has an erect stem, fairly stout at the base, soft-wooded, with smooth green bark, ascending, later twining, the branches green and ropelike, with tendrils. It is a native of Nigeria.

Codd (23) says that in Kruger National Park, *A. spinosa* BURTT DAVY has at the base a massive, swollen, succulent stem, part of which is below the ground. The above-ground portion has a greenish color. From this enlarged stem arise slender twining branches that are armed with straight sharp spines. Numerous creamy-yellow flowers appear on these branches in early summer before the leaves emerge.

Many species of *Adenia* have now been transferred to *Modecca*.

## *Passiflora* LINN.

STEPHEN S. TILLETT

The genus *Passiflora* has long been of interest because of the striking flowers, also the unusual foliage. Nearly 400 species are native to the New World, and a great many have been cultivated at one time or another. The early conquistadores saw in the parts of the flower the Christian symbolism of the Crucifixion, signaling the missionary work they should carry out. There are many interpretations, some of which are indicated in brackets in the following discussion of the complex flower structure.

The plants are generally vigorous growers, well rooted, and prefer soil with good drainage. The vines climb by axillary tendrils, seen by some as the scourges or cords in the symbolism of the Crucifixion; they may be easily trained on trellises or walls. They may be kept under control by pruning, which is often of assistance in producing greater bloom; some varieties will bloom growing in a 4-inch pot.

The stipules at the base of the petiole (the leaf-stalk) may be small, almost like bristles, often falling early, or they may be of ample size, often kidney-shaped. The leaves of some are simple, a few with pinnate veins, but most have 3 to 5 major veins arising from the base of the blade. The majority are 3-lobed in varying degrees, a few with 5 or more lobes, [and seen as the hands of the persecutors], or the middle of the 3 lobes may be much reduced, giving the leaf a long transverse dimension. The petiole almost always has variable glands present, and there may also be moist shiny glands on the under surface of the leaf [the 30 pieces of silver].

The flower (Photograph 213) is subtended by 3 bracts, small, scattered and early deciduous in some, or larger, showy, and often united [by one interpretation, The Trinity]. The 5 sepals may be green or colored, and may have a horn on the back, the 5 petals colored or white [the ten together representing the ten faithful apostles present in Jerusalem at the time of the Crucifixion]. These are supported on a calyx- or floral-tube (an hypanthium), which may be flat, cup-shaped, or

216. PHILESIA MAGELLANICA    217. BILLARDIERA LONGIFLORA

218. SOLLYA HETEROPHYLLA    219. MARIANTHUS RINGENS

elongated and tubular (the last generally red-flowered). Within the perianth is found the corona, which consists of a series of long filaments (radii) and shorter filaments or bristles (pali), the latter either spreading or erect; the radii may be longer than the perianth. These are frequently banded with white, blue and purple, the bands, taken as a whole, forming concentric rings. [These represent to some the crown of thorns, or to others the halo—the striking white rings standing visually out from the blue.] In the species with elongated floral-tubes the corona is often reduced to short knobs or a mere rim.

Within the floral-tube there is a thin membrane (the operculum), either simple or pleated, which generally hangs down or arches over and engages with another (the limen) arising from the base of the stalk that supports the stamens and pistil, thus closing off a nectar chamber in the base of the floral-tube. There is often a ring of tissue (the annulus) associated with the nectary within the nectar chamber. The 5 stamens have versatile anthers; they arch over the corona during the early hours of blooming, then reflex upwards; [those with red spotting seen by some to represent the 5 wounds, by others seen as the 5 hammers used to drive the nails.] The ovary is surmounted by 3 large styles with capitate stigmas [representing the 3 nails, or the whole pistil signifying The Trinity]. These also arch downward during blooming, generally after the stamens have reflexed.

The fruits are edible, though some are not particularly flavorful. *P. alata* and related species "contain the bitter principles maracujin and passiflorin"; a calming drug preparation called "passiflorine" is on the market. Most species seem to be poisonous if cattle eat the herbage, the toxic principle being a cyanogenetic compound.

Where native or naturalized, some of the more important species have been acquired many common names; only the most used are given. In the following listing only the more important species and cultivars are detailed, and these are grouped by relationship as much as possible. For more detailed treatment, see references (3), (4), (22), (84),(170), (171), (172).

Flowers small, usually less than 4 cm. diameter, greenish-yellow to white, the three bracts small and inconspicuous, or absent; operculum generally pleated, the radii in one series, the pali in one series or absent.

These species are grown mostly for the total effect of the foliage.

Glands present, petals absent, stipules small and linear.

*P. coriacea* JUSSIEU. This species is grown for the peltate, transversely oblong leaves, which are often bluish-green, mottled with silver-white along the main veins; the small sessile glands are at or below the middle of the petiole. Mexico to northern Bolivia.

*P. viridiflora* CAVANILLES has leaves of similar texture, but deeply 3-lobed, no pali, the calyx-tube somewhat cylindric (to ¾ inch long) rather than saucer-shaped, and the operculum not plicate. Southern Mexico.

*P. gracilis* JACQUIN has thin leaves with 3 rounded lobes, the 2 to 4 stipitate glands below the middle of the petiole; the fruit is ellipsoidal rather than round, and scarlet-red when ripe. Native in Brazil and Venezuela, but known mostly from cultivation.

*P. suberosa* LINN. has extremely variable leaves, entire to deeply 3-lobed, glabrous to pubescent; radii banded yellow, white and purple; the berry ovoid and dark purple. It is distributed naturally throughout New World tropics; introduced and weedy in Old World tropics and Hawaii.

> Glands present, petals present but small, stipules small and semi-ovate.

*P. warmingii* MASTERS (Colombia, Brazil and Paraguay), *P. morifolia* MASTERS (Mexico, Guatemala, Peru to Argentina and Paraguay), and *P. bryonioides* HBK are occasionally cultivated, and easily confused. All have a single pair of glands near the petiole apex, membranous leaves which are deeply 3-lobed, with short stiff hairs, and a single series of radii with a bluish to purplish band at the base. *P. bryonioides* has filiform petals (4 by 1 mm.—about 1/6 inch long and threadlike), and a glabrous ovary, the other two somewhat oblong, obtuse petals (6 to 8 by 2 to 4 mm.—in greatest dimension about ½ inch long), and the ovary densely pubescent; *P. morifolia* generally has reddish-purple mottling on the sepals.

> Petiolar glands absent, leaves generally transversely oblong and bilobed, occasionally with a reduced or somewhat larger central lobe, stipules linear-setaceous.

*P. trifasciata* LEMAIRE. Cultivated for its striking variegated foliage, generally has leaves 3-lobed, the lobes not widespreading; the variegation along the main veins is yellowish or purplish; the flowers yellowish-white and fragrant. Upper Amazon.

*P. organensis* GARDNER [syn.: *P. maculifolia*] is also cultivated for its foliage, the main veins yellowish- or whitish-mottled above, and purplish beneath; the perianth is cream-colored to dull purple, and the pali absent (present in all the others of this group). Eastern Brazil.

*P. punctata* LINN., norbo or niorbo, has thin-membranous leaves, bilobed, or shallowly trilobed, the lobes truncate, one form in cultivation variegated with purple; the radii are banded yellow, purple and white, the pali are purplish. Ecuador and Peru.

*P. biflora* LAMARCK has quite variable non-variegated, coriaceous foliage, and differs in the shorter, paired peduncles, the yellow pali not capitate, and the fruit globose rather than ellipsoid. Mexico to Colombia and Venezuela.

*P. cheilidonea* MASTERS has coriaceous bilobed leaves with a small center lobe, the radii banded yellow, bluish-violet, and white spotted with violet at base; the pali capitate and grass-green. Colombia and Ecuador.

*P. misera* HBK. has transversely oblong, 2-lobed leaves, one form in cultivation purple beneath; the perianth is white within, the radii purplish, the pali broadly capitate. Panama through northeast South America to Argentina.

*P. lutea* LINN. has thin leaves with three rounded lobes; the petals are yellow-

261

ish-white; the radii greenish-white, the pali pinkish at base. Pennsylvania to Florida, Illinois and Texas.

*P. capsularis* LINN. (widespread in tropical America) has leaves with two non-divergent lobes; the perianth is yellowish-white or -green, the radii white or violet, the pali sometimes present and violet, the ovary occasionally pubescent.

*P. rubra* LINN. (also widespread) differs in the sepals sometimes being red without, the radii shorter, and white with purple base, the short pali frequently present; the ovary is densely hairy, and the fruit tapered only on the stem end.

> Flowers large and showy, usually more than 5 cm. diameter; operculum generally not pleated.

>> Flowers orange-red, red, or red-pink; calyx-tube longer than perianth, radii a band of tubercles; pali absent.

In this group, which was formerly the genus *Tacsonia* (from the common name of "tacso" for many in the Andes), the most important species are *P. mixta* LINN. and *P. mollissima* (HBK) BAILEY, ("curuba" or banana passion fruit).

They are difficult to distinguish, and undoubtedly hybridize among themselves and other tacsonias. Both have leaves with 3 acute lobes; the bracts are united; *P. mollissima* has round rather than angled stems, and these are densely and finely tomentose, as is most of the herbage of this species; *P. mixta* is generally less pubescent, yet the calyx-tube of *mixta* is usually pubescent, and in *mollissima* usually glabrous; *mixta* has 4 to 8 petiolar glands, *mollissima* 8 to 12; the flowers of *mixta* are more orange-red. Both are cultivated for the fruit, but particularly *mollissima;* in Colombia the juice is considered the finest of the passion-fruits, and a wine is also made of it. Both grow wild in the Andes from Venezuela to Bolivia.

*P.* X *exoniensis* BAILEY is a hybrid (*P. antioquiensis* X *P. mollissima*). in which the tube is equal to or shorter than the perianth, which is brick-red to rose-red. *P. insignis* HOOKER, with ovate-lanceolate, toothed leaves, flowers violet to crimson, and a short calyx-tube, is probably a hybrid between a tacsonia and a species of the *P. coccinea* group.

Several other species are occasionally cultivated: *P. jamesonii* (MASTERS) BAILEY (Ecuador) and *P. pinnatistipula* CAVANILLES (Peru or Chile, but commonly cultivated in the Andes). Both have the stipules much divided, *pinnatistipula* with a shorter tube, and the corona of purplish-blue filaments rather than the tubercles that are all that remain on the other tacsonias. *P.* X *rosea* (KARSTEN) KILLIP (*P. pinnatistipula* X *P. mollissima*) is aberrant, with the stamens arising from the middle of the supporting stalk rather than just below the ovary. The toothed stipules and bluish to lilac-purple flowers distinguish *P. cumbalensis* (KARSTEN) HARMS from *P. psilantha* (SOD.) KILLIP, and also from *P. tripartita* (JUSSIEU) POIRET, all of which have entire stipules and rose-colored flowers. All are native to Ecuador, where they are also cultivated, *P. cumbalensis* in Colombia also. They grow in general from Colombia to Peru.

(Flowers large and showy; operculum generally not pleated.)

Flowers red, calyx-tube much shorter than perianth, radii generally fila-mentose, pali present.

*P. manicata* (Jussieu) Persoon has perhaps the most brilliant scarlet flowers. These are offset by the dark purple-blue short-filamentose corona. The leaves are 3-lobed, the petioles have 4 to 10 glands. (Color Plate 159.) Andes, Venezuela to Peru.

*P. antioquiensis* Karsten also has pendent red flowers, with a longer tube, the peduncles very long, the radii of tubercles or short filaments, and, as in none of the others (including the tacsonias), the pali are just above the operculum near the base of the tube. (Photograph 215.) Native in Colombia; cultivated for fruit in New Zealand.

*P.* X *militaris* is a hybrid, possibly between these two, or between one of them and *P. insignis,* the flowers larger and more showy.

*P. coccinea* Aublet (Color Plate 155) (Guianas, Venezuela, and Amazonia) and *P. vitifolia* HBK (Color Plate 161) (Nicaragua to Venezuela and eastern slopes of northern Andes to Peru). Both have a dense pubescence, toothed leaves, the petiole with 2 glands at base, the stipules beside them bristle-shaped, flowers scarlet with very short tubes (to 1.5 cm.), erect radii, and single membranous white pali. *P. coccinea* has unlobed leaves, very large bracts, and the radii usually white, tipped with dark purple. *P. vitifolia* has the leaves deeply 3-lobed, small bracts, and the radii bright red or yellow; it is cultivated in Colombia for the fruit, as is a related species, *P. quadriglandulosa* Rod., in parts of Amazonia.

*P. racemosa* Brotero [syn. *P. princeps*] is one of the finest species, outstand-ing for the hanging pseudo-racemes of 8 or more large, deep red flowers; the ovate to deeply 3-lobed leaves have entire margins and truncate base, and are often purplish beneath; the stipules are large and ovate, the petiole with 2 glands; the calyx-tube is short-cylindric (to 1.5 cm.), the sepals deep-keeled on the back, the radii purple with white tips, the pali red. Brazil.

*P. kermesina* Link & Otto [syn.: *P. raddiana*] has 3-lobed, toothed leaves, truncate or slightly cordate at base; the scarlet perianth becomes reflexed; the erect radii are dark purple, the small pali lighter, and the operculum pleated.

*P.* X *amabilis* Lemaire is considered a hybrid between this and *P. alata;* the leaves are entire, ovate, pinnately veined, the perianth bright brick-red, the long radii and short pali white. *P.* X *atropurpurea* Nicholson (*P. racemosa* X *P. kermesina?*) has foliage like the former, the flowers more like the latter parent, the sepals deeply keeled, purplish, the petals dark blood-red, the corona violet with white spotting. *P.* X *loudonii* Sweet is a hybrid of similar parentage. *P.* X *kewensis* Hort. (considered a cross between *P. caerulea* and *P. kermesina*) has flowers of carmine suffused with blue, the perianth and radii longer than in *P. kermesina.* Eastern Brazil.

*P. sanguinolenta* Masters (Photograph 214) is probably more closely related to *P. rubra,* with similar leaves and pubescence, no petiolar glands, no bracts, and a similar aspect; but the flowers are rose-pink, dull red, or reddish-violet, the calyx-tube elongated (1 to 2 cm.) and ridged, and the operculum is not pleated. Ecuador.

(Flowers large and showy; the operculum generally not pleated.)
Flowers red to white including yellow and greenish tones, calyx-tube bowl-shaped, corona with an erect membrane.

*P. murucuja* LINN. has quite variable leaves, generally transversely oblong, bilobed or trilobed, the petioles glandless; the flowers are red, reddish-purple, to purple and the corona an erect reddish or purplish cylindric membrane. It is grown more often for the foliage. Hispaniola.

Of several species native to the Australian area, the following in cultivation have 3-lobed leaves, the petals about half as long as the sepals, and the corona with a single row of erect filaments surrounding an erect tubular or pleated membrane:

In *P. aurantia* FORSTER [syn. *P. banksii*] the flowers open nearly white and change slowly to bright scarlet or brick-red; the sepals are deeply keeled, the corona filaments and membrane deep red; the petioles have a pair of glands at the apex.

*P. cinnabarina* LINDLEY lacks the petiolar glands, and the corona is yellow, the perianth cinnabar-red to scarlet.

*P. herbertiana* KER has a greenish-white to pale orange-yellow **perianth, the** corona tubular and yellow, a pair of petiolar glands, the leaf lobes blunt.

*P. tetrandra* BANKS & SOLANDER has a greenish-white perianth, the corona cream, the leaf lobes acute. New Zealand.

(Flowers large and showy; the operculum generally not pleated.)
Flowers blue or purplish, calyx-tube bowl-shaped, corona large, in several series.

Leaves unlobed, stipules large.

*P. quadrangularis* LINN. [syn. *P. macrocarpa*] is cultivated throughout tropical America, and in Old World tropics. (Color Plate 152.) Granadilla, giant granadilla, badea, tumbo, and parcha are some of its common names. It is closely related to *P. alata* DRYANDER, which also is native in Peru and Brazil. Both are variable, and often separated with difficulty. They have large, entire pinnately veined leaves, *quadrangularis* with 10 to 12 lateral nerves per side and 3 pairs of petiolar glands, *alata* with 7 or 8 nerves and 1 or 2 pairs of glands; both have squared stems, but those of *alata* are winged, and the stipules narrower. The perianth of *quadrangularis* is generally lighter—white, tinged with pink or crimson; that of *alata* usually crimson or carmine; the radii of *quadrangularis* are as long or longer than the perianth and crinkled at the tips, those of *alata* not so long, and straight; both have radii banded with reddish-purple, bluish-purple, and white. The very large melon-like fruits of *quadrangularis,* common in tropical markets, are greenish-yellow. This species produces a large tuberous root, said to be used as a substitute for yams in Jamaica, but considered poisonous in other areas.

The flowers and fruit of *alata* are very fragrant, and this has been a parent for many hybrids. *P.* X *bournapartea* HORT. (a hybrid between *P. quad-*

264

*rangularis* and *P. alata*) has the foliage of *quadrangularis* and the fragrance and reddish-crimson perianth of *alata,* the filaments banded red, white, and blue. *P.* X *lawsoniana* HORT. (*P. alata* X *P. racemosa*) has somewhat cordate-peltate leaves and a reddish-brown perianth. *P.* X *decaisneana* PLANCHON is of the same parentage, but the perianth bright carmine, the radii banded with dark purplish-blue and white. *P.* X *cardinalis* HORT., with red perianth, is probably of similar parentage.

*P. ligularis* JUSSIEU (granadilla, sweet granadilla, water-lemon) is at once recognized by the 4 to 6 strap-shaped glands on the petiole, which are 1 cm. (⅜ inch) long; the pinnately-veined leaves are cordate, the bracts large and partly united; the perianth is greenish- to pinkish-white. The radii, which are as long as the perianth, are white banded with red-purple. Native from Central America to Venezuela and Bolivia, this species is cultivated in other tropical countries also for the fruit, which is yellowish to tan or purplish, and stiff-shelled.

*P. maliformis* LINN. (sweet-cup, sweet calabash, granadilla de piedra) has ovate leaves, with two petiolar glands near the middle, the stipules narrow; the bracts are very large, partly united, whitish-green, the perianth greenish-white mottled with reddish-purple, the radii white, banded with purple and red-violet; fragrant. The yellowish fruit has a grape-like flavor, the shell often hard enough to need a hammer to open it. West Indies to northern Ecuador; widely cultivated.

*P. oerstedii* MASTERS has generally unlobed, 5 to 7-nerved, ovate-lanceolate leaves, but they may be 3-lobed or mitten-shaped; the large bracts are free, the perianth white, the petals flushed with pink, the radii and pali purple. Mexico to Venezuela, Colombia.

> (Flowers large and showy, blue or purplish; the operculum generally not pleated; calyx-tube bowl-shaped, corona large, in several series.) Leaves unlobed, stipules small.

*P. laurifolia* LINN. (yellow granadilla, jamaica honeysuckle, water lemon, pomme d'or). The leaves are thick-coriaceous, ovate-oblong, with two glands near the apex of the petiole; the bracts are large and free, the perianth red-spotted without and within, or reddish-purple within, the radii very thick, beaded with white and reddish-purple to blue. The fruit has a white-spotted leathery shell, and is quite edible. West Indies, coastal Venezuela, Peruvian Amazonia and eastern Brazil. (Color Plate 158.)

Related and quite similar are *P. nitida* HBK and *P. popenovii* KILLIP, both in upper Amazonia, the former cultivated or native in the Guianas and Panama also.

> Leaves three-lobed, stipules small and linear.

*P. incarnata* Linn. (Virginia to Missouri to Florida and Texas, Bermuda) Maypop, and *P. edulis* Sims (Brazil and Paraguay into Argentina; cultivated and often escaped in most tropical countries) purple granadilla, maracujá, parchita, granadilla, are very closely related. *P. incarnata* has thinner, duller leaves, with

265

finer serrations; those of *edulis* being more coriaceous, often unlobed on young growth, the lateral lobes less ovate than in *incarnate,* although the latter is quite variable; both have a pair of glands at the petiole apex. The bracts are quite large in *edulis* (to 2.5 cm.), smaller in *incarnata* (to 7 mm.), the flowers of *incarnata* generally more lavender, *edulis* generally white; both have long radii crisped at the ends, those of *incarnata* evenly lavender, of *edulis* white with purplish base; the pali of *edulis* are purple, of *incarnata* often white. *P. edulis* has a purple fruit, *incarnata* yellow; but *P. edulis* forma *flavicarpa* DEGENER, with yellow fruits, is the major commercial passionfruit in Hawaii, Australia, New Zealand, and Latin America for the production of canned and frozen passionfruit juice. The related *P. cincinata* MAST has leaves 5-parted to the base, large bracts, purplish or violet perianth, and the banded radii light at the base.

Leaves 3 to 5-lobed, stipules large.

*P. caerulea* LINN. is one of the hardiest and most commonly cultivated species. (Color Plate 160.) It may be recognized by the deeply 5-lobed leaves (sometimes up to 9 lobes), the petioles with 2 to 4 stalked glands; the pale green bracts are very large and broad, the perianth is pinkish or occasionally white, the radii are white with bluish tips and purple base; fragrant. Brazil to Argentina.

This has been a parent of numerous hybrids. The forms 'Constance Elliott', with white sepals and corona, and 'Grandiflora', with flowers 5 to 8 inches across, are possibly hybrids. *P.* X *allardii* LYNCH (*P. caerulea* 'Constance Elliott' X *P. quadrangularis*) has leaves with 3 broad lobes, the petals white shaded with pink, the corona deep cobalt-blue.

*P.* X *alato-caerulea* LINDLEY [syn. *P. pfordtii*], (*P. alata* X *P. caerulea*) is the most commonly grown hybrid; the leaves are 3-lobed, the flowers fragrant, the sepals white, the petals pink-violet within, with upward-curled edges, the radii purple at base, bluer at tips, banded with white in center. 'Imperatrice Eugenie' is believed to be a selection from this hybrid. *P.* X *munroi* HORT. is another hybrid of the same parentage. *P.* X *caeruleo-racemosa* SABINE (*P. caerulea* X *P. racemosa*) has 3 to 5-lobed leaves and purple flowers. *P.* X *belottii* MOORE & AYRES (*P. caeruleo-racemosa* X *P. quadrangularis*) has large flowers with flesh-colored sepals, rose petals, and blue corona; the leaves are 3-lobed. *P.* X *colvillii* SWEET derived from *P. incarnata* X *P. caerulea,* (Color Plate 149.) has toothed leaves with 3 to 5 lobes, the perianth white spotted with red, and the radii banded blue, white, and purple. *P.* X *innesii* HORT. (cited as *P. alata* X *P. quadrangularis*) has the flowers of *quadrangularis,* but the 3-lobed leaves place it, at least for identification, with the present group; the same holds for *P.* X *albo-nigra* REGEL (*P. alata* X *P. kermesina*) also, since it has 5-lobed leaves; the petals are white and the purple corona is white tipped.

*P. violacea* VELLOZO (Bolivia, eastern Brazil, and Paraguay) and *P. amethystina* MIKAN, from eastern Brazil (Color Plate 156), are separated with difficulty; both have 3-lobed leaves with several petiolar glands. The large flowers are generally bright blue in *amethystina* and purplish-blue in *violacea; violacea* has peduncles more than 5 cm. (2 inches) long, the stipules 1.5 to 3.5 cm. (⅝ to 1⅜ inches) long, the horn on the sepals 8 mm. (5/16 inch) or longer, and 4 or 5 rows of dark purple pali; *amethystina* has peduncles less than 5 cm. (2 inches), stipules 0.5 to 1 cm. (3/16 to ⅜ inches), the horn shorter, and 2 or 3 rows of pali; *violacea* has radii as long as the petals, white below, violet above; in *amethystina* the radii are shorter, dark reddish-purple below, blue spotted white in the middle, and pale reddish-purple on tips.

*P. subpeltata* ORTEGA [syn. *P. alba*] white passionflower. This has 3-lobed leaves, the petioles with 2 to 4 minute glands, large bracts, the perianth and corona pure white. Central Mexico to Colombia and Venezuela.

*P. eichleriana* MASTERS differs in having 6 to 8 glands, and the operculum is filamentous in the upper portion instead of wholly membranous. Eastern Brazil to Paraguay.

*P. foetida* LINN. stinking passionflower; love-in-a-mist (West Indian). This plant is extremely variable, but the leaves are pubescent, shallowly 3-lobed to nearly entire, and they have glandular hairs which make them sticky and foul-smelling, especially when crushed; the large bracts are feathery and glandular-hairy; the small flowers whitish, with the corona banded in purple and blue; the fruit generally is red. It is native throughout the American tropics, and is widely escaped and weedy elsewhere. (Color Plate 151.)

*P. cirrhiflora* JUSSIEU (Color Plate 153) is at once recognized by the pedately 5 to 7-foliate leaves, each leaflet with a pair of awns near the base; the sepals are yellowish-green, the petals ivory, the crisped radii red-orange at the base, yellow above. Guianas.

*P. arborea* SPR. is a member of a group of shrubby or arboreous species, this is a tree 18 to 30 feet tall. The leaves are large, oblong, and pinnately nerved, the flowers in a pendulous cluster of 3 to 6, greenish-white, with a short yellow corona. Colombia.


PERIPLOCACEAE—PERIPLOCA FAMILY


## *Periploca graeca* LINN.

*Common Name:* SILK-VINE

This deciduous climber, with slender twining stems that rise to 40 feet, is often planted for ornament in the southern states and California, though the 1-inch flowers with 5 purple corolla-lobes margined with green are rather inconspicuous because of their color. (Photograph 211.) The 4-inch leaves are shiny and handsome, and they hang on long in the autumn; then the stems are bare for several months. The plant has milky juice and is by some placed in the milkweed family (Asclepiadaceae). One advantage of this climber is its very quick growth, which makes it useful for covering an outbuilding or service area. It comes from southern Europe (including Greece) and nearby Asia.

Chinese silk-vine (*P. sepium* BUNGE) of similar appearance, is cultivated in the midwestern states. It is more slender than the Grecian vine and has shown considerable vigor under severe climatic conditions. It requires training on trellises or wires.

## PHILESIACEAE—PHILESIA FAMILY

### *Eustrephus latifolius*  R. BROWN
*ERNEST E. LORD*
[Syn.: *Eustrephus brownii*  F. MUELLER]
*Common Name:* WOMBAT-BERRY

This evergreen wiry-stemmed vine of 10 feet or more, has attractive glossy lanceolate leaves, 2 to 4 inches long, conspicuously parallel-veined. Clustered flowers along the stems are rather small, of starry white, shades of pink, or lavender, followed in late summer by half-inch orange berries. The root tubers are edible. This plant climbs when grown in partial shade with plenty of water. In hot, exposed positions it becomes a bush. It comes from New Guinea, New South Wales, and thereabouts, and is best grown in a cool conservatory. It was originally placed in the lily family.

### *Geitonoplesium cymosum*  A. CUNNINGHAM
*ERNEST E. LORD*

This woody perennial somewhat resembles *Eustrephus,* the strong young twining stems extending for many feet while quite devoid of leaves. These come later, 2 to 3 inches long, narrow and tapering, plentiful along both sides of fine wiry lateral branches. The small, usually reddish flowers (sometimes white or purplish-green) in drooping clusters at branch tips, give place to handsome shiny blue-black berries ½ inch in diameter. This native of eastern Australia is also found in Malaysia, and eastward to the Philippines and Fiji.

### *Lapageria rosea*  RUIZ & PAVON
*Common Name:* COPIHUE, CHILEAN BELLFLOWER

This handsome climber is one of the most prized of glasshouse plants. (Color Plate 165.) It has the useful habit of climbing either on walls or over a trellis, producing many flowers, and casting practically no shade. Native to the Andes, it is seldom grown outdoors in America, or in England, as it is rather difficult to handle. It bears large waxy bell-shaped red flowers that last a long time. There is a white-flowered variety, and many crosses of these two have been established. Under favorable conditions it is evergreen. The fruit is an edible berry.

### *Philesia magellanica*  LAMM.

This formerly was placed in the lily family. It is a very slow-growing, short, stocky, woody, spreading plant, native to the deep woods of southern Chile. In favored localities in England and Ireland it has been grown out-of-doors. (Photograph 216.) The plant grows about 4 feet high, has rather leathery, boxlike

220. PLUMBAGO CAPENSIS    221. CANTUA BUXIFOLIA

222. COBAEA SCANDENS    223. PHLOX DOUGLASII

leaves, and bears showy hanging red flowers 2 inches long, much like *Lapageria,* to which it is related; these two have been hybridized. Chittenden calls *Philesia* "a very beautiful plant."

PHYTOLACCACEAE—POKEWEED FAMILY

### *Agdestis clematidea*   MOCINO & SESSE

This thinly climbing vine, native from Mexico to Guatemala, has become established in Florida and other southern states. In one season, according to Bailey (4), a height of 50 feet was recorded for it, and it is "covered in September with masses of snowy white blossoms in dense clusters, very sweet-scented." The flowers are star-shaped, ½ inch across, in many-flowered clusters 4 to 6 inches long. On this vine, Bailey continues:

> "The red stems come from a tuber which grows half out of the earth, and which is sometimes 100 to 150 lbs. in weight. These tubers look like solid rock, a gray granite color. . . . On account of the ill-smelling foliage, the *Agdestis* cannot be recommended for veranda decoration, but it is a fine plant for covering unsightly objects and outhouses."

### *Ercilla volubilis*   JUSSIEU

This graceful small vine is sometimes included in the genus *Phytolacca.* It has cordate leaves up to 2 inches long and produces dense 2-inch spikes of pale purple flowers, usually climbs by rootlets, though occasionally on a wall it will use discs. This is an excellent thin vine to cover a wall. Bailey (4) refers to it as a climbing shrub from Peru and Chile.

### *Trichostigma humilis*
[Syn. *Rivina humilis*   LINN.]
*Common Name:* ROUGE-PLANT

This is one of four species of small climbers in tropical America, extending into Florida. Stems are rarely more than 18 inches high. The very small white flowers have a pale rose calyx. Bailey (4) says the plants are useful outdoors as summer annuals and can also be grown in the glasshouse.

PITTOSPORACEAE—PITTOSPORUM FAMILY

### *Billardiera floribunda*   (PUTTERL.) F. MUELLER          ※ ERNEST E. LORD ※
[Syn. *Marianthus floribundus*   PUTTERL.]

Twining and climbing plants with attractive flowers are characteristic of the pittosporum family, which is found in the warmer parts of Asia, Africa, and the

Pacific region, 9 genera comprising some 200 species. The 8 species of *Billardiera* are all Australian. Among the western species, *B. floribunda* has been described as a common feature of the great jarrah (*Eucalyptus*) forests near Albany, Australia. Its 5 rolled-back petals ¾ inch long, form showy white flowers in stalked clusters on the twining stems; smooth ovate leaves are 3 to 4 inches long.

The purple apple-berry (*Billardiera longiflora* LABILLARDIERE) is a slender-stemmed twiner from Tasmania and southeastern Australia, outstanding for its cylindrical glossy violet-blue berries, nearly an inch long, carried on the finest of stalks, from late autumn to winter. This is the best known species in Australian gardens. (Photograph 217.) It makes an excellent glasshouse plant. Narrow dark-green leaves are 1 to 2 inches long; tubular yellow flowers with purple markings, 1 to 1½ inches long, widening and lobed at the tips, hang singly from fine stalks not unlike *Correa* blooms.

Another western species, *B. variifolia* DC., with blue flowers in generous clusters and thin berries, is a short-stemmed twiner.

From eastern Australia comes a curious little trailing plant, *B. scandens* SMITH, called common apple-berry or dumplings from its fleshy green berries ¾ inch long, edible, and sweet. It is of little horticultural value, excepting a form called var. *brachyandra* F. MUELLER with deeper yellow flowers and very hairy berries.

The eastern Australian *B. cymosa* F. MUELLER is shrubby, but the branches have a twining tendency, the creamy bell-flowers are shaded purple outside, and the ¾-inch berry is red.

## *Cheiranthera volubilis*   BENTHAM

This slender twiner has half-inch heathlike leaves. The blue flowers with 5 reflexed petals are about ½ inch long, pendent on single stalks. It is found wild only on Kangaroo Island off the coast of South Australia.

Two other climbing species of this Australian genus (there are 5 in all) are the desert-loving *C. filifolia* TURCZANINOW and *C. parviflora* BENTHAM. Both are slender-stemmed, shrubby at the base, the outer branches twining to a few feet only. Flowers of both are a pleasing deep blue with 5 spreading half-inch petals and golden stamens; those of *C. filifolia* are in small clusters and those of *C. parviflora* on long thin stalks. Both are suited to hot dry sandy conditions.

## *Marianthus bignoniaceus*   F. MUELLER            ⚜ ERNEST E. LORD ⚜
*Common Name:* ORANGE BELL-CLIMBER

The name is from the Greek *Maria* and the word for flower, and so is called the "Flower of Mary"; *i.e.,* the Virgin Mary; it was given to the genus by the botanist Huegel on account of the white and blue flowers of the first species seen.

*M. bignoniaceus* is a charming twiner from Victoria and south Australia with long slender stems carrying the pendulous inch-long yellow to orange tubular bell-flowers, tipped with 5 flared petals.

The red bell-climber, also known as Chapman River Bell-flower (*M. ringens*

F. MUELLER) is the most showy of the West Australian species. (Photograph 219.) There are a dozen species, all twiners excepting one. The flowers are more open than on *M. bignoniaceus*. Gardner's *West Australian Wildflowers* describes *M. ringens* as:

> ". . . deserving special comment. It is a plant with broad leathery leaves of a deep green, it carries (in spring) clusters of orange flowers about an inch long with the petals ending in fine points. Restricted to the clay banks of the Chapman River it is now almost extinct."

*M. erubescens* PUTTERL. has similar foliage and clustered 1-inch flowers in late spring and an intense red, climbing small trees in hot dry granite country to a height of 15 feet.

*M. pictus* LINDLEY is called painted bell-flower because its bunches of white or pale yellow bells (in spring and summer) are streaked with violet lines (*pictus* = painted). This species is often shrubby, but its outer growth displays an urge to climb and frequently succeeds.

A white species, *M. caudatus* HUEGEL, is showy in late spring with its clustered open flowers of 5 petals tapered to the base, as though stalked, with a touch of red at the center. Other species are blue-flowered but do not seem as yet to be in cultivation.

## *Pronaya elegans*  HUEGEL

ERNEST E. LORD

[Syn. *Billardiera elegans*  F. MUELLER]

The starry 5 petaled mauve-blue flower of this climber has a subtle delicacy at any time—especially combined with slender twining brown stems also bearing dense clusters of narrow reflexed leaves. The result is a beautiful species; it blooms in its native western Australia throughout spring and summer.

## *Sollya heterophylla*  LINDLEY

ERNEST E. LORD

[Syn. *S. fusiformis*  PAYER]

*Common Names:* BLUEBELL-CREEPER; AUSTRALIAN-BLUEBELL

The strong-growing, narrow-leaved, evergreen climber is often shrubby below but its outer stems extend and twine about anything within reach (Photograph 218.) Clusters of small intense blue pendent flowers, the 5 petals cohering to form inverted cups, make a very showy plant in spring and summer. The sausage-shaped, deep-blue berries may be 1½ inches long. *Sollya* is widely cultivated in warm climates and by a little pruning may provide a neat and useful green coverage for many purposes. It grows about 6 feet high.

The pretty bright blue flowers are too much hidden among the many leaves to be showy and so the plant has never become popular. It is a native of western Australia.

272

## Armeria maritima   WILLDENOW

*Common Name:* SEA-PINK

This perennial creeping subshrub from Eurasia has pink, purple or white flowers, often covering sand banks. In California it is called *A. vulgaris.*

## Plumbago capensis   THUNBERG

꙳ HERBERT G. BAKER ꙳

*Common Name:* LEADWORT (for all species of the genus)

Climbers are rare in the leadwort (plumbago) family, but one is very well known in horticulture for its pale blue flowers (about 1 inch in diameter) produced in large numbers (Photograph 220.) It can be grown in gardens where the winters are generally warm and dry and frosts are only occasional (and never more than 10° Fahrenheit below freezing point). This leadwort is a native of South Africa and, being heterostylous and self-sterile, it is usually propagated vegetatively. Fortunately, this is easily accomplished by cuttings.

It may be grown as a semi-climbing subshrub or may be trained as a climber up any support, such as a greenhouse pillar, an outdoor column, or on a wall. It looks best if it is cut back after flowering. It appears to be almost free of pests. A white variety (var. *alba* Hort.) is also available.

*P. indica* LINN. [syn.: *P. rosea* Linn., *P. rosea* var. *coccinea* Hooker and *P. coccinea* SALISBURY]. Less well known than *P. capensis,* this species is only "more or less" of a climber. Its flowers vary from scarlet to reddish purple. It needs more heat in winter than *P. capensis* and it flowers at that time of the year. A native of southern Asia, it is equally easily propagated by cuttings or can be raised from seed.

*P. zeylanica* LINN. This species is only "somewhat" climbing and rarely reaches above 2 feet in height. Bearing white flowers in long dense spikes, it is an abundant bloomer. Coming from Ceylon and the East Indies, it has been longer in cultivation (since 1731) than any of the other species. Irvine (65) says that *P. zeylanica* is common as a decorative plant in west African villages, a climbing shrub "worth growing."

POLEMONIACEAE—PHLOX FAMILY

## Cantua buxifolia   JUSSIEU

꙳ EDGAR T. WHERRY ꙳

*Common Name:* SACRED FLOWER OF THE INCAS

This member of the phlox family is sometimes listed among vines, presumably because, although it is typically a small tree or coarse shrub, its stems may straggle up through thickets. Its leaves are simple and small, and at the tip of arching branchlets appear pendent red tubular flowers about 3 inches long. (Photograph 221.) A native of the Andes, it is grown outdoors in southern California and in greenhouses elsewhere.

## Cobaea scandens   CAVANILLES

꙳ EDGAR T. WHERRY ꙳

*Common Names:* CUP-AND-SAUCER VINE; PURPLE-BELL CLIMBER

Of the 20 genera in the predominantly American phlox family, only one, *Cobaea,*

**224. ANTIGONON GUATEMALENSE**  **225. POLYGONUM AUBERTII**

**226. POLYGONUM BALDSCHUANICUM**  **227. POLYGONUM TRISTORTUM**

contains species of predominantly climbing habit. While about 20 have been recognized, most of them are rare and little known, but the one treated here is widely cultivated. Originally native in the mountains of Mexico, it has become naturalized well over tropical America.

In mild climates *Cobaea scandens* (Photograph 222) is perennial, but in temperate regions is grown as an annual. The large flat seeds are planted in spring, and the stem elongates rapidly, reaching a length of 20 feet or more. The numerous alternate leaves are pinnately divided into a few coarse leaflets, and they are tipped by a long branching tendril which clings to any available support. The long-stalked flowers arise from leaf-axils through summer and autumn. About 2 inches long and broad, they consist of a green saucer-like calyx and a cuplike corolla with exserted stamens. At first greenish, this becomes dull lavender and ultimately lurid violet-purple. Indigo-blue and pure white albino sports also occasionally appear. Even after the corolla falls, the persistent calyxes, with projecting green cylindric capsules, have a certain ornamental value.

In view of its rapid growth and profusion of bloom over a long season, *Cobaea scandens* constitutes a desirable horticultural subject. It may be grown on a lattice or arbor, is well suited to scrambling over scrubby bushes or even small trees, and will thrive in a greenhouse if sufficiently spacious. In addition to its wide use in tropical America, it is recorded as appreciated in remote Indonesia and is as well known in Europe as in the United States. (Color Plate 35.)

Willis (118) says that *C. scandens* shows very rapid growth, climbs by aid of tendrils (leaf-structures) which are much branched, the branches ending in sharp hooks. The tendril mutates with great rapidity and is highly sensitive to contact (as may be seen by rubbing one side and watching it for 5 minutes); the hooks prevent the mutation from dragging away a branch before it has had time to clasp its support (Darwin, *Climbers,* p. 106). The closed bud stands erect on an erect stalk, but when going to open, the tip of the stalk bends over. There is movement of the stamens and style within the flower, and the stamens shed their pollen before the stigma is ripe. At first greenish with unpleasant smell (fly-flower), the blossom becomes purple with a pleasant honey-like smell (bee-flower). Afterward the stalk goes through several contortions.

## *Phlox douglasii* HOOKER

Although the 66 species of *Phlox* in eastern North America could scarcely be called vines, this species native to Washington and western Montana is a low perennial plant 2 to 8 inches high with stems that spread over the ground. Its flowers are violet, pink, or white, ½ inch across and solitary but numerous. (Photograph 223.)

POLYGALACEAE—MILKWORT FAMILY　　　　　　　⁂ ELIZABETH McCLINTOCK ⁂

## *Bredemeyera floribunda* WILLDENOW

This is a scandent shrub with long branches, liana-like and growing in adjacent trees, bearing alternate, oblong-elliptic leaves to about 4 inches long. The white or greenish-yellow, fragrant flowers about ¼ inch long are borne in terminal panicles.

Bredemeyera contains about 25 species and occurs in South America and the West Indies. It has been considered by some to be a larger genus containing the Australian species now placed in Comesperma. B. floribunda occurs in Colombia, Peru, and Brazil. Bredemeyera was named for Fran Bredemeyer, a Viennese botanist of the early 19th century.

The flowers of Bredemeyera, as well as those in the other genera of the Polygalaceae discussed here, bear a resemblance to those of the papilionate Leguminosae and it is often assumed at first glance that these plants belong to that family.

## Comesperma volubile  LABILLARDIERE
[Syn.: C. gracile  PAXTON; Bredemeyera volubilis  (LABILLARDIERE) CHODAT]
*Common Name:* LOVE-CREEPER

This scandent evergreen shrub displays numerous slender, usually long and flexuous branches, having few alternate lanceolate leaves about ½ inch long. Flowers are blue, rarely white, about ¼ inch long in axillary or terminal racemes to 3 inches long. The name Comesperma means "hairy seed" and alludes to the tuft of hairs at one end of the small seeds.

Comesperma is an Australian genus of about 25 species which formerly were placed in the genus Bredemeyera.

## Securidaca diversifolia  (LINN.) S. F. BLAKE
[Syn.: S. erecta  JACQUIN]
*Common Name:* EASTER-FLOWER

During the flowering season in early spring this is a handsome showy vine with slender arching branches. (Color Plate 167.) Leaves are firm-textured, glabrous or sparsely hairy, shining above, paler beneath, the venation more or less prominent, varying in shape from broadly ovate to elliptic-oblong, 1 to 4 inches long. Flowers are rose or purple, about ¼ inch long, numerous and crowded in axillary or terminal racemes about 4 inches long. Seeds are 1½ to 2½ inches long, winged like a maple. The generic name Securidaca is taken from the Latin word securis, meaning hatchet, and refers to the shape of the wing of the fruit, a samara. The plant is native from Mexico to northern South America and the West Indies.

S. virgata SWARTZ is a scandent shrub with long slender arching branches, scattered elliptic leaves to 2 inches long, and a profusion of bright rose-colored flowers followed by winged seeds 1 to 1½ inches long. It differs from S. diversifolia in its smaller leaves and seeds. West Indies.

S. volubilis LINN. is a scandent shrub, very attractive when in flower, densely hairy at least when young, the leaves elliptic-ovate, 1¼ to 2½ inches long, softly tomentose especially beneath, the venation obscure. Flowers are violet, about ⅜ inch long, in lax terminal or axillary racemes, with a winged seed to 2 inches long. This is similar to S. diversifolia, according to Macbride

**228. CLEMATIS MONTANA RUBENS**    **229. CLEMATIS PANICULATA**

**230. CLEMATIS LASURSTERN**    **231. CLEMATIS X PERLE D'AZUR**

(140), from which it may be distinguished by the leaves, which tend to be smaller, more tomentose, and obscurely veined. *S. volubilis* has been reported from Guatemala but according to Macbride, also Standley & Steyermark (141), it does not occur in Central America, only in northern South America. It is occasionally cultivated, though rarely, in southern California.

*S. sellowiana* KLOTZSCH, which Brazilians call "climbing violet," is a strong woody climber with a thick stem from which rigid branches extend. The leaves are alternate, oval-elliptic, 1 by 2 inches, on short petioles. The flowers are in terminal clusters, in shape somewhat resembling wisteria except that they are of a more violet hue. The fruit is a samara with a very large woody wing. The plant may be grown on a trellis but it is never cultivated in Brazil despite the fact that it is beautiful. It takes many years for it to come into bloom and eventually it becomes a tree.

## POLYGONACEAE—BUCKWHEAT FAMILY ⚜ RICHARD A. HOWARD ⚜

Approximately 40 genera and 800 species of trees, shrubs and herbs, varying in habit to include climbers by twining and by tendrils, belong to the buckwheat family. The plants characteristically have swollen nodes with sheathing stipules, alternate leaves, and unisexual or bisexual flowers on plants which may be monoecious, dioecious, or polygamous. The perianth is undifferentiated into calyx and corolla, it is 5 to 8 parted, and is persistent. The fruit is an achene, commonly sharply angled, and surrounded by the fleshy or dry, accrescent or enlarging perianth tube or lobes. The perianth lobes in fruit may be free, imbricated (overlapping), or developed into large wings or variously keeled.

Cultivated or ornamental vines are found in the genera *Antigonon, Brunnichia, Coccoloba, Muehlenbeckia* and *Polygonum*.

### *Antigonon cinerascens* MARTIUS & GALEOTTI
*Common Names:* ROSA MORADA, BEJUCO DE COLACION

An herbaceous vine with angulate stems, varying from densely pubescent to glabrate. The leaves are ovate-cordate and have a broad but shallow basal sinus with the blades decurrent on the petiole. The dull dirty-pink or purplish-pink flowers are borne in racemes or in racemose panicles. The outer sepals are cordate (heart-shaped) at the base and increase in size from the flowering stage becoming ¾ inch long and wide in fruit. A native of Mexico and Central America.

*A. guatimalense* MEISSNER [syn. *A. insigne* Masters; *A. macrocarpum* Britton & Small]. This robust vine is variously known as colación, confite, San Andrés, and bellisima. It has abundant pubescence on the stems and leaves. The leaves are broadly ovate, with a shallow basal sinus and the blade abruptly running down the petiole. (Photograph 224.) Flowers are racemosely arranged, commonly in widely separated clusters. Outer sepals are ovate, not cordate at the base.

278

Perianth segments are ½ to 1 inch long, making the flowers about twice the size of the more common *A. leptopus*.

The plant is a native of Guatemala, but Meissner, the original author, chose to spell the specific name with an "i" instead of an "e." Hybrids between this species and *A. leptopus* are suspected, in view of the great variation found in the latter species.

*A. leptopus* HOOKER & ARNOTT has a record number of common names: Belle Mexicaine, bellisima, bellosinia, caderna de amor, chain-of-love, confederate-vine, coral-creeper, coralilla, coralina, coral-vine, corollita, corona de la reina, cuamecate, flor de San Diego, flora de San Miguel, fulmina, la vegissima, lluvia, lovers'-chain, Mexican-creeper, mountain-rose, pinkvine, queen's-jewels, queen's-wreath, rosa de Mayo, rosa-de-montana, San Miquelito, Sandwich Island creeper.

Whether herbaceous or woody, in tropical areas it becomes rampant and vigorous, covering trees, buildings, banks, or fields. (Color Plates 148, 150.) The mass of bloom through much of the year has given this plant a reputation as an ornamental rivaling *Bougainvillea*. The tuberous roots are said to be edible and are valued in the native area (Mexico and Central America) for their nutlike flavor. The slender stems are smooth and may be glabrous or pubescent. The axillary branches as well as the inflorescence axis may develop terminal single or forked tendrils by which the plant adheres in climbing. The leaves vary considerably in size and shape, seemingly increasing in size over a long period of growth. They are cordate or hastate-ovate and from 2 to 5 inches in length. The blade does not run down the petiole.

The vines flower throughout the year in many tropical areas but are exceedingly difficult to bring into bloom in hothouses. The flowers vary from pale pink to deep red or may be pale with a darker colored center. They number from a few to 20 or more on each raceme. The branches of the inflorescence, especially when developed terminally, are conspicuously bent like a knee. The outer sepals are rounded, ovate to suborbicular but noticeably cordate at the base. The flowers are attractive to bees and a good-flavored honey is produced. The flowers increase in size with age and the perianth persists in fruit. Dried inflorescences are often valued for their decorative effect. Fruiting varies in different areas and apparently with different clones.

A white-flowered type is found in cultivation and is ascribed only to "horticulture." Although it is called a variety in horticultural literature, various authors have noticed the unusual shape of the leaves or the flowers and have suggested it may be a different species. Graham and Wood have suggested a relationship to *A. flavescens* S. WATSON, a Mexican species with pale greenish-white perianth, as yet not known in cultivation.

*A. leptopus* has been in cultivation a long time and may be one of the first plants taken by the Spanish from Mexico across the Pacific. Curiously, the illustration of this plant in *Curtis's Botanical Magazine* is of a specimen grown from seeds obtained from Hawaii. The white-flowered form is better represented by herbarium specimens from India and Siam than from the New World. The great variation in specimens available for study suggests that field study of native populations is needed for the possibility of hybridity, and crosses with *A. guatimalense* must be considered.

## *Brunnichia cirrhosa* GAERTNER

*Common Names:* AMERICAN BUCKWHEAT-VINE, BUCKWHEAT-VINE, EARDROP-VINE, EARDROPS

Forked tendrils appear at the apex of both the axillary and lateral branches on this semi-woody climber. The leaves are deciduous, alternate, ovate-lanceolate, glossy dark green and often 4½ inches long and half as wide. The flowers are small, greenish-white, and produced in terminal panicles, often 12 to 18 inches long. In fruit the floral tube elongates and becomes leathery or hardened and is topped by the persistent calyx segments. The lower half is slightly curved and is flattened into a ridge or wing on one side.

The plant is native to southeastern United States and is occasionally cultivated in botanical gardens as a curiosity. It flowers in midsummer.

The genus can be distinguished from *Polygonum* by the winged fruiting calyx and by the herbaceous, not membranaceous, sheath at the base of the leaf-stalk. Two African species were formerly included in this genus, giving an unusual trans-Atlantic distribution. Those species have been separated by Hutchinson & Dalziel into the genus *Afrobrunnichia,* which differs from *Brunnichia* in the development of two ridges or wings to the fruiting perianth. The fruit thus produced resembles a spatula, which is straight, not curved or sickle-shaped. *A. erecta* (ASCH.) HUTCHINSON & DALZIEL has been reported in cultivation in one botanic garden.

## *Coccoloba nitida* HBK.

*Common Names:* BLACK-GRAPE, MASARI, PIPOCA

At the base this woody plant often has a thick and heavy trunk, topped by long scrambling branches which are solid in the pith. The portion of the plant most commonly seen and collected by botanists therefore resembles a vine. The inflorescence may reach a length of 15 inches and has the clearest white flowers of any species of the genus, the staminate flowers surpassing the pistillate ones in beauty. The leaves are leathery, shiny, dark green when fresh, and vary considerably in size and shape on the same plant. The fruits, which are regularly produced, are egg-shaped, about ½ inch long, and are capped by the persistent perianth-lobes. The species is native to Trinidad, the Guianas, and Brazil. It is known under cultivation in tropical America, and old herbarium specimens indicate that it was cultivated in hothouses in Europe in the 19th century.

The climbing species of *Coccoloba,* in a fashion comparable to the arboreal forms, may have on the young plants or an adventitious shoots, leaves of very different size and shape from those of fruiting plants. In *C. ascendens,* for example, the normal leaves may be limited to a size of 7 by 5 inches, while the leaves of juvenile branches may be 14 by 12 inches.

In all species of *Coccoloba* the plants are completely dioecious—that is, the male and female flowers are developed on separate plants. The staminate flowers are commonly borne in multiples on the spikes or racemes and the stamens are exserted and conspicuous. In the inflorescences producing fruits, the pistillate flowers are borne singly and the stamens are abortive.

For other *Coccoloba* vines—those with inconspicuous flowers—see Chapter X.

## *Muehlenbeckia adpressa* (Labillardiere) Meissner

*Common Name:* Macquarie Harbour-grape

This plant, native to Australia, often resembles a small shrub under cultivation, but its very slender stems can climb into adjacent shrubs, cover rocks, or progress along wire fences. The leaves vary from rounded and cordate to broadly lanceolate. They may be rounded at the apex or drawn out into long thin tips. The blade may be 1 to 3 inches in length. The flowering spikes are short, rarely 3 inches long, and are either solitary or clustered in the axils of the leaves. The staminate and perfect flowers are mixed in the same inflorescence. The perianth-lobes in flower are thin and may be whitish-cream or green, but when mature the entire perianth becomes very succulent, white in color, and surrounds the nearly globular achene. Much material cultivated as *M. australis* should be referred to this species.

*M. complexa* Meissner. The wire-vine is a deciduous climbing plant with very slender stems often forming masses of interwoven fragile branches. When untangled the stems may be 10 feet in length. The leaves are variable in size and shape on the same plant but they are mostly less than ½ inch in diameter, and can be rounded, broadly oblong or even lyrate. The flowers are borne in small terminal and axillary spikes and the plants may have flowers of two kinds on either single or separate specimens. The flowers are greenish-white and relatively inconspicuous but the perianth forms a chalky-white fleshy cup surrounding a black or chestnut-brown achene. The wire-vine is a native of New Zealand.

The name *Muehlenbeckia* is conserved through the International Rules of Botanical Nomenclature with the spelling differing from that suggested by Meissner. The genus has species in Australia, Tasmania, New Zealand, and Norfolk Island, as well as in the New World in South and Central America. Although the Australian and New Zealand species are frequently cultivated, only a few botanical gardens possess the species of the New World. *M. tamnifolia* (HBK) Meissner extends from Mexico to Argentina and is a vine of high elevations found commonly in the cloud forests. *M. sagittifolia* (Ortega) Meissner is from Argentina, Bolivia, and Paraguay. Several collections which were identified as *M. chilensis* should be referred to *M. sagittifolia*. Neither of the American species is particularly attractive and they apparently are grown as novelties and examples of plants with a Southern Hemisphere distribution, possibly involving Antarctica. *M. sagittifolia* has escaped from cultivation in California and has established itself in at least one ranch as a persistent pest, invading lawns and sprouting continuously from underground portions.

The small leaf size, the variable shape of the leaves, the intricate network formed by the branches, and the fleshy white fruiting perianth contrasting with the black achene constitute the appeal of *Muehlenbeckia* species as cultivated plants. It has been found that all that have already been cultivated can be propagated from either seeds or cuttings.

## *Polygonum aubertii* Henry

*Common Names:* Cascade-creeper; Chinese fleecevine; silver lace-vine

The subherbaceous stems of this vigorous perennial plant may ascend by twining, with the inflorescence branches often separately twisted or bent backward. (Photograph 225.) The plant was discovered in China in 1899 by Père Georges Aubert, who noted that the small white flowers on erect inflorescences contrasted with those on the better-known *P. baldschuanicum*. The leaves of this delicate vine are ovate-cordate and either somewhat the shape of an arrowhead or cut off sharply at the base. When very young the blades may display an attractive bronze coloring. The narrow lateral panicles are generally erect when the stems grow horizontally, and they bear many small greenish-white or pure white flowers. The plants rarely set fruit; they also root from cuttings with great difficulty.

*P. baldschuanicum* REGEL, known as Bokhara-vine or Russian-vine, is often described as the most rampant of the climbing members of the buckwheat family. (Photograph 226.) The species was first found in 1883 by Regel in the province of Bokhara, newly regarded as southern Turkestan. It is hardy only in milder climates of the temperate areas. The stems may become woody and some are reported to reach a diameter of an inch and a length exceeding 60 feet. The leaves are ovate or arrow-shaped, and cordate at the base with the apex either blunt or slender-pointed. The pale pink flowers are produced in quite large numbers in terminal and axillary panicles. The calyx enlarges but slightly in fruit, but the fruits persist, being reddish or even tan in color, and so are attractive until broken from the plant. The plants rarely set seed and are therefore propagated by cuttings. In some areas the plant has become a weed.

*P. cilinode* MICHAUX, fringed black bindweed, is a pubescent perennial, herbaceous vine. At each node there is a ring of downward-pointing hairs. The leaves are broadly ovate, somewhat arrow-shaped at the base. The racemes of few white flowers are in clusters forming panicles. The calyx is obscurely winged in fruit; the achene is smooth and shiny. A native of North America, this species is occasionally cultivated in botanical gardens in Europe.

*P. convolvulus* LINN., black bindweed, is an annual vine with twining stems reaching 4 feet in length. The leaves are narrowly ovate with long pointed lobes at the base. The greenish flowers are borne in short axillary racemes. The achenes are granular on the surface and dull in color. This plant is a native of Europe and was probably introduced into the United States as a contaminant of other seed. It is a vigorous groundcover, attractive when in flower with the light green leaves, and while it is a weed there is an ornamental aspect to its development in trash heaps.

*P. perfoliatum* LINN. The numerous sharp prickles which abound on the stem and petioles of this herbaceous plant aid in its rambling and climbing. Stipules at the base of the leaf-stalks are foliaceous, flaring, and orbicular. Petioles are slender, to 3 inches long, and prickly. Leaf-blades are deltoid in outline, 3 inches long and wide, and peltate (attached to the stalk inside the margin). Racemes are commonly terminal, short, and few-flowered. The large achene is included in the semi-fleshy enlarged calyx. A native of India, this viscous herb is actually cultivated in some European botanical gardens.

*P. tristortum* is a sprawling, large-leaved species with its flowers in cylindrical spikes at the summit of long stalks. (Photograph 227.)

282

## *Lysimachia nummularia* LINN.

*Common Names:* CREEPING JENNY; MONEYWORT; CREEPING CHARLIE

Of the hundreds of these leafy, creeping herbs, found in temperate and sub-tropical areas, Brilmeyer (10) says: "This is a precious little Eastern native, a hardy perennial creeper with button leaves and innumerable yellow flowers almost all summer."

PROTEACEAE—PROTEA FAMILY

## *Grevillea bipinnatifida* R. BROWN

This prostrate-growing shrub is of striking appearance for its unusual leaves, which are rigid and rather prickly, 4 inches long and twice divided into wedge-shaped segments, either deep green or gray-green. (Color Plate 167.) The flowers are dull red, in quite large tapering clusters on long stalks at the ends of the sprawling branches. The plant is best climbing over rockwork or draping from a large container or from elevated ground, where it will readily cover several square yards. West Australian.

The clustered spidery flowers of *G. fasciculata* R. BROWN (Color Plate 166) are brilliant orange-red or scarlet, prolific along the slender branches, in spring almost concealing the narrow 1-inch leaves. The normal form of this species is prostrate or broad-spreading, rarely exceeding a foot or 2 in height, but occasionally a more erect form may be seen. Warm sandy soil is preferred. West Australia.

An outstanding creeper is *G. laurifolia*. This is a remarkable wide-spreading groundcover to 6 inches high from the Blue Mountains of Australia, with egg-shaped leaves 2 to 5 inches long and red flowers in short toothbrush clusters 1 to ½ inches long.

RANUNCULACEAE—BUTTERCUP FAMILY

## *Clematis* LINN.

⚜ J. FISK ⚜

*Common Name:* VIRGIN'S BOWER

*Clematis,* with its long flowering period and masses of flowers of varying shapes and colors is deservedly known as the "Queen of Climbers" (Color Plates 169-175.) Although native to the more temperate regions of the earth, it will do well in warmer climates if planted in the shade. Hill country is of course ideal in such regions. Clematis is a lime-loving plant but will grow quite happily in acid soil so long as it is well fed.

Clematis flowers have no petals, being made up entirely of sepals—but colorful ones. The fruits of a clematis are sometimes almost as delightful as the

232. CLEMATIS X HAGLEY     233. CLEMATIS HIRSUTA

234. CLEMATIS ATRAGENE ALPINA TIBETICA     235. CLEMATIS LAWSONIANA HENRYI

flowers, with the attractive fluffy seed clusters of the numerous species and the huge round whirligigs of some of the large-flowering hybrids, both much used in floral arrangements.

Although the small-flowering species have been known for hundreds of years, it was not until 1850 that any real interest was shown in clematis. It was about this time that plant collector Robert Fortune found in China the large-flowering species that became known as *C. lanuginosa* LINDLEY. When he brought this pale blue variety back to England, hybridizing with the Japanese species *C. patens* MORREN & DECAISNE, previously brought to Europe in 1836, began in earnest. In the next 20 years hundreds of large-flowering hybrids were raised in the nurseries of England and France and many are still with us today, the most famous of them all being the purple *C. jackmainii* MOORE, raised at Messrs. Jackman's Nursery at Woking, England, in 1858 and first flowered in 1862.

During the 19th century clematis varieties became very popular, but a mysterious dying back of many plants caused this enthusiasm to wane. Interest in clematis has revived considerably in the last quarter century, especially when it became more generally known that this wilt is not a killer, and that if swift action is taken the plants can be saved. When a plant collapses it should be cut down to the ground immediately, the roots kept well watered and shaded as they are still quite healthy, then within a few weeks new shoots will appear and the plant will soon regain its vigour. The cause of this collapse is now reckoned to be simply a failure of the stem at the base of the plant to supply enough nutriment to the mass of leaves and flowers during humid spells when demand for moisture is at its peak. One way of preventing this is to layer as many shoots as possible around the plant, thus providing several stems coming from the ground instead of the usual very vunerable single stem.

Clematis plants are always pot grown and so can be planted at any time of the year. They like a cool, moist root run and, as they are deep-rooting plants, the soil should be broken up to a depth of 2 feet if possible, with some good manure in the bottom of the hole. Then put some stones, tiles or pebbles around the stem to keep the roots cool and moist.

The pruning of clematis vines has always been a source of great confusion, but it is actually simple. Those that flower early in the season do so on the old wood, therefore they need no pruning; but those that flower late do so on the current year's growth, and so should be cut back hard to within a few inches of the ground in the early spring. Species need little or no pruning, but if they get out of hand they can be cut back with no ill effect at almost any time.

Clematis can be produced by seed, cuttings, grafts or layers, the latter being the best method for the amateur. A well ripened shoot should be bent over from the plant, twisted, and pegged into a pot filled with good compost and set into the ground; this should be covered with soil and a stone placed on top. In a year's time the pot will be bursting with roots and the shoot can be severed from its parent.

Cuttings can be taken of half-ripened wood and inserted into pots of sand and peat. These should be internodal cuttings; that is, the cut is made halfway between the joints, so that there is only one joint, or node, at the top of the cutting. These root in 3 or 4 weeks if placed under glass and kept shaded. Seed is very chancey and only the species will come true. Hybrids often take 2 or 3 years to germinate and are often inferior to the parents.

Clematis is a cosmopolitan plant found in every country. Some 250 species have been described, chiefly in the temperate zone, but many are found in the warmer parts of the earth as well. The following species are cultivated in the lands where they are native and are used as garden ornamentals.

The sweet autumn clematis (*C. dioscorefolia* LEVEILLE & VANIOT), occasionally grown in the United States on low fences or as a groundcover, produces a mass of fragrant white flowers.

Drummond clematis (*C. drummondii* TURCZANINOW & GRAY), often called "old man's beard," native to the southwestern United States, has creamy-white flowers in the summer followed by quantities of seeds having dull-white feathery appendages. These fluffy seeds often blanket the entire plant. It is excellent for covering fences on adverse sites.

In England the first clematis to flower is the evergreen species *C. calycina* SOLANDER, a native of the Balearic Islands; this produces masses of pale yellow bell-shaped flowers, freckled with red spots within. This is quickly followed by another evergreen with much larger and more handsome leaves, producing scented clusters of white waxy flowers. Next in order of flowering is the European *C. alpina* MILLER with its delightful hanging bells of clear blue. This is low growing and is ideal for the rockery. A double variety, *C. macropetela* LEDEBAIR from China is most beautiful of all the species, with its nodding powder-blue flowers. It reminds one of ballet skirts. The pink form, *C. macropetela markhamii,* is equally attractive; both are plants of medium growth but very free flowering. The most popular of all the species is the Himalayan *C. montana* BUCHANAN-HAMILTON. Its ropelike branches cover everything in its path and it is ideal for covering trees and unsightly buildings. Early in the season it is smothered with masses of anenome-like flowers in varying shades of pink and white. There are several varieties, the best three being *C. montana grandiflora,* pure white, *C. montana* 'Elizabeth', pale pink and sweetly scented and *C. montana rubens,* deep pink. (Photograph 228.) A new variety is just becoming popular, *C. montana tetrarosa* with much larger flowers than the type, an attractive lilac-rose with bronzy foliage.

The beautiful but frail looking *C. florida* THUNBERG *var. bicolor* LINDLEY is a good midseason variety; this comes from Japan and is often taken for a passion-flower with its outer circle of creamy-white sepals and its inner boss of deep purple petaloid stamens, the nearest that a clematis gets to petals. Flowering about the same time is the New Zealand *C. indivisa* WILLDENOW, an evergreen with fairly large, star-shaped, white flowers with bright yellow stamens that give it great charm and distinction.

A handsome and unique variety is the American *C. texensis* BUCHHOLZ. This has urn-shaped flowers of bright crimson, the best color among clematis, and one which makes a vivid contrast borne against the glaucous-green foliage. *C. texensis* 'Duchess of Albany' is an attractive pink variety with flowers that open much

236. ROSA LAEVIGATA     237. ROSA X "ETOILE DE FRANCE" (ON HOUSE), "PAUL'S SCARLET" (ON FENCE)

238. ROSA X "DOROTHY PERKINS"     239. ROSA WICHURAIANA

further than the type. These are semi-herbaceous kinds, needing support, as they do not climb with their leaves as do all other species of *Clematis*.

*C. tangutica* KORSHINSKY and *C. orientalis* LAMARCK are both yellow, a color rare in *Clematis*. The former, which comes from Russia, is covered with small lantern-shaped flowers for many weeks, followed by silky seed-heads; the latter, from Tibet, has very attractive thick sepals which open quite wide and remain in flower a long time; both plants are vigorous and quickly make large specimens. *C. viticellas* LINN. from Spain produces charming, late-flowering varieties with masses of small saucer-shaped flowers which hang downward. The true species is purple but there are red, white, and pink varieties.

Scent is rare in *Clematis,* but it occurs in two late-flowering kinds, *C. flammula* LINN., the scented virgin's-bower from southern Europe, and the sweet autumn clematis of America (*C. paniculata* THUNBERG not GMELIN; now called *C. dioscofolia* LEVEILLE & VANIOT var. *robusta* REHDER.) (Photograph 229.) Both have this added charm to their small white flowers, also both are vigorous and free-flowering.

There are a large number of hybrids, some measuring up to 10 inches in diameter, and the following selection is perhaps the cream of these beautiful and showy blooms:

## Early-flowering

These are in flower for about 6 weeks in the spring. They flower on the previous year's ripened wood and so need no pruning. They often give a second but less profuse display late in the season.

'Barbara Jackman'. A medium-sized variety with soft petunia-mauve sepals striped with a crimson bar. The stamens are cream and the plant grows 8 to 12 feet high.

'H. F. Young'. The best blue clematis to date. Most blues have a certain amount of purple in their make-up, but this one has very little. It makes a plant of 8 to 12 feet.

'Kathleen Dunford! A unique semi-double variety of rich rosy-purple with golden stamens making a plant of between 8 to 12 feet.

'Lasustern'. A very showy plant, covered by masses of enormous deep lavender-blue flowers with an attractive center of cream stamens. (Photograph 230.) Grows 8 to 12 feet high.

'Madame le Coultre.' Also known as 'Marie Boiselott.' One of the best whites. Enormous flowers with yellow stamens often overlapping so much that the effect is of double flowers. A vigorous plant, 12 to 16 feet.

'Miss Bateman'. A very attractive medium-sized white with a prominent center of chocolate-red stamens. It makes a plant 6 to 8 feet high and is one of the first to flower.

'Nelly Moser'. Next to *C. jackmanii,* this is the most popular kind, with its great cartwheel flowers of pale pink with deep carmine bars on each sepal. It grows 8 to 12 feet tall.

155. PASSIFLORA COCCINEA

156. PASSIFLORA AMETHYSTINA
(Rio de Janeiro)

157. PASSIFLORA NITIDA

158. PASSIFLORA MANICATA
(Trujillo)

159. PASSIFLORA SP.
(Rio de Janeiro)

160. PASSIFLORA COERULEA

161. PASSIFLORA VITIFOLIA

162. FORSYTHIA INTERMEDIA SPECTABILIS

163. SECURIDACA DIVERSIFOLIA

164. ZAUSCHNERIA CALIFORNICA

165. LAPAGERIA ROSEA

166. GREVILLEA BIPINNATIFIDA

167. GREVILLEA FASCICULATA

168. GNETUM MONTANUM
(female cones)

'Ramona'. Also known as 'Hybrida Seiboldii'. A well-shaped flower of lavender-blue with dark stamens on a plant of 10 to 16 feet.

'The President'. A deep purple-blue with dark stamens. A handsome variety which often blooms throughout the season and grows 8 to 12 feet tall.

'Vyvyan Pennell'. Doubles are not very popular but this is one of the best, being of violet-blue with splashes of crimson and with golden stamens. Single flowers are produced on the young wood late in the season, as the plant grows 8 to 12 feet tall.

'William Kennett'. A handsome variety with large lavender-blue flowers with crenulated edges, this vigorous grower makes a plant 10 to 20 feet tall.

'Xerxes'. Of deep violet-blue with purple shadings, this flower has rounded sepals and dark stamens. It is a striking variety often flowering throughout the season, growing 8 to 12 feet high.

## Mid and Late-season Varieties

These flower continuously for many weeks on the current year's growth. They all need hard pruning early in the spring.

'Comtesse de Bouchard'. Masses of medium-sized flowers of mauve-pink with yellow stamens appear over a long period on a plant that grows 8 to 12 feet tall.

'Ernest Markham'. Although there are no real red *Clematis* varieties, this is one of the best of the so-called reds. It is a glowing petunia-red with golden stamens; will flower on the old wood if left unpruned, but its main season is late on the young wood. It grows 12 to 20 feet tall.

'Gipsy Queen'. Of rich violet-purple with a velvet sheen, this is a good late variety, free-flowering and vigorous, growing 12 to 20 feet.

'Hagley Hybrid.' A beautiful shell-pink with attractive brown stamens, this is a useful plant for the small garden, growing only to about 6 feet. (Photograph 232.)

'Jackmanii'. The well known popular old-fashioned variety casts a mantle of purple over everything in its reach for weeks on end. It is free-flowering and vigorous, growing to a height of 20 feet or more.

'Madame Edouard André'. A deep velvet-red, medium size with pointed sepals, this is another good variety for the small garden as it rarely gets above 6 feet.

'Perle d'Azur'. The only pale blue among the late-flowering varieties, this is a beautiful sky-blue with green stamens, vigorous and free-flowering over a long period. It makes a plant from 10 to 20 feet tall. (Photograph 231.)

'Ville de Lyon'. Of carmine-red shading to deep crimson around the edges of the sepals, this is a medium-sized flower with golden stamens. The vine grows 8 to 12 feet tall.

There is such great variation in the conformation of clematis flowers, that several other kinds, not further treated in these pages, are shown in Photographs 233 to 235.

## *Naravelia laurifolia* WALLICH

This is a climbing plant with woody stem from the East Indies, with white flowers, numerous petals, and the 4 or 5 sepals petal-like. The leaf-petioles become like tendrils to help the plant climb. A yellow-flowered species, *N. zeylanica,* is found in Ceylon. These plants are closely related to *Clematis.*

RHAMNACEAE—BUCKTHORN FAMILY

## *Berchemia* DC.

※ MARSHALL C. JOHNSTON ※

*Common Names:* SUPPLEJACK; RATTAN-VINE

Some members of this small genus are twining vines and are occasionally planted, although only 2 kinds are cultivated to any extent outside of botanical gardens. The flowers are small but are fragrant and borne in rather attractive bunches. The leaves are deciduous. The stems are tough and woody and usually twine, or are scandent. The 2 species to be mentioned have blunt leaves 1 to 3 inches long with numerous closely parallel lateral veins, easily marking them from all other woody vines.

*Berchemia scandens* (HILL) K. KOCH is a native of southeastern United States, southern Mexico and Guatemala, where it thrives in dense, moist forest, tolerates much shade, and climbs to 75 feet in the crowns of trees; it is hardy as far north as Missouri and Virginia. Its flowers are in short, lateral or terminal racemes or raceme-like panicles with short branches.

*B. racemosa* SIEBOLD & ZUCCARINI is a native of Japan; its panicles are large and spreading, showier than those of *B. scandens,* the branches being elongate and themselves raceme-like. It is hardy slightly farther north than is *B. scandens.*

## *Ceanothus prostratus* BENTHAM

*Common Name:* TRAILING CALIFORNIA-LILAC; SQUAW-CARPET

There are 3 varieties of this trailing or semi-climbing form of a favored garden plant in California, all have matlike growth with stems to 10 feet in length, some of the branches rooting themselves as they go. They are ideal plants for slopes and banks, preferring a sunny position. Characteristic blue flowers are produced in clusters at the tips of short leafy branchlets. The 3 kinds are var. *prostratus* BENTHAM, var. *laxus* JEPSON, and var. *occidentalis* MCMINN.

Eight other species of prostrate *Ceanothus* grow in the same manner. These are:

C. *arcuatus* MCMINN, arching ceanothus
C. *diversifolius* KELL., trailing ceanothus
C. *fresnensis* DUDLEY EX ABRAMS, Fresno mat
C. *gloriosus* T. J. HOWELL, Point Reyes creeper

240. ROSA MOSCHATA    241. ROSA BANKSII

242. RUBUS DELICIOSUS    243. WALDSTEINIA TERNATA

C. *griseus* (Trellease) McMinn var. *horizontalis* McMinn, Carmel creeper
    (Color Plate 176)
C. *pinetorum* Coville, Kern ceanothus
C. *pumulis* Greene, Siskiyou mat
C. *thyrsiflorisus* Eschscholtz var. *repens* McMinn., Creeping blue-blossom

Generally speaking, these species are not cultivated because they are both difficult and short-lived. Dr. M. A. Nobs at the Carnegie Institution of Washington, at Sanford, California, an authority on *Ceanothus,* writes:

> "Hybrid *Ceanothus* are generally much more tolerant and long lived. There are a number of splendid forms which have been introduced and are readily available in the nursery trade. Among the ground cover types are X. *C.* 'Far Horizons' and a number of derivatives of *C. gloriosus,* including 'Bamico', 'Emily Brown', and 'Tuttle'."

For the most complete treatment of the genus, both taxonomically and horticulturally, see (169).

---

ROSACEAE—ROSE FAMILY                              ⚘ MARGARET E. COON ⚘

## *Rosa* Linn.

From a strictly botanical point of view, the members of the Rosaceae are not climbers as they have neither tendrils nor discs for support, nor do they twine. Some have thorns (*Rosa, Pyracantha, Crataegus, Chaenomeles, Rubus*), but these do not actually serve as a method of attachment for support. Some genera have creeping stems or runners enabling them to cover a wide space in a short time (*Luetkea, Fragaria, Dryas, Waldsteinia*). Others have stems that are quite limber and grow extremely long in one growing season (*Rosa*).

The flowers of the Rosaceae are considered some of the most primitive when it comes to structure, but one genus—*Rosa*—is reputed to contain some of the most beautiful and most colorful flowers known to man. Sappho, the Greek poetess, bestowed the title "Queen of Flowers" upon the rose. Keats wrote: "the sweetest flower wild nature yields, a fresh-blown musk rose!"

Of all ornamental plants, only the rose will produce such a variety of color over such a long period for so little care. From the earliest blooming species to the "last rose of summer"; from the smallest, under 6 inches in height, to the tallest—who knows how many feet?—can be found some rose or roses to fit any purpose and grow under almost any condition. Nearly every color is available: white, pink, and every shade of red; occasional hints of green, brown, and blue; and, in design, one-color, bi-color, multi-color, picotee, striped, and, under some climatic conditions, even spotted. Flower form ranges from the simplicity of the flat, five-petaled species to the elegant perfection of the double, high-centered hybrid tea, and the size can be from ½ inch across for a single bloom to 6 inches. The flowers may be borne singly on a long slender stem, in clusters, or in garlands gracefully swaying in the breeze.

Most of the rose species, at least 125 generally recognized, originated in Asia and Europe with a few (18) in North America. Attention in this book centers on the species and cultivars (cultivated varieties) that are known as climbers and ramblers or trailers. There are large-flowered or small-flowered climbers, once-blooming or repeat-blooming; upright and rambling, arching, or trailing and creeping. The majority of the climbing species have small, single, white, non-recurrent clustered bloom. They are more readily adapted to warm climates, and come from the subgenus *Eurosa* and the section Synstylae, with the sections Banksianae, Bracteatae, Laevigatae and Indicae. These have been inter-crossed, outcrossed, nature-crossed, and man-crossed to the point where tracing their ancestry is all but impossible.

Most modern cultivated climbers have been bred for the temperate regions where the growing season is relatively short and winters are severe. There is need for modern, repeat-blooming climbers adapted to an almost continuous growing season.

For more information on climbers, consult bibliography numbers 153 to 159.

Under normal conditions, bloom should not be expected on most climbing roses until the third season, although some climbing forms of hybrid teas and floribundas will bloom in less.

*R. arvensis* HUDSON [Syn. *R. repens, R. silvestris, R. candida*]. The field rose is deciduous and creeping in habit, flowers are thin, small (1½ inches), single, white, and solitary or in few-flavored clusters in June or July. It has been described by some as scentless; others attribute to it a slight musklike fragrance. Europe and possibly Asiatic Turkey are its native habitats. *R. arvensis* crosses readily with other roses and one group known as Ayrshire roses has *R. arvensis* as one parent. 'Elegans,' with semi-double, clustered, white flowers on a vigorous plant, is probably the best known of this group. There are also some natural hybrids with other species. Two have a trailing habit: *R. X paulii* REHDER (*arvensis* X *rugosa*), with single 2½-inch, white flowers in clusters; and *R. X ruga* LINDLEY (*arvensis* X *chinensis*) with semi-double, light pink, fragrant flowers with hardiness that seems to have been picked up from *chinensis*.

*R. brunonii* LINDLEY, Himalayan musk rose is listed by some authors as a separate species; however, in more recent listings one will find it as *R. moschata nepalensis*. It is very similar to *R. moschata*, but has hairy branches and downy leaf undersides when young, while *moschata* is smooth.

*R. helenae* REHDER & WILSON, discovered by E. H. Wilson in central China in 1907, is a vigorous, deciduous climber, more upright with long arching canes reaching 15 feet; it has fragrant white flowers about 1 inch in diameter in loose clusters, blooming in June and July. Again, as with many rose species, this has synonyms: *R. floribunda* BAKER, *R. moschata micrantha* CREPIN, and *R. moschata helenae* CARDOT. Shepherd (155) indicates that the species has been used as an understock for strong-growing cultivars.

*R. moschata* HERRMANN, musk rose is a native from Iran to southern China;

grows to 40 feet in warm humid areas; in temperate regions it reaches 10 feet; is at its best when growing over other plants. Flowers are creamy white; 1½ inches in diameter, fragrant, and produced in clusters. (Photograph 240.) As mentioned previously, some authors list *R. brunonii* as a variety of *moschata*, others believe *moschata* has been lost to cultivation and what is now called *moschata* is really *brunonii*, the pubescence of *R. brunonii* being the main difference.

*R. moschata* has been frequently used as a parent for bringing roses several steps up the evolutionary ladder to Noisettes and hybrid musks. Many of the cultivars are more upright than the species and have repeat blooming. This species crosses readily with others. *R. gallica* X *R. moschata* resulted in *R. X dupontii* [syn. *R. moschata nivea*], an upright but spreading bush, with a flesh-colored bud opening to a white, 3-inch, fragrant flower borne in clusters. This hybrid was used by Roy Shepherd as one of the female parents of the cultivar 'Conrad Hilton'.

*R. cerasocarpa* ROLFE is similar to *R. moschata* but its 1 to 1½-inch white flowers are borne in panicles instead of corymbs and it can be distinguished from *R. helenae* by its leaves—5 large leathery leaflets instead of 7 to 9. This strong climber of central China bears its flowers in June and is hardier than *R. moschata*.

*R. filipes* REHDER & WILSON, from western China, has many-flowered panicles of ¾ to 1-inch, fragrant white blossoms in June and July and reaches 10 to 20 feet although some authors claim it is only a semi-climber. This again is similar to *R. moschata*.

*R. leschenaultiana* WIGHT & ARNOTT while similar to *brunonii* and *sempervirens* is close to *moschata* with white 1¾ inch flowers in clusters. Crepins listed it as *R. moschata leschenaultiana*. In southern India where it is native, this rampant climber may reach 60 feet. It is not hardy in cool climates.

*R. longicuspis* BERTOLONI [syn. *R. lucens, R. willmottiana, R. irridens* and *R. charboneaui*] was found in western China and is tender, but the reddish canes can reach 10 to 20 feet. Flowers white, in clusters; petals are silky on back.

*R. phoenicea* BOISSIER, thought to be a parent of the damask rose, blooms in June with the white, 1¼ to 2 inch-flowers borne in clusters. Native to Asia Minor, *phoenicia* is less vigorous than *moschata* but still a strong, half-evergreen climber.

*R. rubus* LEVEILLE & VANIOT [syn. *R. ernestii*], blackberry rose, indigenous to central and western China and again belonging to the *moschata* group, blooms in June with 1-inch white flowers in heavy clusters on vigorous canes up to 20 feet in length.

*R. sinowilsonii* HEMSLEY, from China, with shining, dark green foliage, is similar to *longicuspis*, but the flower buds are rounder and they open to 1½ to 2-inch, white, loose-clustered blooms in June and July.

*R. multiflora* THUNBERG [syn. *R. polyanthos, R. sylvestris cheusanica, R. thyrsiflora, R. intermedia*], multiflora japonica and polyantha simplex. The Japanese rose is more upright and arching than climbing. A deciduous shrub from the area of China, Japan, and Korea, it produces many single white, sometimes light pink, ¾-inch blooms in clusters during late May and June. It is used quite frequently as a conservation or highway hedge and chiefly as understock for our more popular hybrid teas, floribundas, etc. As its seeds germinate readily and are scattered by the birds, it can pop up in unwanted places: *R. multiflora* is a parent of the multiflora ramblers and also of some of our polyanthas and floribundas. There are also botanical varieties: *carnea,* with double pink flowers; *gentiliana* or *cathayensis,* pink; and *platyphylla* with double purple flowers, known as 'Seven Sisters' and less winter hardy than the species. Some of the more popular multiflora hybrids are 'Crimson Rambler', 'Tausendschön', and 'Veilchenblau'.

*R. maximowiczii* Regel [syn. *R. faureiri, R. granulosa*] from Manchuria and Korea is only a partial climber, being more sprawling in its growth. Flowers, 1 to 1¼ inches, are white and borne in small, many-flowered clusters. There are two varieties, *jackii* (jack rose), which is similar in bloom but the canes are void of bristles, and *pilosa,* which has fine hairs or bristles on the canes. The latter has been crossed with hybrid teas, producing several hardy climbers that are once-blooming, among them 'Prairie Moon'—large, double, fragrant, and creamy white, and 'Maytime'—large, single, and shell-pink.

*R. sempervirens* Linn., also known as the evergreen rose because of its green stems and persistent foliage during a mild winter, is a native of southern Europe and northern Africa. Two-inch, single, white, slightly fragrant flowers are borne in loose clusters during June and July on vigorous canes reaching over 20 feet. *Prostrata,* a less vigorous plant, with fewer flowers, is a botanical variety. Crossed with other species, *R. chinensis* in particular, *R. sempervirens* produces double-flowered and upright hybrids.

*R. setigera* Michaux [syn. *R. rubifolia*] is the only climber native to North America. Called the prairie rose, its 2-inch, single, pale pink flowers on trailing canes brighten its habitat during late June and July. The species is vigorous, stems reaching 10 feet in a season, disease-resistant and adaptable to various climatic conditions; although it is said not to be hardy in far northern states, it does grow in Ontario. There is some evidence of a dioecious nature so plants to be used as pollen parents should be carefully chosen. *Tomentosa* seems to be a hardier botanical variety. Some of the more familiar commercial cultivars are 'Baltimore Belle', 'Doubloons', and 'American Pillar'; the latter two are climbers—double yellow and single deep pink respectively.

*R. watsoniana* Crepin [syn. *R. multiflora watsoniana*], bamboo rose, said to have originated in Japan, at times is classed as a variety of multiflora, being similar in growth habit (upright, arching, but smaller). The pink flowers are small (½ inch), loose-petaled, and are borne in many-flowered, long panicles or clusters.

*R. wichuraiana* Crepin [syn. *R. luciae, R. bracteata*], a half evergreen, creeping shrub with small 1½-inch, single, white flowers in loose clusters, has probably contributed more to the popular hybrid climbers than any other species. (Photograph 239.) The species itself, from the eastern China and Japan, is trailing, late-flowering (July to September), and vigorous, with attractive, disease-resistant foliage and stems which, if trained upright, are more subject to winter injury at zero temperatures than if left to trail. *R. wichuraiana* has produced cultivars that are upright, climbing or creeping. Some of the better known climbers are:

'American Pillar'—single, deep pink with white centers
'Dorothy Perkins'—double, deep pink (Photograph 238)
'Dr. W. Van Fleet'—double, fragrant, cameo-pink, hybrid tea form
'Albertine'—double, coppery yellow
'Climbing American Beauty'—fragrant, deep rose-pink
'Silver Moon'—semi-double, creamy white
'City of York'—semi-double, fragrant, creamy white

There is a natural hybrid, *R.* X *jacksonii,* a single, 2-inch, bright crimson from *R. rugosa* X *R. wichuraiana.* The diploid cultivar 'Max Graf' (bright pink, profuse, non-recurrent bloom on trailing canes) is a probable hybrid of the same parentage and is a forerunner of a new group of tetraploid species, *R. kordesii,* which are quite vigorous shrubs and climbers with profuse, fragrant, and usually recurrent bloom. The following are some of the recent (since 1952) introductions of *R. kordesii* or of its hybrids:

'Alexander von Humboldt'—scarlet
'Aurora'—double, orange-yellow, upright
'Bad Neuenahr'—double, scarlet
'Dortmund'—3-inch, single, red with white center
'Flammentanz'—double, crimson, non-recurrent, upright
'Hamburger Phoenix'—orange red
'Ilse Krohn'—very double, white, non-recurrent
'Köln am Rhein'—deep salmon-pink
'Leverküsen'—double, pale yellow
'Parkdirektor Riggers'—semi-double, recurrent, velvety crimson
'Raymond Chenault'—semi-double, red, free bloomer
'Zweibrücken'—double, deep crimson, recurrent

*R. luciae* Franchet & Rochebrune [syn. *R. luciae fujisanensis, R. fuji-sanensis, R. jasminoides, R. hakonensis, R. franchetii*] has fewer leaflets than *R. wichuraiana,* to which it is related, and it is also semi-evergreen, but less hardy. The flowers are smaller (¾ to 1¼ inches), fragrant and borne in clusters of 3 to 20 flowers in July and August. It is a native of Japan, Korea, and eastern China. Some authors say it is upright; others list is as climbing or prostrate.

In addition to the previous species from the Systylae section of *Rosa,* which contains most of the climbers, the sections Indicae, Banksianae, Bracteatae, and Laevigatae have a species or two that trail or climb.

*R. odorata* Sweet [syn. *R. indica odoratissima, R. thea, R. chinensis fragrans*], better known as the tea rose, has long, half-evergreen canes which sometimes climb. Flowers, blooming from June through September, are white, light pink, or yellow, fragrant, can be double or semi-double and are usually solitary rather than the clustered or corymb-type bloom of the Systylae section.

The bloom fragrance is likened to that of crushed fresh tea leaves. Being from a part of China where the seasons change gradually, this species does not tolerate the sudden temperature changes of our northern temperate region, but adapts readily to southern sections of the United States. *R. odorata,* through a series of natural and man-made crosses, is a parent of our modern hybrid teas, which are mainly of bush form, 3 to 5 feet. However, due to its inherited climbing tendencies, many hybrid teas sport to the climbing form.

Besides the species *R. odorata,* there is the variety *pseudindica* LINDLEY, also known as 'Beauty of Glazenwood', 'Fortune's Double Yellow', or 'Gold of Ophir', that will reach 20 feet or more. This somewhat tender plant has double, fragrant flowers of rose-pink tinged with salmon-yellow.

Formerly known as *R. X odorata gigantea,* the species *R. gigantea* COLLETT, from China and Burma, is vigorous, reaching 40 feet, with creamy-white to pale yellow, fragrant, solitary flowers; but it is tender. Its variety *erubescens* has blush-pink flowers and may be the same as *R. chinensis grandiflora* described by Willmott.

*R. chinensis* JACQUIN [syn. *R. sinica, R. indica, R. nankinensis*], the China rose, Bengal rose, or monthly rose, while normally considered a bush type, in the wild state it is sometimes climbing. It is mentioned here only as the precursor of the repeat-blooming or monthly roses and a parent of such types as Bourbons, Boursaults, Hybrid Chinas, Noisettes, Polyanthas, Hybrid Perpetuals, Teas, Hybrid Teas, and Miniatures; all of which have climbing forms or themselves have long rambling canes that can be easily trained.

There are only two species in the Banksianae section. Both are from China and are climbing.

*R. banksiae* AITON, Banks' rose or Lady Banks' rose, is quite vigorous, reaching 20 feet, and the canes are almost devoid of thorns or prickles. (Photograph 241.) Small white or yellow flowers, 1 inch or less, single or double, are borne in open clusters during May and June. The plant is tender in the north but grows well in warm areas.

There is one in Tombstone, Arizona, that covers 2,700 square feet. In addition to the species there are two varieties: *albo-plena*—double, white, fragrant, and *lutea*—double, yellow, and with some fragrance.

*R. X fortuniana* LINDLEY [syn.: *R. fortuneana*] is a cross between *R. banksiae* and *R. laevigata,* but while having the same general appearance as *banksiae,* it is slightly hardier. The flowers are double, white, about 3 inches across, and borne singly. This species does well in poor, sandy soils and has recently proved successful as an understock for roses to be grown in Florida.

*R. cymosa* TRATTINICK [syn. *R. microcarpa, R. sorbiflora, R. indica, R. fragariaeflora, R. amoyensis, R. esquirolii*]. Indigenous to most of China, this climber, to 15 feet, produces compound clusters of many small white flowers in June. The foliage is shiny, dark green on the upper surface. Its hardiness is questionable in cooler climates.

*R. bracteata* WENDLAND [syn. *R. macartnea*], Macartney rose, from southern China is acclimated to southeastern United States to the point of being a pest in pasture lands, but because it readily spreads by underground stems it has been used for erosion control in areas where adaptable. The large, solitary, white, single blooms are fragrant (as of apricots) and are borne in June, July, and sometimes later in the summer. 'Mermaid'—with single, pale yellow flowers, recurrent bloom and attractive foliage—is a hybrid of *R. bracteata,* not too hardy in the northern parts of the United States, but half-evergreen and rampant in the south.

*R. laevigata* Michaux [syn. *R. sinica, R. cherokeensis, R. ternata, R. hystrix, R. camellia, R. nivea*], cherokee rose, state flower of Georgia, though of Chinese origin, has also been naturalized in the southeastern United States, and while it may grow farther north, it seldom blooms. It is single, large (2 to 3 inches across), white, fragrant, blooming in May and June. (Photograph 236.) Two well-known hybrids are 'Silver Moon,' described under *R. wichuraiana* and *R.* X *anemonoides* Rehder, anemone rose or pink Cherokee. This is hardier and has large, single, pink, repeat bloom, but pollen is sterile in many instances. 'Ramona' (red Cherokee) is a light crimson sport with repeat blooms.

## Modern Climbers

Two species have been prominent in the blood lines of our modern climbers; these are *R. multiflora* and *R. wichuraiana.* Some of the better known hybrid cultivars of these are:

'Dorothy Perkins'—fragrant, rose pink, dark glossy foliage, vigorous, non-recurrent.

'Dr. W. Van Fleet'—fragrant, pink fading to white, non-recurrent.

'Hiawatha'—single, deep crimson with white center, non-recurrent.

'Paul's Scarlet Climber'—vivid scarlet, profuse bloom, slightly recurrent. (Photograph 237.)

From some of these hybrids have come others:

'New Dawn'—a 'Dr. W. Van Fleet' sport with double, fragrant, bush-pink, recurrent bloom; it received the first U. S. plant patent.

'Blaze'—a semi-double, scarlet, recurrent bloom from 'Paul's Scarlet Climber'.

'Spectacular'—fragrant, scarlet-red, double, clustered, recurrent bloom, again from 'Paul's Scarlet Climber' crossed with a *multiflora* seedling.

From 'New Dawn' as the female parent came:

'Blossomtime'—very fragrant, profuse, double blossom, cameo pink, the reverse a darker pink, on semi-climbing or arching canes. Blooms first year.

'Coral Satin'—fragrant, coral, double, recurrent bloom.

'Don Juan'—large, double, very fragrant, dark red with recurrent bloom, some the first year.

'Gladiator'—everblooming, double, fragrant, rose-red. 'New Dawn' seedling is a pollen parent.

'White Dawn'—double, fragrant, white, clustered, recurrent bloom.

'Yellow Creeping Everbloom'—very vigorous, yellow, recurrent bloom.

And from 'White Dawn' come two hybrids. One, 'Viking Queen', is a very fragrant, deep pink, double, profuse, recurrent bloom on a low-growing, semi-

244. CHIOCOCCA ALBA      245. HEDYOTIS SP.

246. MANETTIA COCCINEA      247. MANETTIA BICOLOR

prostrate plant which blooms the first year and makes an excellent ground cover. The second is 'Sea Foam', white to cream-colored flowers of recurrent bloom borne in clusters in vigorous, trailing, semi-prostrate canes. Excellent for low walls and step borders.

A recent Italian hybrid of *R. banksiae lutescens* is 'Purezza'. This produces spirea-type garlands of double, fragrant, white blooms in the spring. In warm climates it will sometimes repeat.

As it is impossible to keep up with the many commercially available bush roses, it is just as impossible to keep up with their climbing sports. Name a popular bush rose and 9 times out of 10 it will have a climbing form. Some of these are more prolific than the bush type; others are not.

There are 'Climbing Peace', 'Climbing Queen Elizabeth', 'Climbing Chrysler Imperial', 'Climbing Crimson Glory', 'Climbing Fashion', 'Climbing Spartan', 'Climbing Pinocchio' ('Rosenmärchen'), 'Climbing Cecile Brunner', to name just a few. And of all the All-America Rose Selection winners, only two are classed as climbers: 'High Noon', a double, fragrant, lemon-yellow, with recurrent bloom which is best suited for warmer climates, and 'Golden Showers', a large, double, fragrant, yellow bloom which is abundant and recurrent, borne singly or clustered and usually appearing the first year.

## *Rubus* LINN.
*Common Name:* RASPBERRIES

This genus is more noted for its fruit than for its flowers. Those species which might qualify as climbers have inconspicuous, small, white, open-clustered flowers. There are, however, three species (all native to North America) which are grown especially for their flowers—though the fruit of all is delicious; *R. deliciosus, R. odoratus,* and *R. spectabilis.* The growth habit is more upright and arching than it is climbing or twining. Generally the canes of *Rubus* are biennial in nature, so to keep the plants in good condition the old canes should be cut out each year after the blooming and/or fruiting is finished.

## *Rubus deliciosus* JAMES
[Syn. *R. roezlii, Oreobatus deliciosus*]
*Common Names:* ROCKY MOUNTAIN FLOWERING RASPBERRY; BOULDER RASPBERRY

*R. deliciosus* is arching, thornless, deciduous. The canes reach 6 feet and produce white, single, roselike flowers about 2 inches in diameter on solitary stems in May and June. (Photograph 242.)

*R. orodatus* LINN. [syn.: *R. grandifolius, Bossekia odorata, Rubacer odoratum*], flowering raspberry. This is a deciduous, thornless shrub of 6 to 8 feet. The 1½ to 2-inch, purple, fragrant flowers are borne in broad clusters from July through September in the northern hemisphere.

*R. spectabilis* PURSH [syn.: *Parmena spectabilis*] salmonberry. The fragrant, purplish-red, 1-inch flowers are borne singly or a few together on long stems in late spring. Canes are vigorous, smooth, and can attain a length of 15 feet.

## *Waldsteinia ternata* FRITSCH
[Syn.: *W. sibirica; W. trifolia*]

A little-known genus containing 5 species which are native to the United States and eastern Europe. (Photograph 243.) Because of their low creeping habit (4 to 10 inches), they are best suited for rock gardens. The ½-inch, yellow, star-shaped flowers are generally borne in small clusters on the tips of the stems rather than along their entire length. The general plant appearance is strawberry-like and the species *W. fragarioides* [syn.: *Dalibarda fragarioides*] has a common name of barren-strawberry. The other species besides *W. ternata* are *W. geoides, W. idahoensis,* and *W. lobata.*

RUBIACEAE—COFFEE OR MADDER FAMILY    ※ JULIAN A. STEYERMARK ※

## *Amaralia*

This little-known genus of African climbing shrubs is worthy of cultivation. The flowers are tubular and 5-lobed. In *A. bignoniiflora* (WELWITSCH) HIERN the 2½-inch-long flowers are first pink, turn eventually red, then orange, and are subtended by a calyx which is green mottled with crimson.

In *A. calycina* (G. DON) K. SCHUMANN, the smaller inch-long corollas are white, yellow, or pink, with the tube darker spotted on the inside, and with smaller, shorter calyx-lobes. In both species the leaves are glabrous or nearly so. In *A. calycina* they are prominently ribbed. In both species the fruit is edible.

## *Chiococca*

This genus of about 6 species comprises shrubs or small trees, some of which often develop climbing or trailing branches. They are all native to tropical America, extending from South America to Central America, Mexico, and the West Indies and Florida.

The pendent, flattened or rounded pearly-white fruit is very attractive and ornamental in such species as *Chiococca alba* (LINN.) HITCHCOCK. This species has axillary clusters of small, creamy-white tubular flowers and shining, thick, ovate leaves. (Photograph 244.) In other species the flowers may be tinged with lilac. *Chiococca alba* is the commonest species. It and other species of the genus merit cultivation.

## *Cosmibuena*

This genus consists of about 6 species, mostly of shrubs or trees which inhabit portions of Central and South America. One of the species, *C. triflora* (BENTHAM) Kl., found in Venezuela and British Guiana, is an epiphytic shrub, which may develop elongated and climbing branches.

248. MUSSAENDA ERYTHROPHYLLA    249. UNCARIA AFRICANA

250. LEPTACTINA DENSIFLORA    251. GONZALUGIA HIRSUTA DICOCCA

The flowers, resembling those of *Hillia,* are very fragrant and showy. The white corollas attain a length of 5½ inches. The shining, dark green, oval or elliptic leaves are very attractive. This species deserves to be introduced into cultivation. Like *C. grandiflora* (RUIZ & PAVON) RUSBY [syn.: *C. obtusifolia; C. latifolia*], which is sometimes cultivated, propagation is by either seed or cuttings.

## *Emmeorhiza umbellata* (SPRENGEL) SCHUMANN

This is the only species, although a variable one, of the genus, but has a wide geographical range in South America, extending from Venezuela south to Brazil along the Andean chain of mountains to Bolivia. It is a slightly woody or soft-stemmed, high-climbing vine with conspicuously veined, rich green leaves and small white tubular flowers, which are arranged in dense umbellate clusters. With its small, conspicuously veined leaves, which form a dense cover over any supporting object, the vine is a most attractive one which merits cultivation. So far as known, it has not been introduced into cultivation.

## *Euclinia longiflora* SALISBURY

Sometimes known also as *Randia macrantha* (SCHULTES) DC., this is usually a scrambling shrub or small tree, but may also climb. The handsome, trumpet-shaped, fragrant flowers are white to pale yellow with reddish-brown on the outside. They may reach 10 inches in length and hang solitary from the tips of the branches.

This species is native to tropical Africa, where it is found from Sierra Leone to Angola, Sudan, and Uganda. It is common on the Ivory Coast. It has been cultivated at Kew Gardens, and deserves to be more widely grown. As in *Randia,* the fruit has a black pulpy interior which is edible.

## *Ferdinandusa*

This genus is found in the West Indies and South America, where about 13 species are known. Most of them are trees or shrubs, but some, such as *F. speciosa* POHL of Brazil, are climbing shrubs. The numerous, showy, scarlet flowers, up to 2½ inches long, are produced at the ends of the branches. The oblong or linear-oblong, bluntly pointed leaves, up to 6 inches long, are shining and glabrous on their upper surface. This handsome climbing shrub deserves to be introduced into cultivation. Other members of the genus have white, green, yellow, or flesh-colored flowers, which are usually very fragrant.

## *Gardenia*

While this genus of about 60 species usually comprises shrubs or trees, at least the following two are climbers to a greater or lesser degree.

*Gardenia abbeokutae* HIERN, native of Africa from Tanganyika, as well as Sierra Leone to French Cameroons, is of great ornamental value and has been cultivated at Kew Gardens. It possesses spines. The leaves are dark green and shining, elliptic, 5 or 6-nerved, and acuminate. The creamy-white or white, funnel-shaped flowers are very fragrant, 2 to 3 inches long, more than 1 inch in diameter, and they hang from long stalks.

The second climbing species of *Gardenia, G. fernandensis* HIERN, likewise found in Africa, specifically from Sierra Leone to Gabon and Portuguese Congo, may climb as high as 80 feet. It has purple fluted stems and broadly oblong-elliptic leaves rounded at the apex. The fragrant flowers are white, but turn yellowish in age. They are crowded at the ends of short lateral branchlets.

[EDITOR'S NOTE: In the Tribe Gardenia to which *Gardenia* belongs, climbers are found also in the genera *Sherbournea* (10 species in tropical Africa), *Atractogyne* (3 species in west Africa, and *Bertiera* (30 species in tropical America and Africa).]

## Gonzalagunia

About 15 species are known from the tropical regions of South and Central America and the West Indies. While the members of this tropical genus are usually considered as trees and shrubs, some of them may have elongated or drooping branches, which may give the appearance of clambering or half-climbing. The fruits are usually an attractive ivory-white color, but also may be black, and are developed on long, slender, drooping branches. The tubular flowers are usually slender and white or pink.

*G. sessilifolia* STANDLEY, from Ecuador, is a shrub with slender climbing branches covered with small white flowers and white rounded fleshy fruits. The attractive white fruits lend a charm to this and other members of the genus, which deserves a place among cultivated plants.

*G. hirsuta dicocca* K. SCHUMANN (Photograph 251) is native of Guadeloupe in the French West Indies.

## Hedyotis capitellata   WALLICH

This species is exceptional in belonging to a large tropical genus of about 120 species, whose members usually consist of shrubs or even small herbaceous plants. This sprawling herbaceous plant is distributed from southern China to western Malaysia. (Photograph 245.)

## Hillia

This genus includes about 20 species of mainly shrubby or woody plants, some often climbing in trees by their elongated stems, others growing in the upper crotches and on the trunks of trees as air plants (epiphytes). Most of the species are found in South American forests, but a number of them also occur in Mexico, Central America, and the West Indies. All have very showy, usually pleasantly fragrant flowers. The funnel-shaped or tubular flowers are usually white or cream-colored, but may also be in shades of green, and in some species they may attain a length of 6 inches.

Only a couple of species, *H. tetrandra* SWARTZ and *H. parasitica* JACQUIN

169. CLEMATIS X CRIMSON STAR

170. CLEMATIS X HULDINE

171. CLEMATIS X JACKMANII

172. CLEMATIS FLORIDA SIEBOLDII

173. CLEMATIS X ETOILE VIOLETTE

174. CLEMATIS X RAMONA

175. CLEMATIS ARMANDII

176. CEANOTHUS GRISEUS HORIZONTALIS

177. MUSSAENDA ERYTHROPHYLLA

178. PORTLANDIA GRANDIFLORA

179. MUSSAENDA FERRUGINEA VAR. PALLIDIOR

180. MUSSAENDA ELEGANS

181. MITCHELLA REPENS

182. MACROSPHYRA LONGISTYLA

183. STREPTOSOLEN JAMESONII

184. SOLANDRA GUTTATA

185. PARTHENOCISSUS HIMALAYANA

186. SOLANUM RANTONETTI

187. DECUMARIA BARBARA

188. TROPAEOLUM TRICOLOR

189. CONGEA TOMENTOSA

190. VIOLA SCANDENS

191. PETREA VOLUBILIS ALBA

192. PETREA VOLUBILIS

193. PETREA KOHAUTIANA

194. GMELINA HYSTRIX

195. CLERODENDRUM THOMSONAE

196. FARADAYA SPLENDIDA

[syn. *H. longiflora*], have been introduced into cultivation, but the other species of the genus should be grown not only for their beautiful and fragrant flowers, but as well for their thick, dark green, handsome foliage.

## Leptactina

This genus is closely related to *Gardenia*. About 25 species are known, all from tropical Africa. While most of the species are shrubs, at least one, *L. manii* HOOKER F., is known as a climber. It has highly fragrant, very large clusters of flowers 6½ inches long with the tube 4 inches long and silky on the inside of the throat. The leaves are oval, wavy-margined, and up to 5½ inches long by 2½ inches wide. Conspicuous green, globose stipules are inserted between the bases of each pair of leaves.

This handsome species deserves to be cultivated more widely than at present.

*L. densiflora* HOOKER F. is a West African climber (Photograph 250) with splendid white flowers that are prized for their delicious fragrance. In Guinea a perfume is made from them.

Willis (118) spells the generic name *Leptactinia*.

## Macrosphyra longistyla    (DC.) Hiern

Sometimes placed under the genus *Gardenia,* this native of west tropical Africa is mainly a climbing shrub with creamy-white flowers arranged in several- to many-flowered terminal clusters. The showy flowers vary in length from 1¼ to 3 inches and are strongly sweet-scented. The projecting style, 3 to 4 inches long, gives the plant its specific name. The branchlets and evergreen leaves are 2 to 7 inches long and densely pubescent when they first appear. This species is often cultivated in gardens of Asia and Africa. (Color Plate 182.)

Another species, *M. brachysiphon* WERNH., with similar azalea-pink or brick-red and yellow flowers, also grows wild in West Tropical Africa.

## Malanea

This genus comprises mainly climbing plants included in 21 known species of tropical South America. The foliage is often made very attractive with sunken nerves or with a prominent network of nervelets of decorative appearance. In most of the species, the leaves are large or medium-sized, but in *M. microphylla* STANDLEY & STEYERMARK, of the Venezuelan Guayana Highlands, they are small. The small whitish flowers are produced in dense branching clusters, followed by purple or blackish and bony, fleshy fruits.

Although the genus is not known in cultivation, so far as our records go, many of the species deserve to be introduced because of their attractive foliage.

## Manettia

This is one of the few, solely climbing genera of the coffee or madder family (Rubiaceae). About 80 species are encountered within the genus, which is

252.   CORREA REFLEXA     253.   BERGENIA CORDIFOLIA

254.   HYDRANGEA PETIOLARIS     255.   PILEOSTEGIA VIBURNOIDES

native to Mexico, Central America, South America, and the West Indies. South America is the home of most of the known species.

The vines of this genus usually have slender and soft or wiry stems, and do not attain the thick, woody stems encountered among the climbers of many other groups of plants. Colors of the flowers in this genus vary from bright red, scarlet, pink, blue, purple, and white, to combinations of red and yellow. The tubular corolla is always 4-parted.

Although many native species have been described, relatively few of these have been introduced into cultivation. Nevertheless, these graceful and easily grown climbing plants are particularly useful to train over trellises, rafters, or pillars.

Among the most frequently cultivated, *M. bicolor* PAXTON of Brazil, commonly known as papagallo (parrot) is best known. (Photograph 247.) Its inch-long flowers, scarlet in the lower half and yellow at the tips, are very showy and cover the vine with blossoms most of the year. This vine grows easily in ordinary soil and is often grown in semi-shade in a tub.

Other species in cultivation are *M. cordifolia* var. *glabra* (CHAMISSO & SCHLECHTENDAHL) SCHUMANN of Peru, Brazil, Argentina, with bright red flowers. It is commonly known as coral. *M. inflata* SPRAGUE, with contrasting red and yellow flowers, is a native of Uruguay and Paraguay, and is sometimes grown as a hothouse plant. Many of the blue and purple-flowered species are also desirable subjects for cultivation, but they have not yet been introduced.

*M. coccinea* WILLDENOW in the French West Indies has deep red flowers. (Photograph 246.)

### Mitchella repens   LINN.

*Common Names:* PARTRIDGE-BERRY, SQUAW-BERRY, TWIN-BERRY

Trailing evergreen plant, often used in rock gardens, native from Nova Scotia to Florida and west to Texas and Guatemala. It has pairs of small, white, fragrant flowers that are followed by scarlet berries. (Color Plate 181.)

### Morinda

About 60 species of this genus are known, native of the tropics of both the Old and New World, extending north in the western hemisphere to Florida and the West Indies. While most of the members of this genus are shrubs or trees, a few become climbing or have subclimbing branches.

The species are characterized by an orange-colored dye in their roots and the joining together of the flowers and fruits into fleshy heads. What appears to be a single fruit is actually a group of several separate flowers joined by their ovaries, as in the pineapple.

Among the climbing or subclimbing species are *M. yucatanensis* GREENMAN of Yucatan, and *M. roioc* LINN. of Central America and the West Indies, which is both shrubby and semi-climbing. The flowers of these are white, leathery, and 5-lobed. The fruit of some species is edible.

## Mussaenda

While most of the approximately 40 species of this genus are small to large shrubs, at least a few of them become climbers to a greater or lesser extent. All of the species of *Mussaenda* are native to tropical Africa, Asia, and Polynesia.

*M. elegans* SCHUMANN & THONNING from west tropical Africa is called by Irvine (65) "a fine decorative shrub, well worth a place in the garden." (Color Plate 180.) He says it climbs to 30 feet and in April and May it bears flowers that are velvety orange-red or brownish-red or flame-colored followed with a yellow center 2 inches in diameter.

*M. erythrophylla* SCHUMANN & THONNING, from the wet forests of the Congo, has sulphur-yellow corollas surrounded by large crimson or bright scarlet bracts 3½ inches long by 3 inches wide. (Photograph 248 and Color Plate 177.) *M. arcuata* is a climbing shrub from the forests of Uganda, Africa, with beautiful yellow and brown flowers.

*M. ferruginea* var. *pallidior* (Color Plate 179) is a white-flowered New Guinea variety.

## Paederia

Most of the 20 species of this group of climbing shrubs are native to tropical and temperate Asia, with only a few known from tropical America. The small whitish or purple or lilac flowers are tubular or funnel-shaped, and occur in axillary clusters.

*Paederia diffusa* (BRITTON) STANDLEY of Bolivia and Peru has deep purple flowers. Some of the species, such as *P. foetida,* produce an offensive odor when bruised. This has tubular, lilac-purple flowers in panicles up to 1½ feet long. It is native to the Himalayas, China, and the Malay Archipelago.

Other species are *P. scandens* and *P. tomentosa,* both with deciduous leaves and flowers ½ to ¾ inch long. The fruits are globose, orange in *P. scandens* and greenish-orange to brown in *P. tomentosa.* Owing to the offensive smell, they are little grown.

## Pentagonia

About 20 species of this genus are known from South and Central America. Most of them have spectacularly large leaves, while several of the species are unusual in having deeply cut leaf-blades, a very rare condition to be found in the coffee family (Rubiaceae) in which the leaves are normally without any teeth or lobing.

While usually they are trees or shrubs, one of the species, *Pentagonia peruviana* STANDLEY, recorded only from Ecuador (despite its ill-chosen name), is doubtfully reported to be a climbing shrub, on the basis of the collector's field notes. The funnel-shaped, creamy-yellow flowers are slightly over an inch long.

## Portlandia

This genus of about 10 species comprises usually trees or shrubs, native of Mexico and the West Indies. Probably the best known of these in cultivation is

*Portlandia grandiflora* LINN. of the West Indies, known as tree-lily. (Color Plate 178.) Usually it is considered a shrub, but sometimes becomes climbing in habit, as noted by Jex-Blake in the Singapore Gardens. The large lily-like flowers, fragrant at night, are pure white with a 7-inch-long corolla. The edges of the corolla-lobes are tinged with shell pink.

This species prefers semi-shade and grows slowly, but deserves a conspicuous part of the shrub border in warm climates.

## Psychotria

This is the largest genus of the coffee family (Rubiaceae), the estimated number of species approaching 500. The genus is found in both the Old and New World tropics. Although usually trees, shrubs, or nearly herbaceous plants, a few species of *Psychotria* are epiphytic in habit, growing high up in trees as air plants. Of the latter type, a few, such as *P. parasitica* SWARTZ of the West Indies and South America, often climb tree trunks with their elongated stems.

The foliage of this species is dark green and the spreading, fleshy or leathery, ovate to elliptic-oblong leaves are very attractive. The small white flowers are set on reddish stalks at the ends of the stems.

Another species, *P. sulphurea,* of the Fiji Islands, is a small climbing shrub with sulphur-yellow flowers.

## Sabicea

This genus of usually climbing plants includes about 70 species distributed in the tropics of the New World, Africa, and Madagascar. Most of them are low climbers, ascending to 15 or 20 feet. They do not have such climbing devices as hooks or tendrils, but usually sprawl over shrubs, hedges, small trees, or along river banks. The small flowers occur in few- to many-flowered clusters along the sides of the stems, where the pairs of leaves occur. The flowers are funnelform or tubular, and white, flesh-colored or roseate.

Some species, such as *Sabicea velutina* BENTHAM of Venezuela, Brazil, and British Guiana, are attractive vines because of the dense white wooliness covering the stems and lower surfaces of the leaves. Other species have appeal because of the silky outer surface of the flowers or because of the edible fruit.

## Schradera

This is one of the few climbing genera of the coffee family (Rubiaceae), and it includes 35 presently known species, which occur mainly in South America, but also in the West Indies.

The genus is easily recognized because of the arrangement of the flowers in heads surrounded by closely fitting bracts at the base of the heads. Usually 3 or more tubular white flowers are grouped together. At maturity the heads form into a fleshy fruiting mass.

Although the species are rarely cultivated, they deserve to be better known, as all of them have attractive, dark green and usually thick leaves, combined with the oddly different white heads of flowers.

A Jamaican species, *S. involucrata* (Swartz) Schumann (previously grown as *S. cephalotes*), is in cultivation.

## Uncaria

About 30 species of this genus are known, most of them native to Asia, but a few in the western hemisphere from the southern United States and Mexico to South America.

They are characterized by having stout, hooked spines by which they climb and cling. The yellowish or white flowers occur in dense heads and are fragrant, thus serving as good bee plants. They form dense coverage, but the spines may make them objectionable to some growers. For protective covers they would have an advantage in keeping away intruders.

Attractive shining leaves are found in *U. guianensis* (Aublet) Gmelin, the common species of South America.

*U. africana* G. Don is a West African climber. (Photograph 249.) The species are scattered all through the tropics, and are distinguished by the axis of the inflorescence changing over and becoming a climbing hook.

In Malaysia *U. gambir* (Hunter) Roxburgh produces gambier, a valued source of tannin.

The genus has sometimes been called *Ourouparia,* a name no longer accepted.

RUTACEAE—RUE OR CITRUS FAMILY

## *Correa reflexa* Labillardiere          ⚘ ERNEST E. LORD ⚘
[Syn.: *C. speciosa* Andrews, *C. rubra* Sm.]

Several forms of this very variable and popular evergreen Australian shrub are scandent or spreading in growth habit, extending to 4 or 5 feet in width while not above 2 feet high. (Photograph 252.) Leaves of the various forms differ so widely in size, shape, and texture, that one could take them for more than one species. The flowers similarly vary in both shape and coloring. So far few have been sufficiently definited to be given varietal or cultivar names, but one believed to be a hybrid is known as *C.* X *manni.* This has smooth leaves and the flower-bells are uniformly coral-red. Its growth is spreading and bushy. Blooming for 6 months on end it has proved a first-class garden subject. One form of the species, var. *virens,* has quite attractive flowers of greenish yellow.

## *Luvunga* Buchanan-Hamilton          ⚘ BENJAMIN C. STONE ⚘

Most members of the citrus family are trees, shrubs, or herbs, but some of the dozen species of *Luvunga* may occasionally climb. It is found in lowland or hill forests from Ceylon to New Guinea. The leaves are composed of 3 leaflets; usually there are straight or hook-shaped spines in the axils. Flowers are white, fragrant,

256. PHILADELPHUS MEXICANUS

257. SCHIZOPHRAGMA INTEGRIFOLIA

258. SCHIZOPHRAGMA HYDRANGEOIDES

259. CYMBALARIA MURALIS

usually crowded in axillary clusters. The fruit is a berry with a thick rind, averaging about 1 inch in length. Though attractive, the plants are seldom seen and are scarcely known at all in cultivation.

## Okenia hypogaea   WALTER SCHLECT & CHAMISSO

This is an annual prostrate herb, native of Florida, the stems and branches creeping, fuzzy and sticky. The 2-inch leaves are fleshy, on thick stems. Calyx of the conspicuous, infertile flowers is deep purple, 1 inch wide on young plants, 3 inches wide on old ones. The plant grows on the coastal dunes and hammocks of south Florida.

## Paramignya   WIGHT

A few of the score of woody species in this Indo-Malayan genus may have vinelike branches, but they are virtually unknown in cultivation.

Most of them are spiny plants, with leaves that appear jointed. The fruit is a resinous berry.

SAPINDACEAE—SOAPBERRY FAMILY

## Cardiospermum halicacabum   LINN.
Common Names: LOVE-IN-A-PUFF, HEART-SEED, HEART-PEA, BALLOON VINE

This woody perennial vine, usually grown as an annual, is one of a dozen species of climbers native to warm regions, mostly in America. They get their names, both scientific and common, because the 1-inch black, balloon-like seed has a heart-shaped white spot on it. Children enjoy this feature. Frequently cultivated in California is another species, *C. hirsutum* WILLDENOW. This creeper is densely hairy on stem and leaves. Though it has inconspicuous flowers it is useful in covering arbors as it is evergreen.

## Paullinia thalictrifolia   JUSSIEU

This is one of the few among 125 species of *Paullinia* vines which Firminger (37) says are grown for the beauty of the flowers. These are white as a rule and clustered at the branch tips. The vines climb by tendrils. Chittenden (22) says that "this is a beautiful climber grown on a trellis or pillar, or it can be trimmed back for exceptionally handsome foliage in a pot."

## Serjania communis   CAMBESSEDES VAR. glabrata

This is the only one of some 200 species of twining and climbing shrubs in the genus *Serjania,* native to tropical America, that is frequently seen in cultivation. Brilmeyer (10) calls it a twiner with "gorgeous silver-marked divided foliage and lavender flowers," and says it is sometimes used as a foliage fence in mild-climate gardens. *S. cuspidata,* a yellow-flowered species, is grown as a greenhouse vine.

## Bergenia cordifolia STERNBERG

This immigrant from Siberia has a large thick rootstock which produces running stems in colonies of plants, with large thick waxy leaves, and flowers among the foliage. (Photograph 253.) All species of *Bergenia* are spring-blooming plants with leaves often rising a foot or more from the ground.

## Decumaria barbara LINN.

Common Name: WOOD VAMP

A deciduous, woody, root climber that is most commonly grown as a greenhouse curiosity. It is a native of the southeastern United States where it grows in very moist habitats and climbs on trees or rocks. (Color Plate 187.) The glossy green leaves are ovate to elliptic and usually less than 5 inches long. The inflorescences of fragrant, white, fertile flowers generally are about 3 inches in diameter. The flowering season lasts several weeks in late spring or early summer. Winter interest is provided by the small fruits, which open by the disintegration of tissue between the conspicuous ribs. Although its use is limited by its intolerance to low temperatures and soil moisture, it is relatively free of insect pests.

*D. sinensis* OLIVER is similar but less robust than the preceding species. In spite of somewhat smaller inflorescences and leaves, its evergreen or semi-evergreen nature makes it a more desirable plant than the preceding. A native of central China, it is cultivated mostly in western Europe as a wall plant. At one time grown as a pit-house plant in the northeastern United States, it now seems to have been lost in this area.

## Hydrangea LINN.

This well-known genus has been placed, along with *Decumaria, Pileostegia,* and *Schizophragma* (treated before and after this genus), in a separate family, the Hydrangeaceae. It is now considered more appropriate to group these with others in the saxifrage family.

## Hydrangea anomala D. DON

Common Name: CLIMBING HYDRANGEA

The horticulturally important genus *Hydrangea* is known primarily by its ornamental shrubby species. Few persons therefore are aware that there are more climbing species than shrubby ones. This species is a deciduous, woody, powerful root climber and is the best known climber of the genus. Subspecies (or species) *H. petiolaris* (SIEBOLD & ZUCCARINI) McCLINTOCK (Photograph 254.) is similar but has fewer stamens. This eastern Asiatic species has extraordinary flexibility in uses: it can be grown as a free-standing fountain plant, or, to best advantage, on large rocks, walls or trees. It is extremely hardy and comes into flower before most other hydrangeas. The climbing shoots have attractive yellowish-orange bark which irregularly peels into large, thin flakes. Inflorescences, which are borne terminally on the lateral shoots, are usually 6 inches or more in diameter. They are composed of both fertile and sterile flowers. All 4 calyx-lobes of the sterile flowers are much enlarged, being ½ to ¾ inch long and nearly as broad. Calyx-lobes generally are whitish but are found with orange-green to pinkish hues as well. The small persistent fruits open by means of an apical pore between the recurved styles. The plant is grown in western Europe and temperate United States.

*H. serratifolia* (HOOKER & ARNOTT) PHILIPPI F., a native of Chile and Argentina, is the southernmost of all hydrangeas. As it occurs at high altitudes, therefore in relatively low temperatures, it has been found hardy in Britain, though not as robust as *H. anomala*. The large compound inflorescences generally lack sterile flowers, so it is not as showy as the preceding species. It is, however, evergreen.

## *Philadelphus mexicanus* SCHLECTENDAHL
*Common Name:* MOCK-ORANGE

This is a difficult genus distributed mostly in the United States, and popular in cultivation for the showy white flowers. *P. mexicanus* (Photograph 256) is a shrub with slender drooping branches, lending themselves to cultivation as a vine.

## *Pileostegia viburnoides* HOOKER F. & THOMSON

This evergreen, woody, root climber (Photograph 255) is grown as a wall plant in western Europe and southern California. It is native to India, China, Formosa, Hong Kong, and the Ryukyu Archipelago. The elliptic, leathery leaves are 2 to 6 inches long with nearly entire margins. Inflorescences are composed entirely of fertile white flowers and are up to 7 inches long and 11 inches in diameter. The flowers, which appear in late summer, have been described as either "fragrant" or "ill-smelling." Since it is adaptable to either tree or rock climbing, the potential of this species has not been fully realized. Fruits are of the same type described for *Decumaria*.

## *Schizophragma hydrangeoides* SIEBOLD & ZUCCARINI
*Common Name:* JAPANESE HYDRANGEA-VINE

Trees or walls are equally suitable as a background for this deciduous woody root climber. The 4 to 6-inch light green leaves, resembling those of *Hydrangea*, are ovate to heart-shaped with a coarsely dentate margin. (Photograph 258.) The climbing shoots, with dull gray bark, are restricted to that function, with only the lateral branches bearing leaves and terminal clusters of flowers. Seldom exceeding 6 inches in diameter, the inflorescences are composed of several hundred small fertile flowers and up to a dozen sterile ones. The sterile flowers are remarkable in that a single calyx-lobe of each is greatly enlarged and becomes petaloid. In well grown specimens the white calyx-lobe is ovate to lanceolate and may become 4 inches long and 3 inches broad. As the sterile flowers are arranged on long pedicels about the periphery of the inflorescence, a halo effect is achieved. The blooming period appears to be quite long because

314

260. **MAURANDYA BARCLAIANA**    261. **MIMULUS LUTEUS**

262. **LOPHOSPERMUM SCANDENS**    263. **RHODOCHITON ATROSANGUINEUM**

of the persistence of the sterile flowers. Fruits are of the same type as those described for *Decumaria*. Grown mostly in the United States and western Europe, this is among the very best climbers for cold temperate climates.

*S. integrifolia* OLIVER (Photograph 257) is similar to the preceding species but far more variable in important horticultural features such as size, shape, serration, and pubescence of leaves; size of inflorescence; and size and shape of the sterile flower calyx-lobe. A number of varieties have been described but they are based only on extremes of the variabilities just mentioned. The 2½ to 8-inch leaves are ovate to broadly elliptic with the leaf margin entire to strikingly dentate. Inflorescences vary from 6 to 12 inches in diameter and are composed of both fertile and sterile flowers. The single, enlarged calyx-lobe of each sterile flower is ovate to broadly elliptic and varies from ¾ to 3½ inches by ⅜ to 2 inches broad. Color of the sterile lobe varies from yellow to cream or white. There is little question that this is the most spectacular plant of all the climbing members of the saxifrage family. It is somewhat tender and does not perform as well in the United States as in western Europe.

## SCROPHULARIACEAE—FIGWORT FAMILY      ※ JOHN W. THIERET ※

The Scrophulariaceae, a family of about 250 genera and 5,000 species, is well known in horticulture for the snapdragon and the foxglove, but it contributes little to the world of vines. Some of the vines considered here have been known under several generic names. The nomenclature used in this account is that of Werner Rothmaler, the most recent student of the Antirrhineae, the tribe to which they mostly belong.

### *Cymbalaria muralis*   GAERTNER, MEYER & SCHERBIUS

[Syn.: *Antirrhinum cymbalaria* Linn.; *Linaria cymbalaria* (Linn.) Philip Miller; *Cymbalaria cymbalaria* (Linn.) Wettstein]

*Common Names:* KENILWORTH-IVY; COLISEUM-IVY

Native to northern Italy and the Adriatic region and widely used as a basket, wall, and rock-garden plant, *C. muralis* has become naturalized in many other parts of the world. (Photograph 259.) It is a trailing or climbing, annual or perennial herb. The leaves opposite or alternate, are ½ to 1 inch wide and may be rounded, heart-shaped, or kidney-shaped in general outline but have 5 to 7 angular or rounded lobes. The solitary axillary flowers, reminiscent of those of the snapdragon, are about ½ inch long. They are violet with a yellow palate and have a short spur near their base. After flowering, the long and slender pedicels curve downward and may bring the seed-capsule to or even below the surface of the soil. The Kenilworth-ivy is easily grown, doing well in moist shady spots and reseeding itself readily. It grows without attention—even as a weed—in many greenhouses.

264. VERONICA BUXIFOLIA    265. CESTRUM FASCICULATUM

266. CESTRUM AURIANTIACUM    267. CESTRUM PURPUREUM

*C. muralis* var. *maxima,* sometimes considered a separate species (*C. pallida*), has paler to white flowers about twice as large as typical Kenilworth-ivy.

## *Epixiphium wislizeni* (ENGELMANN) MUNZ

Bearing solitary, axillary, blue flowers about 1 inch long among the somewhat heart-shaped triangular leaves, this native of southwestern United States and adjacent Mexico might be of interest to the grower of unusual vines. It is, however, not well known horticulturally. For the synonyms of the species see (142).

## *Lophospermum erubescens* G. DON
[Syn. (143)]
*Common Name:* CLIMBING LOPHOSPERMUM

Of the 4 species of *Lophospermum,* 2 are vines, climbing by means of their twining petioles and pedicels. Their leaves are long-petioled, and the blades, to 6 inches wide and long, are triangular to heart- or arrowhead-shaped. The flowers are solitary and axillary. Their corollas, open-throated and 1½ to 3 inches long, are tubular for much of their length and have 5 spreading lobes. Lophospermums are good perennial woody-based vines for the greenhouse, but they are almost always treated like tender annuals, flowering the first season from seed and making fine trellis plants.

*Lophospermum erubescens* has rose or rosy-pink corollas, which are pubescent outside, and ovate calyx segments. It is widespread as a wild plant from Mexico to northern South America and in Jamaica.

*L. scandens* G. DON [syn. *Maurandia lophospermum* Bailey; *Maurandya erubescens* (G. DON) Gray var. *glabrata* Johnston; *Asarina lophospermum* (Bailey) Pennell].

This species, native to Mexico and Central America, is similar to the preceding, sometimes being considered a variety of it. It too is known as climbing lophospermum. (Photograph 262.) Its corollas, purplish-rose, are glabrous externally, and its sepals are lanceolate-ovate. The corolla-lobes are more pointed than those of *L. erubescens,* which are obtuse or notched.

## *Maurandella antirrhiniflora* (HBK) ROTHMALER
[Syn. (144)]

This species is an attractive one for use as a basket plant or as a climber for windows or greenhouses. Though perennial, it is usually grown as an annual. It reaches 6 feet in height, climbing with its twining petioles and pedicels. The leaves are triangular with a heart-shaped base. The flowers, solitary in the leaf-axils and about 1 inch or more long, have a whitish tube, a bluish to reddish limb, and a yellow palate. They resemble snapdragon flowers except that their throat is not completely closed by the palate. Native to southwestern United States and Mexico, *M. antirrhiniflora* is naturalized in places outside its original range, as in Florida, the Bahamas, Bermuda, and Jamaica.

268. IOCHROMA GRANDIFLORUM  269. SOLANDRA LONGIFLORA

270. SOLANDRA GRANDIFLORA　　271. SOLANDRA MAXIMA

## *Maurandya barclaiana* LINDLEY
[Syn.: *Asarina barclaiana* (Lindley) Pennell]

*Common Name:* BARCLAY'S MAURANDYA

Maurandyas, climbing by means of twining petioles and pedicels, are fine vines for winter bloom in the greenhouse. (Photograph 260.) Usually, however, they are used for summer flower out-of-doors and are treated as annuals, blooming the first season from seed. Their leaves are more-or-less triangular or arrowhead-shaped and have a cordate base. The handsome, solitary, axillary, long-pediceled flowers are 1½ to 3 inches long. The throat of the corolla is open, there being no palate.

Of the 2 climbing species of *Maurandya,* both of Mexican origin, *M. barclaiana* appears to be the more commonly cultivated. It is available in several color forms. The tube of the flower is greenish, but the limb ranges from deep purple to rose or white. The sepals are conspicuously hairy.

*M. scandens* (CAVANILLES) PERSOON [syn. *Usteria scandens* Cavanilles; *Maurandya semperflorens* Ortega; *Asarina scandens* (Cavanilles) Pennell]. This climbing maurandya is similar to the preceding but can be distinguished by its glabrous calyx and by the color of its flowers, the tube being whitish, the limb lavender.

## *Mimulus luteus* LINN.

*Common Name:* MONKEY-FLOWER

Of the 150 species of *Mimulus,* a few are decumbent to prostrate plants with stems rooting at the nodes. They may have sticky foliage. Many of them are showy in flower.

*Mimulus luteus,* from Chile, is a smooth perennial with decumbent stems to 2 feet long and with yellow flowers that are red spotted. (Photograph 261.)

*M. moschatus* Dougl., the Musk Plant, native from British Columbia to California, is a yellow-flowered perennial with spreading and creeping stems. Formerly it was much cultivated for its musky odor, but the scented form has apparently been lost, and the plants currently grown are odorless.

## *Neogaerrhinum filipes* (GRAY) ROTHMALER
[Syn. (145)]

*Common Name:* YELLOW TWINING SNAPDRAGON

This native of far western United States is an annual with bright yellow, solitary, axillary, snapdragon-like flowers about ½ inch long. The lowermost leaves are ovate, while the uppermost are lanceolate. *N. filipes,* though it might be grown as a curiosity, is horticulturally of little significance.

*N. kelloggii* (GREENE) THIERET [syn. (146)], lax snapdragon. This California species is similar to the preceding except that its flowers are blue. Like *N. filipes,* it is of little consequence horticulturally.

320

## *Rhodochiton atrosanguineum*   (ZUCCARINI) ROTHMALER
[Syn. (147)]

*Common Name:* PURPLE BELLS

*Rhodochiton atrosanguineum,* native to Mexico, is especially notable for its unusual flowers, which are pendulous and solitary in the leaf axils. (Photograph 263.) The 5-lobed, inch-wide calyx is broadly bell-shaped and flaring. The corolla, about 2 inches long, is tubular and has 5 erect rather blunt lobes a bit unequal in size. The calyx and corolla, as I have seen them, are deep purple, with the corolla darker than the calyx, although they have been described also as being "blood-red" or "purple-red." The leaves are long-petioled and taper to a point from a heart-shaped base. Both leaf- and flower-stalks twine. This attractive perennial climber, which will bloom the first season from seed, is usually treated as an annual.

## *Veronica buxifolia*   BENTHAM

This smooth evergreen New Zealand shrub (known also as *Hebe buxifolia*), with branches prostrate in one variety, bears small white flowers in clusters among the upper leaves. A somewhat similar species is *V. chathamica* (*Hebe chathamica*).

*V. prostrata* Linn. of Eurasia, has sterile stems creeping on the ground, and erect flowering stems 2 to 8 inches high. Several other of the 200 or so species of *Veronica* may have a prostrate habit of growth, including *V. filiformis* Sm., *V. montana* L., *V. officinalis* Linn., and *V. repens* DC. (Photograph 264.)

SOLANACEAE—NIGHTSHADE FAMILY

## *Cestrum diurnum*   LINN.

*Common Name:* DAY-JASMINE

☀ V. T. STOUTEMYER ☀

This native of the West Indies is a tall upright, often scandent shrub bearing spikes of white flowers which have an intense fragrance by day. These are followed by small black berries. The leaves are large, up to 5 inches long, and are dark green above, lighter beneath.

The coral jessamine or purple cestrum, *C. purpureum* (LINDLEY) STANDLEY is valuable for its everblooming character. (Photograph 267.) This is frequently known under the synonum *C. elegans*. It is a tall leggy, scandent, evergreen shrub with entire ovate-lanceolate leaves. The deep reddish-purple flowers are scentless and are borne in clusters near the tips of the branches, which tend to arch over in a pendent manner. Since the stems tend to be bare near the base, facer plantings may be needed. A variegated-leaved form is known and the variety *smithi* has bush-rose flowers. This and other cestrums are popular glasshouse shrubs in cold climates.

*C. fasciculatum* MIERS is similar but more erect in habit, with flowers of redder coloring (less purplish), in tighter clusters, and appearing later. (Photograph 265.)

The orange cestrum, *C. aurantiacum* LINDLEY, a native of Guatemala, is a tall scandent shrub with alternate leaves. (Photograph 266.) It is grown for the showy flowers, which appear in a bright golden or orange-yellow glow in late summer or fall. They are scentless. The plant should be pruned after blooming. It thrives on a rich soil with abundant moisture. In Europe it is a popular conservatory plant and it is widely distributed in tropical countries.

## *Iochroma* BENTHAM                                  ※ V. T. STOUTEMYER ※

All species of *Iochroma* are tall shrubs similar to *Cestrum*. Several kinds are cultivated in mild-temperature areas. Since they tend to be leggy at the base they are often planted with lower facer shrubs. They are not properly vines but are often used against walls or in conservatories where they are grown in the vine manner. The generic name is often spelled *Jochroma*. This tall scandent shrub from Colombia with deep blue tubular flowers is often cultivated in England as a wall shrub, growing to 15 feet.

*I. fuchsioides* MIERS is from Peru and generally has orange-scarlet flowers, although a white-colored type is also known. *I. cyaneum* (LINDLEY) M. L. GREEN is a species from Ecuador with flowers in a varying range of violets and purples. *I. grandiflorum* BENTHAM, which bears pendent clusters of long funnelform flowers in rich purple, is an especially handsome plant for glasshouse culture or for outdoor use in mild climates. (Photograph 268.) It comes from Ecuador.

## *Solandra* SWARTZ                                  ※ PETER S. GREEN ※

A genus consisting of perhaps 10 species native from Mexico to northern South America and the West Indies, of which 4 are known in cultivation. These species all constitute tall climbing shrubs seen to best advantage when given plenty of room (some will grow 200 feet long or more) and trained, for example, up and along the front of a house or balcony. The evergreen leaves are undivided, lustrous and leathery, and they set off the very large, showy and fragrant flowers, which are produced singly (or rarely in pairs) at the tips of branches. Plants grow rapidly if given space, sun, and water. They thrive best, however, with good drainage, and some species flower more abundantly when given a rest period with a restricted supply of water. They may be grown in the open in subtropical and tropical regions but, in other areas, will grow well under glass if given space.

## *Solandra grandiflora* SWARTZ
*Common Name:* SILVER CHALICE; SILVER CUP

Native to the West Indies, this species prefers a more tropical climate than those from Mexico. The sweetly fragrant, funnel-shaped flowers (Photograph 270) are about 8 inches long, greenish-white at first, tinged with purplish lines within; they eventually turn yellowish-brown with age. The crenulated edge of the corolla is folded back and the tube constricted below the throat into a relatively short narrow portion which is contained within the tubular calyx.

272. **SOLANUM JASMINOIDES** 273. **SOLANUM CRISPUM**

274. **SOLANUM MACRANTHERUM** 275. **SOLANUM WENDLANDII**

*S. guttata* D. Don. (Color Plate 184.) Much less well-known in cultivation than the other species, (the name often mistakenly applied to *S. maxima*), this native of Mexico is most easily distinguished by the fine pubescence of the leaves and calyx. The dark cream or pale yellow flowers have 5 prominent purplish lines in the throat and a noticeably crenulated edge to the lobes.

*S. longiflora* Tussac. Gabriel's trumpet, trumpet-vine, copa de leche. This is distinguished from the other species by the flowers, about 10 inches long, with the narrowly tubular part of the corolla much longer than the calyx. (Photograph 269.) These flowers, which are fragrant at night, are white at first, with 5 purplish lines running down the throat, but eventually turn yellow and deepen further in color with age. A native of the West Indies, it prefers more tropical conditions than *S. maxima*.

*S. maxima* (Sesse & Mocino) P. S. Green [syn.: *S. "guttata"* Hort., *S. "nitida"* Auct., *S. hartwegii* N. E. Brown], cup of gold, golden chalice, copa de oro. Perhaps the most striking species of this remarkable genus, this vine bears rich yellow, more cup-shaped flowers, 6½ to 7 inches long and 5 to 6 inches across, more or less abruptly contracted into a narrow tube. (Photograph 271.) There are 5 dark purplish-brown lines within, passing into the tube and, as they age, the mellowly fragrant flowers take on an orange tinge. The edges of the corolla lobes are tightly folded back so that the slightly crenulate edge is often hidden. A native of Mexico, this species is reputed to stand a touch of frost. It is frequently grown under the wrong name (*S. guttata*).

## *Solanum jasminoides* Paxton                     ⁂ V. T. STOUTEMYER ⁂
Common Name: Potato-vine; Jasmine Nightshade

This is an attractive and vigorous vine from Brazil with small, refined foliage and wiry stems. It blooms constantly during the warmer part of the year. (Photograph 272.) The clusters of white or pale mauve-tinted flowers resemble flowers of potato, to which it is related, hence the name. Types with a pure white color are preferable. Types with large flowers and also with both white and yellow variegated leaves are known. The vine will thrive in a cool conservatory but also is quite useful in the milder areas of the United States, where it can lose leaves without permanent injury during cold periods. Pruning may be needed to thin out the mass of twining stems.

This vine is good for covering trellises, fences, and pergolas, and in mild areas where the leaves persist, it is sufficiently dense for partial screening, although it may not provide full shade. It is a useful but not spectacular ornamental.

*S. macrantherum* Dunal is a scandent shrub from the tropical regions in southern Mexico. (Photograph 274.) The leaves are large and entire. The star-shaped violet flowers are borne in large, many-flowered cymes and have a pleasant odor. They are followed by small red fruits.

The blue solanum, *S. rantonnetii* Carriere (Color Plate 186) native in Paraguay and Argentina. This is a scandent shrub which can be pruned to a variety of forms, including standards. The small leaves are not notable, but the violet flowers are borne in abundance during the entire year. Variant forms are

276. DAPHNE CNEORUM EXIMUM  277. TROPAEOLUM PEREGRINUM

278. CLERODENDRUM SPLENDENS  279. CLERODENDRUM SPECIOSUM

known and a large-flowered type is generally stocked by nurseries. Fruits are red. Excess watering may promote vegetative growth at the expense of flowering.

The Brazilian nightshade or tomatillo, *S. seaforthianum* ANDREWS, is successful only under tropical conditions. It is a scandent shrub with variable leaves, ranging from simple to divided into 3 to 5 or more parts. The violet flowers are up to an inch in diameter and are borne in large clusters. The red fruits about 1/3 inch in diameter, attract birds. This species may be planted in shade. It is popular in Florida but rarely grown in California. The plant is named for Lord Seaforth, who introduced it from the West Indies.

The Costa Rican nightshade, giant potato-vine, or paradise-flower, *S. wendlandii* HOOKER F., when in flower is a strikingly effective vine, suited to warm subtropical or tropical areas which are virtually free of frost. (Photograph 275.) This species was named for the German botanist, Herman Wendland. It is a coarse-foliaged vine of rapid growth with quite large leaves having great variations in form, from simple or lobed to trifoliate. A few thorns are present, frequently on the underneath midrib of the leaf. Bare stems at the base are apt to be a problem and it is sometimes most effective when combined with other plants of more attractive foliage. The vine tends to be deciduous in winter. Severe pruning may be needed to keep it in bounds and to produce new flowering wood. It should be watered and fertilized abundantly and used only in well-lighted areas in the subtropics. It is especially attractive when grown against high walls or buildings; these can provide additional warmth in marginal areas. Heavy trellising and other supports may be needed. A well-grown specimen in bloom over a long period in late summer or fall is an unforgettable sight. The individual flowers are over 2 inches across and are borne in terminal cymes which can be almost a foot across. The color is a striking lilac-blue or mauve and the bright yellow centers of the flowers give a sharp contrast.

*S. lycoides* LINN. from Peru has large deep mauve flowers with yellow centers.

*S. crispum* RUIZ & PAVON is a small shrub with drooping herbaceous branches and slightly crisped leaves. The flowers are purplish-blue in terminal clusters and the small fruits are yellowish-white. (Photograph 273.) There are a number of horticultural varieties, among them *S. crispum autumnale* ('Glasnevia') and *S. crispum ligustrinum* with subcordate leaves.

Out of the many species of *Solanum,* the later Peter Riedel of Santa Barbara, California, has left notes which indicate that the following species have probably been tried in that area:

> *S. endlicheri*—from Peru, with 1-inch edible fruit.
>
> *S. gayanum*—Chile. Woody stems and blue flowers.
>
> *S. lambii*—a woody vine of northern Mexico with stellate-pubescent leaves and branches.
>
> *S. lanceifolium*—a scandent shrub ranging from Mexico and the West Indies to South America, with white flowers in clusters.
>
> *S. lentum*—of similar habit and natural range, but with violet flowers and red fruit.

*S. lundelli*—a woody vine of British Honduras.

*S. pensile*—an attractive tall climber from Guiana, with white-centered violet flowers and violet fruits.

*S. rubidum*—a scandent shrub from Costa Rica with violet flowers.

*S. worsleyi*—a climber from Brazil with edible fruits.

## *Streptosolen jamesonii*  MIERS
❀ V. T. STOUTEMYER ❀

Few plants give a showier display of orange to orange-red blossoms for a long period of time than *Streptosolen jamesonii* native of Colombia and Ecuador. (Color Plate 183.) It prefers warm, sunny sites for best performance. As it is badly damaged by frost it is used as a scandent groundcover or wall shrub for landscaping only in practically frost-free regions. In other areas, it has long been a favorite in cool conservatories, either as a pillar plant or trained in various ways for urns or pots.

The flowers are small and tubular and have various tones of brilliant orange-red color. They are borne in large terminal clusters. The leaves are relatively small and are deeply rugose and hairy. Pruning should be done after flowering. It is propagated easily by greenwood cuttings.

STERCULIACEAE—STERCULIA FAMILY

## *Mahernia verticillata*  LINN.
[Syn.: *M. odorata*  Hort.]
*Common Name:* HONEYBELL

This twiggy South African shrub, one of a dozen species, develops long, extended, woody branches that lend themselves to cultivation in the vine manner. It is frequently grown out-of-doors in warm areas and in the glasshouse. Brilmeyer (10) says this shrub has needle-like segments to the leaves, sweetly fragrant, yellow bell flowers, and bristly stems. Although sometimes used as a basket plant, it is more frequently found as a high-reaching climber in glasshouses, cascading its flowers down from far above.

SYMPHOREMATACEAE—SYMPHOREMA FAMILY
❀ HAROLD N. MOLDENKE ❀

## *Congea tomentosa*  ROXBURGH
*Common Names:* LAVENDER-WREATH; SHOWER-OF-ORCHIDS; WOOLLY CONGEA; JAPONESA; KA-YAN; LLUVIA DE ORQUIDEAS; TAMAKANWE; TERCIOPELO

This genus *Congea* contains about 11 species and 5 named varieties. All are vines or climbing shrubs with quite handsome inflorescences. (Color Plate 189.) The *woolly Congea* is the most widespread of the species in the wild state and is also the one most commonly seen in cultivation. It is native from East Pakistan and the Assam and Manipur areas of India to Burma, Thailand, Laos, Vietnam, and the Yunnan region of China, probably commonest in Burma. Under favorable conditions it is a strong deciduous climber, suitable for growth on trellises, roofs, fences, and arbors. The elliptic-ovate leaves, which are opposite on the twigs, are usually sharp-pointed at the apex, slightly heart-shaped at the base, 3 to 7 inches long, and densely soft-hairy beneath. The small white flowers are usually arranged in 7's (rarely 5's or 9's); they are sessile and almost hidden by 3 large violet, pink, or purple 1-inch bracts, which remain persistent several weeks after flowering. They are the showiest feature of the plant. The cymes are arranged in a large, loose, terminal panicle, from 2 to 10 on each of the 10 to 30 branches of the panicle. A large well-developed plant may have over 100 panicles and the display is then understandably quite spectacular.

The flowering panicles hold well in water after being cut. If gathered early in the flowering season and stored in bundles, base up, until dry, they will keep for many months for use in dry arrangements. Usually the bracts acquire color in late October, become brilliant in the beginning of the new year, then gradually darken until March or April, when the new growth starts. If no seeds are produced, propagation may be effected by stem cuttings, though they tend to root with difficulty. Variety *nivea* MUNIR, also cultivated, may be distinguished by its more ashy-white pubescence.

*C. vestita* GRIFFITH is much like *C. tomentosa* but has its individual flowers stalked, and the floral bracts are often deeply notched at their apex. Another commonly cultivated species is *C. griffithiana* MUNIR, which has four spatulata or oblanceolate bracts under each of the flower-clusters.

## *Sphenodesme involucrata*   (PRESL) B. L. ROBINSON
*Common Names:* FIVE-POINTS-CLIMBER; YAN DUK

The genus *Sphenodesme* contains some 15 species and 9 varieties, most of which are climbers. It is closely related to the previous and following genera, but its involucral bracts are always 6 in number, and the stamens are only 5 or rarely 6. In *Congea* the bracts are 3 or 4 and the stamens only 4 per flower, while in *Symphorema* the bracts are 6, but the stamens 6 to 18 in number. The five-points-climber is a rather common forest vine from India and eastern Pakistan, Burma, and the Andaman Islands, eastward to Indochina, Thailand, and Malaya and north to Formosa and Hainan. It sometimes attains a length of 50 feet, with white or pink, slightly odorous flowers, the stamens in which are hidden within the corolla-tube. Its branches and young leaves are brownish- or rusty-pubescent. The inflorescence is large and paniculate, borne in the upper leaf-axils, and yellowish-hairy throughout. The bracts are white at first, later turning purplish-red, spatulate in shape, and slightly unequal in size. The flowers are rather small, sessile, 7 per head, with a funnelform corolla.

The related *S. pentandra* JACK has exserted stamens, an elongated style, and glabrous leaves, bracts, and calyx. It has a rather similar geographic distribution. Both species are sometimes encountered in cultivation in tropical regions.

In the Bornean *S. racemosa* (PRESL) the flowers are greenish-yellow. The

**280. HOLMSKIOLDIA SANGUINEA**  **281. LANTANA CAMARA**

**282. LANTANA MONTEVIDENSIS**  **283. OXERA PULCHELLA**

Malayan *S. ferruginea* (GRIFFITH) BRIQUET has white or yellowish sweet-scented flowers, and sometimes climbs to 45 feet into trees of virgin forests or evergreen jungles. In *S. mollis* CRAIB, of Indo-China and Thailand, the flowers vary from greenish or yellowish to white, ashy-gray, or even bluish. The remaining species and varieties in the genus are quite similar.

## *Symphorema luzonicum*   (BLANCO) FERNANDEZ-VILLAR

*Common Names:* BALABAI; MALABULAON; MALASIAD; MALASIAG; MALASKOG; MULAUING-BAGING; PAMULAK-LAKIN

This is a small genus with only 3 known species, native to India, Ceylon, and Burma, through Thailand, to the Philippines and Java. The Philippine species, *S. luzonicum* is a stout liana or scrambler, the stems very much twisted and fluted when old, the youngest parts gray-tomentose, the older parts smooth. The ovate or ovate-oblong leaves are leathery, 2 to 4 inches long, and about 1½ inches wide, pointed at the apex, subtruncate at the base, smooth on both surfaces, and without any teeth. There are 6 conspicuous white bracts forming an involucre beneath an equal number of small blue flowers, which normally bloom from February to April.

The Indian *S. polyandrum* WIGHT also has leathery, but larger and saw-toothed or wavy-edged leaves, the white flowers to an inch long, with many stamens, and the bracts broadly obovate. It is a rather rare plant, found in dry open situations and in deciduous monsoon-forests. It blossoms profusely during February and March, when it is devoid of leaves. One sometimes finds it cultivated.

In *S. involucratum* ROXBURGH the leaves are thin, toothless or only slightly toothed, the white flowers are only ½ inch long, with few stamens, and the bracts linear-spatulate. It occurs in India, Burma, and Ceylon to Thailand, and is described as a rampant climber, ascending even the highest trees in moist or dry deciduous forests, with gray, close-grained, rather heavy wood, used for fuel by the natives. The plant normally flowers in March and April.

## THYMELAEACEAE—MEZEREUM FAMILY

## *Daphne cneorum*   LINN.

This low evergreen shrub to 1 foot high has trailing pubescent branches. It is native of the mountains of Europe and is prized in American gardens for its terminal heads of fragrant pink flowers. (Photograph 276.)

## TILIACEAE—LINDEN FAMILY

## *Glyphaea brevis*   (SPRENGEL) MONACHINO

This exceptionally pretty plant is common in gardens in West Africa. Irvine (65) calls it a "spreading or straggly shrub, woody climber, or small tree up to 20 feet high," and reported it often planted in West African villages as a living fence. It has conspicuous golden and yellow flowers in few-flowered clusters 3 times a year.

## Grewia natalensis

Firminger (37) says this is a scandent South African shrub with pretty purple flowers. He adds that most of the Indian species of *Grewia* require a lot of space in the garden and scarcely compensate the grower for his trouble. They are horizontal vines that creep but do not climb.

⚶ J. SOUKUP ⚶

TROPAEOLACEAE—NASTURTIUM FAMILY

The *Tropaeolaceae* is a family with 2 genera: *Tropaeolum,* about 90 species distributed from Mexico southward to Chile and Argentina, and *Magallana,* only 1 species from Patagonia. In *Tropaeolum* only 9 species are important to horticulture.

## Tropaeolum majus  LINN.

*Common Names:* NASTURTIUM; INDIAN-CRESS

The garden nasturtiums are glabrous annual herbs climbing by sensitive petioles. Leaves are shield-shaped, rounded, or somewhat kidney-shaped, the margins wavy, lobed, or angled, with about 9 nerves radiating from the petiole. The flowers, which grow singly on succulent stalks, are large and showy with vivid colors in the very familiar yellow-orange-red-mahogany range. The calyx is of 5 distinct sepals, one produced into a spur; the 5 petals of the corolla are distinct and all are clawed, the lower ones being narrower and fringed on the claws, also spotted. Stamens are 8, distinct and unequal, the anthers are 2-celled. The pistil is solitary; the ovary superior, 3-lobed, and 3-celled, 1 ovule in each cell.

The plants bloom best in sunny places and in porous, rather poor soil; rich soil results in much attractive foliage but few flowers. They are subject to attacks of aphids; dusting or spraying with a contact insecticide is effective.

*T. peregrinum* LINN. Canary-creeper; canary-bird vine. This annual glabrous vine (Photograph 277) has roundish but lobed leaves, the stalk attached to one side of the center. Flowers are sulphur-yellow, the lower petals small, long-stiped, fringed, and with 4 or 5 long hairs; the upper petals red-dotted near the base.

*T. azureum* MIERS is a very graceful climber. Leaves are 4 or 5-parted nearly to the base, the lower ones with very narrow lobes. Flowers are small and dark blue. The corolla is wide-spreading; the spur is smaller than the sepals. (Chile.)

*T. dipetalum* R. & P. The stem is vigorous; leaves are doubly 5 to 7-lobed, heart-shaped at the base, with large 3-lobed stipules. Flowers are red, the 3 lower petals are lacking; the spur is about an inch long and curved. (Peru.)

331

*T. olmoncense* MANSFELD is a slender climbing species, with leaves broader than long, the margins entire or wavy. Sepals are red, petals yellow and sawtooth-fringed, the upper 2 with a chocolate spot. (Peru.)

*T. peltophorum* BENTHAM is a more or less pubescent species, except for the under parts of the leaves and the petals. Leaves are long-petioled, peltate (the stalk attached in the center), roundish with slightly wavy margins, and 3 or more points at the ends of nerves. Flowers are like a slender tube of orange or scarlet, with large upper petals, the lower ones coarsely toothed and fringed at the base. (Colombia-Peru.)

*T. pentaphyllum* LAMARCK. This slender perennial climber has tuberous roots. Leaves are palmately compound with 5 elliptic-lanceolate leaflets. Flowers are of 2 red petals, more than an inch long, the spur large, red and green, and abruptly thickened at the tip.

*T. polyphyllum* CAVANILLES. This may be either a prostrate or climbing perennial. Leaves are peltate, with 7 to 9 (rarely 11) narrow divisions. Flowers are sulphur-yellow or ochre-colored, the upper petals with a shallow notch at the apex. Sepals are sharp-pointed with the spur is short. (Chile-Argentina.)

*T. speciosum* POEPPIG & ENDLICHER is a perennial vine that grows from rhizomes. Leaves are peltate, parted to the base into generally 5 or 6 lobes, the stipules also slightly lobed. The calyx is red, the spur about 1¼ inches long and dark red; petals are red, the upper ones wedge-shaped and notched, the lower ones greatly narrowed at the base. (Chile.)

*T. tricolor* SWEET. This is a tuberous perennial species. (Color Plate 188.) Leaves are peltate, divided almost to the base into 5 or 6 lanceolate, ovate, or nearly linear lobes. The petals are small, spoon-shaped, and yellow. The calyx and spur are purplish, the calyx lobes purplish or green. (Chile.)

---

VERBENACEAE—VERVAIN FAMILY ⚜ HAROLD N. MOLDENKE ⚜

## *Clerodendrum thomsonae* BALFOUR F.

*Common Names:* BAF-FLOWER; BLEEDING-HEART; BLEEDING-HEART GLORYBOWER; GLORYBOWER; SOUTHERN BLEEDING-HEART; CORNELL-FLOWER; BALAO DE SAO JOSE; ALA DE ANGEL; BANDERA DANESA; BRINCO DE DAMA; CLARA LISA; CLEMATIDA; CRENDOLINDA; FUGSIA; ARETE DE INDIA; JAMAIQUINA; LAZO DE AMOR; MATA-VINE; MIL FLORES; MISTERIOSA; PASION DE CRISTO; PERAGUT DE THOMSON

In the huge vervain family there are numerous vines and vinelike climbers. Probably the best known are in the genus *Clerodendrum,* of about 560 species and varieties of wide geographic distribution, but most abundant in tropical and semitropical Asia and Africa. The bleeding-heart glorybower (Color Plate 195) is a vigorous evergreen, twining vine to about 21 feet in length, which makes a fairly dense shade and is admirably suited for growing on arbors and trellises. In temperate zones it is most satisfactory in greenhouses, where it may bloom continuously. It has been in cultivation since 1861 when it was introduced into Great Britain by a West African missionary. The shiny green leaves are borne in pairs, are ovate-elliptic and sharp-pointed, 5 to 6 inches long and up to 3 inches wide, smooth, and rounded at the base. The flowers are produced in loose cymes of 5 to 50 near the ends of the branches, mainly in the summer months. The calyx is large, creamy-white, and baglike, almost entirely surrounding the crimson-red corolla, whose slender tube is about an inch in length. After blooming is over, the calyx turns violet-pink and the fleshy fruits are blue. In its native haunts this beautiful plant is found from Senegambia to the Congo, but it is now common in cultivation—and sometimes naturalized—in all tropical and subtropical lands.

Closely related and often confused with the former is *C. umbellatum* var. *speciosum* (DOMBRAIN) MOLDENKE, almost as widely cultivated, but easily distinguishable by its calyx-lobes extending only part way to the base. The true *C. umbellatum* POIRET is found naturally from Senegambia to the Cameroons, Congo, and Uganda. It is a climbing or scrambling shrub or woody vine with rather slender stems and branches, which are densely hairly when young. The leaves are very thin, mostly elliptic or ovate-elliptic, 1½ to 5 inches long, 1 to 2¾ inches wide, long-pointed at the tip, toothless, rounded at the base, and more or less finely hairy, especially beneath. Its white flowers are pink in the throat and at the base of the front lobe; the calyx is green. (Photograph 279.)

Still another handsome climber in this group is *C. splendens* G. DON, found wild in deciduous and secondary forests, common in clearings on old farms, from Senegal to Angola and the Congo and now widely cultivated in tropical countries and in greenhouses elsewhere. (Photograph 278.) The ovate or lanceolate leaves are glandular-dotted beneath, to 6 inches in length and 3½ inches wide, usually more or less heart-shaped at the base, shiny and wrinkled. The flowers are borne in large, dense, many-flowered, very showy, terminal, 4-inch panicles, the corollas being bright red or brilliant scarlet, passing into bright yellow or even white, the tube ¾ to 1 inch long, and the exserted stamens fully an inch in length. The calyx turns pink or red after the corolla has fallen. This plant is a dwarf climber of exquisite beauty when in good condition. It is well suited for low fences in subtropical lands, where it will do well in either sun or shade. It is almost perfect when trained to grow around a pillar or on a system of wires arranged some distance from and parallel to a greenhouse roof. Pruning requirements consist of removing wood that has flowered, selecting the best of the new growth, and tying in.

Probably the giant of all the vines in this group is *C. buchholzii* GUERKE, which may climb 100 feet to the tops of the tallest jungle trees from Guinea to Gabun, Angola, and Ugonda, with stems to 1 inch in diameter. Its rather small, slender-tubed, white flowers are produced in dense inflorescences, often 7 inches long, on the branches and on even older wood, sometimes near the ground. The corolla is nearly 1 inch in length. The fruits are red, enclosed by a white inflated calyx.

Another species producing flowers on its old stems, or even from an underground rhizome, is *C. schweinfurthii* GUERKE, native from the Sudan and Cameroons to the Congo and Tanganyika. It gradually develops a climbing habit, and, if unrestricted, may rise 10 or more feet. The dazzling white clusters of flowers erupting along the basal parts of the stem in late spring and early summer render it most impressive.

333

Of especial interest is *C. triplinerve* ROLFE, widespread in Africa, whose branchlets are ridged and hollow when old, and are then pierced and occupied by ant colonies. The flowers are small and white in many-flowered panicles.

## *Faradaya*   F. MUELLER

The genus *Faradaya* contains about 23 species and varieties of high-climbing vines in Indonesia, Melanesia, Polynesia, and Australia, all so much alike that they are usually rather difficult to distinguish except by the expert. Five species of the genus are found in cultivation in tropical regions of both the Old and New Worlds.

## *Faradaya splendida*   F. MUELLER
*Common Names:* BUKU; KOIE-YAN; LATARA; MUMUNI; PITUTU

In this widespread Pacific species, *F. splendida,* the showy white flowers appear in large terminal clusters in the spring of the year. Their tubes are over an inch in length, with their lobes another ¾ inch long. They have the fragrance of carnations. The large fleshy fruits are about the size and color of a hen's egg. The leaves are smooth, oval, pointed, and 6 to 12 inches long, with prominent veins.

In *F. vitiensis* (A. GRAY) SEEMANN, from the Fiji Islands, the inflorescences are only axillary, not terminal. (Color Plate 196.)

*F. neo-ebudica* GUILLAUMIN, with white funnelform corollas, climbs to the tops of the highest rain forest trees in the Fiji, Tonga, and New Hebrides Islands, and produces large orange or reddish fruits.

*F. ovalifolia* (A. GRAY) SEEMANN, limited to the Fiji Islands, has leaves that are coppery on the under surface.

## *Gmelina philippensis*   CHAMISSO
*Common Names:* BRISTLY BUSH-BEECH; ALIPUNG; ALIPUNGA; BAGA-BABUI; BETEBET; BOSEL-BOSEL; BULANGAN DURI; CHING CHAI; KALULUT; KUMBIL; PANIKTIK; SOUSOU; TULONGAN

Of the 47 species and varieties recognized in the genus *Gmelina,* a few become vines. Probably the best known of these is the bristly bush-beech, often cultivated, but originally from the tropical region extending from India to the Philippines and Indonesia. It is a large spiny scandent shrub, often sprawling like a bougainvillea. The pretty lemon or orange-yellow flowers are in dense terminal cymes, subtended by very large yellowish to purple bracts. The pendulous corolla is 2 inches wide and has a curiously inflated tube. The very similar *G. asiatica* LINN. also often develops a scrambling habit and produces yellow allamanda-like blossoms in short terminal clusters, flowering nearly throughout the year in its native haunts. (Color Plate 194.)

## *Holmskioldia sanguinea*   RETZIUS
*Common Names:* CHINESE COOLIE HAT-PLANT; CHINESE HAT-PLANT; CHINESE-HATS; CHINESE-UMBRELLAS; CUP-AND-SAUCER; JAPANESE-UMBRELLA; MANDARIN-HAT; PARASOL-FLOWER; SCARLET HASTINGIA; SOMBRERO-FLOWER; PARAGUITA CHINO; RELAMPAGO JAPONES; SOMBRERO CHINO

There are 17 recognized species and varieties in the little genus *Holmskioldia.* Of these by far the best known is *H. sanguinea.* (Photograph 280.) This is a

284. VERBENA MARITIMA    285. VITEX SIMPLICIFOLIA

286. VITEX TRIFOLIA    287. TRIBULUS CISTOIDES

straggling shrub, sometimes vining, 6 or more feet tall, the long pendent branches often sprawling gracefully to the ground. The bright green ovate leaves are up to 5 inches in length and 3½ inches wide, rather long-pointed at the tip. The flowers are in dense terminal racemes. The calyx is saucer-shaped or shield-shaped, about the size of a quarter and normally of a bright reddish-orange color. The 1-inch-long corolla is tubular, curved, and usually bright scarlet, but there are orange and yellow varieties. The plant is native to the subtropical Himalayan region of India but was introduced into cultivation in 1796 and is now found in gardens all through the subtropical and tropical world, as well as in greenhouses elsewhere. Prefers to grow in sunny well-drained soil, flowering practically throughout the year. Outside it is a prime favorite of hummingbirds and sunbirds.

[EDITOR'S NOTE: In the botanical garden at Bangalore, India, is a deep red-flowered form and also a bright yellow-flowered form of this plant.]

## *Lantana camara* VAR. *aculeata*   (LINN.) MOLDENKE

*Common Names:* CLIMBING LANTANA; HEDGE-FLOWER; PINK-SAGE; PRICKLY LANTANA; PRICKLY-SAGE; CAMARA DE ESPINHO; CARIAQUILLO; LILAC LANTANA

Lantanas are very widespread in subtropical and tropical lands all over the world, often with a tendency to become weedy and pestiferous. At least 242 species and varieties are recognized, not including purely horticultural forms. Some of these species have a distinct tendency to become vinelike, climbing into trees or sprawling over surrounding vegetation. Best known of these is doubtless the West Indian *L. camara* var. *aculeata,* whose tetragonal stems are conspicuously armed with rather stout and recurved thorns which assist the plant in climbing. The many small flowers are arranged in tight flat-topped heads on elongated stalks in the upper leaf-axils. (Photograph 281.) They usually open yellow and change through orange to pink or rose-color. The plant blooms intermittently throughout the year. The opposite leaves are 1 to 4 inches long, toothed, and rough to the touch. The entire plant has a strong, persistent odor. It is drought-resistant, and will thrive in any kind of soil provided that the location is sunny. The fruits are fleshy, blue-black in color, and relished as food by many birds. Old plants may attain a height of 25 feet, with a stem diameter of almost 5 inches.

In peninsular Florida there is a practically prostrate species, *L. depressa* SMALL, with procumbent or semi-procumbent branches and all yellow flowers. From Uruguay and adjacent portions of Argentina, Paraguay, and Brazil we have obtained the weeping or trailing lantana, *L. montevidensis* BRIQUET, which has very small gray-green leaves and rosy-lavender flower-clusters. (Photograph 282.) It is valuable for hanging baskets or to trail over rock-piles and banks.

## *Oxera pulchella*   LABILLARDIERE

*Common Names:* ROYAL-CLIMBER; SHOWY OXERA

The strictly New Caledonian genus *Oxera* comprises no less than 39 species and varieties. Included are many climbers, often extremely handsome when in bloom, with large white or yellowish flowers. Only *O. pulchella* (Photograph 283) has

336

thus far been introduced into cultivation. It may climb to 30 feet on tall trees along the ocean bluffs of its native island. Its funnel- or trumpet-shaped, ivory-white to greenish-white flowers are 4-lobed, bear 2 protruding stamens and have a conspicuous calyx. The opposite evergreen leaves are oblong to lance-shaped, often 5 inches long, sometimes entire and sometimes with scalloped edges. The vine blooms several times a year, with about 40 flowers 2 inches long in 2- or 3-forked clusters. The stems are corky and the fruits fleshy. In cultivation this plant requires plenty of water and good drainage in a fairly cool spot, never against a hot wall.

The closely related *O. oblongifolia* VIEILLARD is a liana with handsome white tubular flowers, while *O. palmatinervia* DUBARD is described as a large yellow-flowered liana, climbing far up into forest trees. *O. robusta* VIEILLARD produces its golden-yellow flowers on the wood of the old cable-like stems. In *O. subverticillata* VIEILLARD. the flowers are also borne on old stems.

## *Petraeovitex wolfei*   SINCLAIR

This is a woody climber with the upper flowering branches slender and pendulous, native to Malaya. The leaves are mostly trifoliolate but sometimes have only 1 or 2 leaflets. The paniculate inflorescences contain numerous yellow bracts which render them quite showy. The deeply 5-lobed calyx is reminiscent of *Petrea*. The plant prefers an acid soil. The closely related *P. multiflora* (J. E. SMITH) MERRILL in this Indo-Malaysian genus scrambles over roadside vegetation and climbs into trees in swampy forests of New Guinea, the Solomon Islands, Moluccas, and New Britain, sometimes attaining a length of 120 feet, with a stem diameter of more than 1 inch. It produces cream-colored or white flowers in paniculate spikes. In the damp forests along small streams and on moist ridges at low altitudes in Borneo it is replaced by *P. membranacea* MERRILL, with very lax, few-flowered red cymes and long-stalked flowers.

## *Petrea volubilis*   LINN.

*Common Names:* BLUEBIRD-VINE; PURPLE-WREATH; QUEEN'S-WREATH; ROUGH-LEAF; SANDPAPER-VINE; TWINING PETREA; STAPELIA-FLOWERED PETREA; ADELFA; ADOLFINA; CHAPERRO; CHAPARRITO; CHOREQUE; ESTRELLA AZUL; FLOR DE JESUS; FLOR DE SANTA MARIA; BEJUCO DE CABALLO; JAZMIN; LENGUA DE VACA; RASPA-SOMBRERO; SOLTERO

The genus *Petrea* comprises 41 species and varieties of woody plants with mostly hard and leathery leaves, some of which are climbers of outstanding beauty and therefore are widely cultivated. All are native to tropical America. Best known is *P. volubilis,* originally from Mexico and Central America, which may grow as much as 40 feet into forest trees and when in flower or young fruit is extremely showy in the manner of a wisteria. (Color Plate 192.) Its simple leaves are opposite on the stems, short-stalked, 2 to 8 inches long, and, when mature, as rough as sandpaper to the touch on both surfaces. The many violet or blue flowers are borne in large terminal racemes often a foot in length. Usually the conspicuous calyx is a lighter shade of blue than the small trumpet-shaped corolla, and, after flowering, this calyx persists for several weeks and eventually expands into a dry ashy-gray star-shaped structure which serves as a wing for the dispersal of the seeds. In cultivation this magnificent evergreen twining vine flowers 4 times a year and is very suitable for growing on arbors or trellises in the open sun. There is a white-flowered form, VAR. *albiflora* (STANDLEY3 MOL-DENKE. (Color Plate 191.)

Closely related is *P. kohautiana* PRESL (Color Plate 193), a West Indian vine, differing chiefly in having its leaves smoother, practically stalkless, and decidedly heart-shaped at the base, and the calyx-tube only very finely instead of densely pubescent. There is a white-flowered variety. Also widely cultivated is the Brazilian *P. racemosa* NEES, with more or less wavy or almost saw-toothed leaf-blades. In northern South America *P. bracteata* STEUDEL is a common heavy woody liana or bush-rope, spreading itself over shrubbery and climbing high into the jungle trees, with very abundant erect or finally drooping, crowded racemes, often 18 or more inches long, extremely ornamental when in full flower, with lilac or lavender calyxes and purple or blue corollas. In *P. macrostachya* BENTHAM, of the Guiana rain forests, the flower-clusters may become over 2 feet in length. The Peruvian *P. peruviana* MOLDENKE has its amazing fruiting-calyx almost 3 inches wide when fully expanded.

## *Verbena hybrida* VOSS
*Common Names:* GARDEN VERBENA; GARDEN VERVAIN

One of the largest genera in the entire *Verbenaceae* is the type genus, *Verbena*, with more than 380 accepted species, varieties, and named hybrids, not including purely horticultural forms. A few of these natural species have procumbent or trailing stems and deserve a place in the present book. Best known is the widely cultivated garden verbena, originally derived by the crossing and recrossing of several South American parental species. In warm lands it is a perennial, although often grown as an annual. It blooms all through the year in warm lands, with masses of trumpet-shaped flowers closely aggregated on spikes which at first are flattened and headlike and later elongate. The corollas vary through almost all imaginable shades and tints of pink, red, blue, purple, and even yellow and white; sometimes they are handsomely variegated or have central "eyes" of a different color are white. The general appearance is much like that of a low or trailing phlox. The plants prefer plenty of sunshine, they root easily, spread rapidly, and may be propagated by seeds, cuttings, or divisions.

In peninsular Florida a wild species, *V. maritima* SMALL, trails its wiry stems and branches often for many yards over coastal sand dunes and beaches. (Photograph 284.) Its rather small, bright-green, somewhat lobed leaves are slightly fleshy and the dense erect flower-clusters are vivid blue-purple to lilac, rose, or lavender. From southern Brazil to northern Argentina we find *V. lobata* VELLOZO, in several varieties, creeping beneath low shrubs and over rocks. It has curious triangular-ovate, often deeply 3-lobed, very thin-textured, hairy leaves and violet to lilac or purple flowers. In Argentina and adjacent areas *V. incisa* HOOKER is very common on sunny grassy campos and pampas, its blood-red flowers contrasting with its ash-gray foliage and enlivening the landscape. Most spectacular of all, however, is *V. peruviana* (L.) BRITTON, also a native of southern temperate South America, with flowers so brilliant scarlet as almost to hurt the eyes of the observer! It creeps over the ground in sunny exposed places in much the manner of *V. incisa,* but its leaves are much smaller, bright green, and far less hairy. Its flowers are unquestionably among the most brilliant known.

*V. phlogiflora* CHAMISSO is sometimes a low creeping herb, while sometimes it assumes the role of a climber and ascends to 6 feet into surrounding vegetation. It is found in southern Brazil, Paraguay, Uruguay, Bolivia, and northern Argentina, producing masses of large blue, violet, or purple flowers in very showy erect trusses. *V. platensis* SPRENGEL, from the same general geographic area, has mostly pure white flowers fading to pink, 1½ inches long, with the fragrance of jasmine.

## *Vitex trifolia* LINN VAR. *simplicifolia* CHAMISSO

This is a very common prostrate or semi-prostrate, creeping, shrubby plant throughout the Indo-Pacific and Australian area. The obovate leaves are 1-foliolate and usually very white-hairy beneath, mostly sessile. The mostly terminal floral panicles are erect and few-flowered. The corollas vary from blue through lavender to purple. The plant is valuable as a sand-binder along beaches and is quite resistant to salt spray.

EDITOR'S NOTE: Some botanists refer to this variety as *V. rotundifolia* LINN. F., while others look upon the species and its variety as 2 separate species. For those who hold the latter opinion, some distinctions may become evident in Photographs 285 and 286.

VIOLACEAE—VIOLET FAMILY

## *Corynostylis hypanthus* MARTIUS & ZUCCARINI

This is one of 4 species in a genus of climbing shrubs native to tropical America. They have alternate leaves and large white flowers in clusters on long thin stems. Of the 5 petals, the lower one (the largest) has a long hollow pouch behind it which is compressed at the sides and is constricted to measure about 2 inches long.

## *Viola scandens* WILLDENOW

This climbing plant is found in thickets and mountain forests from southern Mexico through Central America. Often shrubby below, (Color Plate 190) it forms dense tangles over other plants with stems 4 feet long or more. The leaves, 1 to 1½ inches long, are triangular, sharp-pointed, and shallowly heart-shaped at the base. The small flowers about equal the leaves: the white petals are striped in lavender.

## *Tribulus cistoides* LINN.

*Common Names:* Abrojo; Anglo; Burr-nut; Caltrop; Capres; Jamaican-buttercup; Nohu; Police Macca; Puncture-vine; Turkey-blossom

This pantropical weed of warm, dry, usually sandy habitats is one of the few trailing members of the caltrop or bean-caper family, a group composed primarily of shrubs and trees. The burr-nut is a prostrate or low-spreading perennial herb, with stems up to several feet in length that can be trained for climbing. (Photograph 287.) It is cultivated for the attractive, bright yellow flowers 1 to 2 inches in diameter, borne alternately along the stem on stalks as long as the contrasting dark green, opposite, even-pinnate leaves 1½ to 3 inches long. The 5-lobed fruit splits at maturity into 5 spiny nutlets that may prove uncomfortable for animals or barefoot humans.

The burr-nut is grown as a garden plant in Central America, the West Indies, and west Africa. It is also occasionally cultivated as a groundcover and sand binder in southern Florida, where it is commonly encountered as a roadside weed.

# X

## *Vines Left Out of This Book*

The title of this book, *Flowering Vines of the World,* is in effect misleading. All vines have flowers and yet several thousand of them have been omitted from the pages of this volume for reasons that seem adequate.

The purpose of this book fundamentally is to give the gardener a guide to the chief ornamental vines that are or ought to be cultivated for the attractiveness of their flowers. Actually, gardeners grow many other excellent vines on which the flowers are the least important feature. This supplementary chapter classifies these excluded climbers into 14 groups. Some representative examples are given under each heading. A thousand names might have been added, but these should be enough.

### 1—VINES OF EXCESSIVE SIZE

In the tropical jungles, lianas (also spelled lianes) are enormous climbers that put their foliage and flowers among the treetops, often 200 feet in the air. They are of no interest whatever to the ordinary gardener. Some of the most spectacular flowering vines in the world are species of *Bauhinia* in the treetops of the Malayan jungle, seen only at a distance and, with two exceptions, never brought into cultivation even in their native land. Some of these are also called *Phanera.*

*Anamirta paniculata* (Menispermaceae) is a little-known liana in the forests of India. A sister vine, *A. cocculus,* produces berries that are the source of "cocculus inducus," a product used by the Chinese as a fish poison.

*Anodendron paniculatum* (Apocynaceae) is one of 10 species in this genus of giant climbers that send their twisted woody stems up the trunks of forest trees from Ceylon to China. (Photograph 288.)

*Bucklandia populnea* (Hamamelidaceae). This noble Himalayan vine that grows to 100 feet has heart-shaped evergreen leaves that are tinged orange on the margins.

*Cocculus macrocarpus* (Menispermaceae). This Indian species is the largest vine in this genus, 1 or 2 members of which are occasionally cultivated for their attractive bright green leaves of variable shapes. Since their flowers are inconspicuous, they are treated in Part IV.

*Entada phaseoloides* (Leguminosae). Gogo-vine, elva climber, matchbox-bean. This enormous liana (Photograph 289) was formerly called *E. scandens.* It entranced Fairchild (35) when he visited the Botanical Garden of Buitenzorg in Indonesia. Its "bean" pods are hard and woody, 4 to 5 feet long and 4 inches broad, and contain many hard flat seeds. Fairchild wrote:

288. **ANODENDRON PANICULATUM**   289. **ENTADA PHASEOLOIDES**

290. **STRYCHNOS**   291. **HIPPOCRATEA**

"Treub took me to see one of the 'sights' of the garden, a proper liana in the shape of a gigantic vine over a foot through at the ground, which had climbed up and spread itself over eight of the magnificent *Canarium* trees. . . . It was for all the world like a gigantic grape vine. . . . . Of the gigantic liana, *Entada scandens,* I did succeed in getting some seeds. They grew; in fact they grew too much. . . . When it did bloom I gave up, for of all messy looking flower clusters, the famous *Entada scandens* took the prize. The individual flowers were small and of a dirty green color and had nothing about them that was attractive."

*Hippocratea* (Celastraceae; formerly Hippocrateaceae). This tropical genus contains about 120 species of woody climbers. The long tough stems of some of the African species are used for building bridges. (Photograph 290.)

*Machaerium* (Leguminosae). Among the 150 species of *Machaerium* found from Mexico to South America are many large climbers, medium to very large in size, climbing by sensitive lateral shoots and recurved thorns. They are not in cultivation.

*Metrosideros* (Myrtaceae). A genus of about 30 evergreens in Polynesia and New Zealand. While some *Metrosideros* species are known in coolhouse cultivation (*see* under the Myrtaceae in Chapter IX), others have a reputation for the power of their growth. *M. robusta,* for example, may germinate high up in the crotch of a tree, send down aerial roots which eventually will carry its stem to the ground. There it will develop subterranean support and in time assume the figure of a tree. The plant pictured in Photograph 190 was once a tiny vine beside a *Dacrydium* tree, a relative of the yew in the Eastern Hemisphere. The vine grew enormously, engulfed the tree, killed it, and went on to assume treelike proportions itself. The *Dacrydium* tree rotted away, and 14 school boys recently crowded into the hollow interior where the tree once stood.

*Strychnos* (Loganiaceae). Many species of the strychnine family in Malaya are huge climbers. (Photograph 291.)

*Uvaria* (Anonaceae). More than 100 species of this genus are scattered from tropical Africa through Madagascar to southern Asia. Most of them are lianas with recurved hooks. *U. purpurea* from Java with purple-red flowers is cultivated in some tropical countries. Flowers are about 1 inch across, the 6 petals overlapping in 2 rows. For others, see Part IV, Inconspicuous Flowers.

*Willughbeia zeylanica* (Apocynaceae). Enormous vine, climbing by long whiplike leafless shoots. Handsome round pink fruit. India.

## 2—VINES THAT ARE WEEDS

The second group to be omitted are the unwanted vines. These range from noisome pests, including poison-ivy, to great climbers like kudzu (*Pueraria* species), which was brought to this country from China with the good intention of preventing erosion of steep banks. It has remained, unfortunately, to swamp roadsides in the southern states and elsewhere with enormous mounds of foliage that cover other plants, including big trees, and it is now rather a nuisance. A good many vines that have pretty flowers occasionally must be classed as

292.  ABRUS PRECATORIUS        293.  AMBROSIA HISPIDA

294.  PUERARIA HIRSUTA        295.  RHUS TOXICODENDRON

weeds, notably many morning glories, of which there are 700 different kinds, and passion-flowers, which are not far behind with close to 500 species.

*Abrus precatorius* (Leguminosae). Rosary-pea. This twining herbaceous climber to 10 feet has gone wild in Florida and is frequently a nuisance climbing over other plants. The flowers are inconspicuous, but short pods open to expose bright red beadlike seeds with a black eye, very attractive but poisonous to eat. (Photograph 292.)

*Ambrosia hispida* (Compositae). Creeping ragweed. This evergreen prostrate shrub with branches often several yards long is a native of Florida beaches. (Photograph 293.)

*Amphicarpaea monoica* (Leguminosae). Hog-peanut. This is one of half a dozen species of herbaceous perennial vines native to eastern North America and India, none of them of much horticultural value. It has rather large white or purplish flowers and big pods but is not cultivated.

*Convolvulus arvensis* (Convolvulaceae). Bindweed. This noxious perennial weed (Photograph 298) is a nuisance in the garden and difficult to eradicate. It should never be planted.

*Galium* (Rubiaceae). This genus comprises about 400 species, mostly weedy in temperate regions but occasionally found at high elevations in the tropics. Goose-grass or cleavers (*G. aparine*), with small bristly leaves, is a persistent weed, and yellow bedstraw (*G. verum*), introduced from Europe, is a troublesome creeper in gardens.

*Gonolobus laevis* (Asclepiadaceae). Vining milkweed is a weedy member of a genus of about 70 species of prostrate or climbing shrubs or subshrubs native to tropical America, a few of which are cultivated as greenhouse plants for their attractive flowers.

*Hydrocotyle verticillata* (Hydrophyllaceae). Marsh-pennywort. Dollar-grass. This is typical of 100 kinds of widely distributed species of this pennywort weed which grow in damp soil over much of the world. Its stem is prostrate and roots at the nodes. It bears round leaves up to 2 inches across, each attached near the center, and often somewhat cupped.

*Lysimachia nummularia* (Primulaceae). Moneywort, creeping heddy, Charlie, or Jenny. This prostrate perennial herb whose stem is 1 or 2 feet long, is sometimes cultivated in baskets or as a ground cover, but it has a tendency to be weedy. Its small flowers are yellow. The inch-long, opposite leaves are roundish, sometimes heart-shaped at the base.

*Mucuna pruriens* (Leguminosae). Cowage, cowitch. This common weed in southern pastures is troublesome because of stinging hairs that cover the pods. However, a variety of it (or a species sometimes known as *Stizolobium deeringianum*) is the Florida velvet-bean, a useful fodder. (Color Plate 106.)

*Passiflora* (Passifloraceae). Many of the passion-flower vines are weeds. Even the maypop (*P. incarnata*) in parts of the southern states can be troublesome.

*Pueraria thunbergiana* (Leguminosae). Kudzu. Grown as a blanket for the earth to stop erosion, this Asiatic vine is also useful as fodder. Along highways in the southern states, however, it is too happy, for it smothers all neighboring

**296.  SMILAX HAVANENSIS**     **297.  SMILAX BONA-NOX**

**298.  CONVOLVULUS ARVENSIS**     **299.  TRAGIA INVOLUCRATA**

foliage, including shrubs and trees. A species that behaves similarly, *P. hirsuta*, is shown in Photograph 294.

*Rhus toxicondendron* (Anacardiaceae). Poison-ivy. "Leaflets three, leave it be." This is truly poisonous and should never be touched with bare hands. (Photograph 295.)

*Smilax* (Liliaceae). Greenbrier. While 2 or 3 of the some 200 species of cosmopolitan climbers in the genus *Smilax* are cultivated in glasshouses for winter greenery, 2 species are weeds in Florida: *S. havanensis* and *S. bona-nox*. (Photographs 296 and 297.) Appropriately, many in the genus known as greenbriers are thorny.

*Solanum triquetrum* (Solanaceae). Texas nightshade. A somewhat low herbaceous climber which is found as a weed in southern and western Texas and in large areas of northern Mexico where it is called "hierba mora" among other local names. The typical potato-type flowers occur in small clusters, ranging in color from white to purple.—V. T. S.

*Tragia involucrata* (Euphorbiaceae). Nose-burn. These are climbing or twining stout herbs with pungent or stinging hairs which cause an intense skin irritation that continues for hours. (Photograph 299.) Common in Bihar forests, India.—J. K. M.

## 3—VINES WITH ORNAMENTAL FOLIAGE

Omitted also are the many foliage vines which are cultivated both as house plants and in the garden for the beauty of their leaves.

These include woodbine (grape relatives in the genus *Cissus*), and the several kinds of wandering-Jew. Such climbers have a place in a book on vines, but not in one devoted primarily to displays of flowers. English ivy might also be included here, but this is placed with equal appropriateness in the next part, on *Vines with Inconspicuous Flowers*.

*Bosea amherstiana* (Amaranthaceae). A magnificent variegated-leaved form of this Himalayan evergreen climbing shrub is in cultivation in Australia. The ovate, 3 to 7-inch, rather puckered, long-pointed leaves are richly margined in deep cream.

*Cissus* (Vitaceae). Several of the 325 species in warm countries are tendril-climbing shrubs, often with fleshy stems, sometimes cultivated in glasshouses. The flowers are inconspicuous but the fruit is often showy. *C. incisa*, marine-ivy or ivy-treebine, makes an unusually heavy cover because of its large fleshy leaves. (Photograph 301.) From Missouri and Kansas to Texas it has been found native on many adverse sites, crawling over rocks at the entrance of bat caves, or among juniper trees or in other difficult places.

*Cissus* is similar to and closely related to the common grape. *C. antarctica* and *C. striata* are grown outdoors in California for their heavy foliage well suited to blanketing arbors. *C. sicyoides* (Photograph 303) is a tall tendril-climbing plant from South America which extends into south Florida. In the tropics it is called season-vine. *C. acida* is a smooth climber with fleshy branches, long stout tendrils and rigid leaves, sharply toothed at the tip. (Photograph 300.)

300. CISSUS ACIDA    301. CISSUS INCISA

302. CISSUS QUADRANGULARIS    303. CISSUS SICYOIDES

This South American vine is sometimes planted in south Florida and Arizona and occasionally elsewhere in the South. *C. quadrangularis* is a quick-growing climber with very thick fleshy stems. (Photograph 302.) The few leaves are kidney-shaped. The stems are reportedly eaten by natives of Ceylon. The round fruits are bright red, the size of a pea.

*Fittonia verschaffeltii* (Acanthaceae). This is one of 3 species of Peruvian creepers much used in glasshouses for the brilliant variegation made by the red or white venation of their large heart-shaped leaves. In this particular species, the leaves are dull green, often yellowish, veined carmine. Planted in moist shady places, this tall herbaceous perennial becomes a pretty jungle of creeping plants. (Photograph 304.)

*Iresine* (Amaranthaceae). Bloodleaf. Several species of this scandent perennial shrub are cultivated as bedding plants for their brilliant foliage in various tones of red.

*Muehlenbeckia complexa* (Polygonaceae). Wire-plant. Tall climber in California, though often grown in hanging baskets. Flowers are small and greenish white, but the white-cupped fruits become conspicuous.

*Nepenthes* (Nepenthaceae). Pitcher-plants. About 60 species, some epiphytic and some climbers, found mostly in boggy places in the tropics of the Old World. The pitchers, which are of remarkable structure, are extensions of the leaf tips. (Photograph 305.)

*Parthenocissus quinquefolia* (Vitaceae). Virginia-creeper or Woodbine. This vigorous, high-climbing vine, which has always been a favorite, has 5 rather thick leaflets about 6 inches long, emanating from a central point. In the autumn they turn scarlet and crimson. The branched tendrils have adhesive tips. It is native from New England to Florida and west to Mexico. (Photograph 307.)

*P. inserta,* also called by the same common names, is a low vine often rambling over bushes and rocks. It is native from New England to the Rocky Mountains.

*P. tricuspidata* (Photograph 306), commonly called Japanese-ivy or Boston-ivy, is another high climber clinging closely by tendrils which are tipped with disks. This is a Japanese vine with glossy foliage.

*P. himalayana* is a vigorous high climber in India and China with tendrils adhesive-tipped. The leaves are dark green, smooth above, trifoliate, to 5 inches long. The autumn color is a rich red. In var. *rubrifolia* the leaflets are smaller, purplish at first. Color Plate 185 shows this vine on a 150-foot spruce tree.

*Phanera vahlii* (Leguminosae). Brown hairs densely cover the square woody stem and also make the petioles, veins, and margins of leaves on this large, vigorous climber look brownish. Both leaf surfaces, particularly the lower one, are also hairy. Leaves are cut halfway along the midvein and are sometimes expanded to 10 inches on both sides. Tendrils are axillary and large. Flowers, which are 1 inch across and in terminal or axillary clusters, are produced abundantly during the summer, opening in the morning and fading in the afternoon. At first their 6 petals are white, then they gradually turn light pink. They are densely hairy on the under surface. (Photograph 308.)

304. FITTONIA VERSCHAFFELTII    305. NEPENTHES

306. PARTHENOCISSUS TRICUSPIDATA    307. PARTHENOCISSUS QUINQUEFOLIA

This vine is an evergreen, fast-growing climber suitable for pergolas or high walls.—T. K. B.

*Setcreasea purpurea* (Commelinaceae). Purple Queen. This creeper from Mexico has smooth stems a foot or more long bearing pink flowers, and the stems, leaves, and bracts are all some shade of purple. Frequently used as a ground-cover in Florida and Hawaii. (Photograph 309.)

*Tradescantia fluminensis* (Commelinaceae). Wandering-Jew. This is one of 40 species from South America with leaves 1 to 3 inches long, green, green and white, yellowish and white striped, or purple on the underside. The flower petals are white, but the vines are cultivated only for their attractive foliage. *T. blossfeldiana* from Argentina produces many-flowered clusters of ½-inch blossoms with petals edged in rose, the base white. See also *Zebrina pendula*. (See Color Plate 43 and Photograph 310.)

*Tripogandra multiflora* (Commelinaceae.) This Jamaican plant is often cultivated as a basket plant in glasshouses in the United States, for its clustered white flowers. Its stems will climb if opportunity offers.

*Uvaria afzelii* (Anonaceae). While most members of this large tropical genus are jungle lianas, 2 or 3 are cultivated (See Part I). This one (Photograph 311) is a native of West Africa.

*Zebrina pendula* (Commelinaceae). Wandering-Jew. This trailer comes in several forms, all with quite ornamental leaves, often planted in rockeries and baskets. (Photograph 310.) This is also known as *Tradescantia zebrina*.

*Editor's Note:* For other vines with attractive foliage, see under "Inconspicuous Flowers" (Part 4), *Ampelocissus, Ampelopsis, Fatshedera,* and *Hedera;* under "Fruits" (Part 5), *Actinidia* and *Gaultheria;* and under "Groundcovers" (Part 6), *Asarum* and *Vancouveria*.

## 4—VINES WITH INCONSPICUOUS FLOWERS

Climbers whose flowers are inconspicuous are legion, and some of these can be equally well classed under *Ornamental Foliage*. Many of them are familiar garden subjects, like the English ivy on the chimney.

*Ampelocissus latifolia* (Vitidaceae). An extensive climbing vine with brick-red flowers and black succulent berries which are sweet and juicy. (Photograph 312.) Common in Bihar and Orissa forests, India.—J. K. M.

*Ampelopsis* (Vitidaceae). This close relative of the grape comprises about 30 species mostly from China and elsewhere in eastern Asia; two species grown in the United States. All of them are ornamental, frequently vigorous vines with handsome foliage and ordinarily small or inconspicuous flowers. Frequently they have showy fruit clusters in autumn, sometimes red or blue, occasionally other colors. *A. arborea* of the southern United States (Photograph 314) is a slender climber sometimes bushy. Fruit dark purple ½ inch wide. *A. brevipedunculata* is particularly handsome in fruit, bright blue. *A. heterophylla* from Korea has fruit that is porcelain blue. *A. orientalis* from Asia Minor has bright red fruit resembling currants. Monkshood vine (*A. aconitifolia*) from northern China has

308. PHANERA VAHLII          309. SETCREASEA PURPUREA

310. ZEBRINA PENDULA         311. UVARIA AFZELII

fruit that is orange or yellow. Because of its heavy foliage, it is often used on fences as snowdrift barriers. (Photograph 313.)

*Aneilema biflorum* (Commelinaceae). The 60 species of *Aneilema* from Indomalaysia are narrow-leaved, blue-flowered, perennial trailing plants allied to *Commelina,* often cultivated in glasshouses. *A. biflorum* from Australia and *A. sinicum* from China are found in collections in England and the United States. In gardens of northern Queensland *A. gramineum* is a creeping annual to 6 feet with white flowers, tinged violet, in loose terminal clusters.

*Bidens rubifolia* (Compositae). Few climbers other than this are numbered among the 230 species of these annual herbs. None have any horticultural interest.

*Carludovica* (Cyclanthaceae). Palmlike plants from one of which Panama hats are made. Several climbers are in the genus.

*Centella asiatica* (Umbelliferae). [Syn.: *Hydrocotyle asiatica; H. cordifolia*] Indian pennywort. A strong-growing perennial groundcover, with stems rooting at the nodes and rounded leaves ½ to 1 inch across. (Photograph 315.) Pink and white flowers are in small heads. The chief value of this often low-rated creeping herb is its fondness for swampy and poorly drained soil, where most such creepers would not survive. It occurs naturally in tropical and subtropical regions of all continents except Europe. According to Neal (84) this vine has been planted in Indonesia and Ceylon to prevent soil erosion.—E. E. L.

*Coccoloba ascendens* (Polygonaceae). Liana laur, liane cacao, cuchape. A stout scrambling woody liana ascending to the tops of the tallest trees in the Lesser Antilles ranging from Martinique south to Trinidad and Tobago and recently reported from wild collections in the Guianas and Venezuela. The stem cambium is uniformly developed and active and the stem is occasionally hollow. The leaves are leathery when fresh and an attractive dark green and waxy in appearance. The racemose inflorescence bears inconspicuous cream colored flowers. The pistillate flowers develop into fruits to 1 inch long and nearly as thick, and these are borne on stout pedicels. The fleshy perianth tube is purple and vascular when fresh and becomes corky and fragile when dry. The achene is chestnut brown and smooth and shiny. As is true of most species of *Coccoloba* the fruit is reported as edible but is usually insipid, astringent or flavorless. *C. ascendens* is cultivated casually in several botanical gardens in the West Indies.

*C. dussii.* Raisinier marron, raisin marron. A woody liana native to the Lesser Antilles and found wild or cultivated in islands south to Trinidad and Tobago. In contrast to most lianoid species of *Coccoloba,* this vine develops a flattened stem through the bilateral activity of the cambium which produces two distinct zones of growth on opposite sides of the stem. These wings of secondary xylem reveal large vessel pores when cut. The leaves of this species tend to be ovate or oblong, leathery, slightly curved and to 7 by 4 inches long and broad. The inflorescence is delicate, to 6 inches long and the flowers and fruit are borne on thin pedicels. The fruits are nearly spherical, less than ½ inch in diameter, dark blue-purple in color and the fruiting perianth is extremely astringent.—R. A. H.

*Cocculus carolinus* (Menispermaceae). Carolina moonseed. Twining small shrub, only occasionally cultivated; leaves of diverse shapes; inconspicuous

312. **AMPELOCISSUS LATIFOLIA**     313. **AMPELOPSIS ACONITIFOLIA**

314. **AMPELOPSIS ARBOREA**     315. **CENTELLA ASIATICA**

flowers. *C. trilobus,* snailseed. Small twining evergreen garden shrub, also with inconspicuous flowers but with bright green foliage. For another species see Part I.

*Coprosma baueri* (Rubiaceae). Looking-glass plant. This normally is a shrub or small tree but under provocation it will climb. (Photograph 316.)

*Deeringia baccata* (Amaranthaceae). Australian climber to 12 feet, with greenish flowers.

*Euonymus* (Celastraceae) has several climbers and trailers among its approximately 150 species, most of which are native in Asia. While their flowers are scarcely noticeable, most of them bear colorful small fruits. The leaves of most species are elliptic; some are evergreen. The hardiest evergreen climber in the genus is *E. fortunei,* which occurs in several forms with colored or variegated leaves, notably var. *colorata,* the foliage of which turns purple in autumn, giving the plant the name of purple-leaf wintercreeper. *E. obovatus,* the running strawberry-bush, native from Ontario to Kentucky, takes root from the branches as they trail along the ground. *E. radicans,* evergreen, grows naturally in similar fashion, but will climb against a wall if given opportunity.

*Fatshedera lizei* (Araliaceae). This hybrid shrub, derived from *Hedera helix* and *Fatsia japonica,* is often trained as a vine in California. The leaves, about twice the size of those of English ivy, are similarly lobed.

*Ficus pumila* (Moraceae). Climbing fig. Out of the 2,000 species of *Ficus,* many are climbers. Of immediate horticultural interest is this species, also known as *F. repens,* an ivy-like evergreen creeper that covers walls solidly, adhering to brick, stucco, or other surfaces by many tiny rootlets. (Photograph 318.) Its deep green leaves are 1 to 4 inches long. When allowed to overtop the wall, the plant becomes treelike. The shaggy fig (*F. villosa*) also occasionally cultivated in Florida, has larger, more pointed leaves (Photograph 317) and is hardier than the climbing fig.

*Fumaria* (Papaveraceae). Chiefly Mediterranean, with a score or more of species, this genus of herbaceous plants contains a number of climbers. The leaves are divided into narrow segments.

*Gurania malacophylla* (Cucurbitaceae). Strong, hairy South American perennial climber with large lobed leaves; male and female flowers produced separately.

*Hablitzia* species (Chenopodiaceae). This is a curious vine from extremely dry areas in the Caucasus. It lives as a perennial underground, and from that stem a climbing shoot is given off annually. This climbs by sensitive petioles.

*Hedera helix* (Araliaceae). English ivy. This familiar vine scarcely needs to be described. (Photograph 319.)

*Juniperus horizontalis* (Cupressaceae). Creeping juniper. This is a procumbent shrub with long trailing branches. Of similar creeping growth is *J. sabina* var. *tamariscifolia.* (Photograph 320.) Both are frequently used as groundcovers.

*Menispermum canadense* (Menispermaceae). Moonseed. A strong semiwoody climber of twining habit to 15 feet, a mass of twisting stems. It is excellent for growing over an old tree. The flowers, freely produced, are greenish-yellow, not showy.

*Nitraria schoberi* (Zygophyllaceae). Nitre-bush. An amazing plant from

316. COPROSMA BAUERI    317. FICUS VILLOSA

318. FICUS PUMILA    319. HEDERA HELIX

the sandy deserts and arid saline regions of Australia and central and western Asia. (Photograph 322.) As a shrub of originally around 3 feet in height it spreads laterally by its outer creeping growth, binding the sand by a strong rooting system. If buried or partially covered by moving surface sand its rigid upper stems rapidly grow through the sand, repeating the process as often as more sand may continue to raise the ground level. Thick green or glaucous leaves average an inch in length, tiny white flowers are in small branching clusters and are followed by purplish or golden berries (drupes) half an inch or more long. The generic name derives from niturum (saltpeter), on account of the salt plains of Siberia where the plant was first found, and the species commemorates Dr. Gottlob Schober (d. 1739) who conducted scientific exploration in Asiatic Russia. There is one other species, North African.—E. E. L.

*Pisonia aculeata* (Nyctaginaceae). This big climbing shrub of the Pacific Islands, often with a thick trunk, has tiny inconspicuous yellowish-white flowers. They are followed by small ribbed, oblong, sticky fruits that exude a viscid liquid. Willis (118) comments:

> "One of the few fruits which are able to cling to feathers. On some Pacific Islands birds and even reptiles are ensnarled and disabled and eventually killed."

*Rhipogonum scandens* (Liliaceae). This is a tough climber, very common in the New Zealand bush. It has pretty red berries 1/3 inch in diameter. It is commonly called "supplejack" by the New Zealanders, pronounced *sooplejack.*

*Tetragonia trigyna* (Aizoaceae). Where support is available on coastal sands, dunes, or rocky places, this trailing shrub or subshrub becomes lianoid. It has tiny yellow flowers. (Photograph 321.)

*Sargentodoxa cuneata* (Sargentodoxaceae, formerly placed in Lardizabalaceae). This is a single species of a twining shrub native to China. It grows to 25 feet or more and bears half-inch 6-parted, greenish-yellow flowers in clusters, the female ones followed by small blue-black fruits. The relationship is so close that this plant has also been known as *Holboellia cuneata,* which was never shifted from the Lardizabalaceae.

*Sinofranchetia chinensis* [syn. *Holboellia chinensis*]. Small white flowers with 6 petals hang in clusters on this Chinese vine in the Lardizabalaceae. Leaves are parted into 3 leaflets about 4 inches long. Fruits are small purplish berries. The vine climbs to 30 feet or more.

*Schrankia* (Leguminosae). This genus contains a number of prickly shrubs that are either decumbent or scandent. Most of them grow in semi-tropical regions; none is ornamental.

*Scleria barteri* (Cyperaceae). Vine-razor. This African sedge climbs over shrubs and trees to heights of 20 feet or more, rendering them impenetrable because of the sword-edged leaves. Some 200 species of *Scleria* are found in the tropics. (Photograph 327.)

*Thymus serpyllum* (Labiatae). Creeping thyme, mother-of-thyme. Bailey (4) says this creeping perennial has wiry, prostrate stems, rooting below, sending

320. JUNIPERUS SABINA TAMARISCIFOLIA 321. TETRAGONIA TRIGYNA

322. NITRARIA SCHOBERI 323. TILLANDSIA

up erect stems. He continues: "A common plant in old gardens, prized as an evergreen edging and as covering for rockwork and waste places; also runs wild. The leaves are sometimes used for seasoning."

*Tillandsia usneoides* (Bromeliaceae) is one of 1,400 species in 50 genera in this family in the forests of the West Indies and tropical America. Most are epiphytic plants, many with gorgeous flowers. Some extend their growth along tree limbs to establish new plants, but they are not true vines in the sense usually understood. However, Spanish-moss (*Tillandsia usneoides*), also called old man's beard, long-moss, and vegetable horsehair (Photograph 323) comes nearest to being a vine. At the base of a larger plant, each of the stems is wound around its support. The plant then climbs and its branches soon become pendent. As each tip grows on downward, the older parts die away. In this genus the flowers are insignificant.

*Triphyophyllum peltatum* (Dioncophyllaceae). This is an astonishing West African climber because it bears three entirely different kinds of leaves which are designed for three different purposes. (Photographs 324-326.) One long, narrow leaf gathers chlorophyll to feed the plant. Another kind of leaf terminates in a pair of hooks which harden and help the plant to climb. A third kind of leaf terminates in a long, curling glandular process which exudes a sticky liquid that does attract bugs but has nothing to do with the pollination of the flowers. These appear elsewhere on the vine and are insignificant. For further details of its extraordinary form see the *Garden Journal of the New York Botanical Garden,* January-February 1965.

*Ventilago* (Rhamnaceae) is a genus of about 35 species of climbing shrubs, mostly Chinese and Indian. They bear small white flowers usually in leafless clusters at the tips of the branches. Willis (118) says some of them climb by hooks.

*Vincetoxicum* (Asclepiadaceae). Angle-pod. This genus contains about 75 species of twining or trailing, woody or herbaceous perennial vines with heart-shaped leaves and small greenish or purplish flowers. Several species are native in the United States from Pennsylvania southward but apparently are not in cultivation.

## 5—VINES THAT YIELD FRUIT OR OTHER CROPS

### (edible, useful or ornamental)

These plants are enormously important in their own right: the grape is prized everywhere for its flavor; the pumpkin has huge flowers; the bittersweet is a cherished decoration. Another example is the firethorn (*Pyracantha* species), which is not a vine at all but is grown as such in many gardens and is frequently a handsome addition to the landscape. Its "crop" is the decorative fruit it yields. There are large numbers of these fruiting vines that are important, but they do not belong among the ornamental flowering plants.

*Actinidia* (Actinidiaceae). The attractive leaves, which are variously downy, in some species curiously colored, and mostly finely toothed, are of equal interest

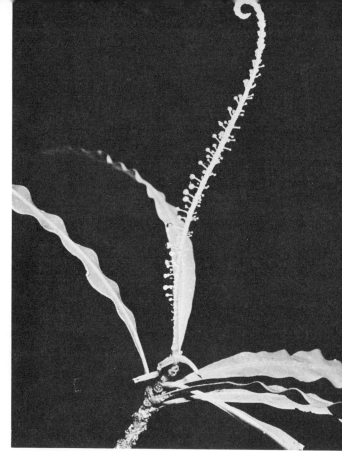

324. **TRIPHYOPHYLLUM PELTATUM**    325. **TRIPHYOPHYLLUM PELTATUM**

326. **TRIPHYOPHYLLUM PELTATUM**    327. **SCLERIA BARTERI**

with the small sweet fruits of the dozen or more cultivated species of *Actinidia*. Averaging 4 or 5 inches in length, the leaves in most species are ovate, sometimes heart-shaped at the base. On *A. kolomikta* they are frequently tipped or half-marked with white or pink. The berries on these Asiatic vines appear in many different colors—yellow on the species illustrated. (Photograph 328.)

*Blastania garcini* (Cucurbitaceae). A pretty Indian annual climber with 5-lobed leaves and pale green flowers. The fruits are globose, red when ripe.—J. K. M. (Photographs 330 and 331.)

*Cardiospermum* (Sapindaceae). Balloon-vine; heart-seed. About 15 species of herbaceous vines of the world's warm regions. The fruits are bladdery; the seeds have a heart-shaped white spot on a black background.

*Chiogenes hispidula* (Rutaceae). Creeping snowberry. This evergreen trailer is frequently cultivated in rockeries where it makes a mat. It bears white bell-shaped flowers and snow-white fruits.

*Citrullus vulgaris* (Cucurbitaceae). Watermelon. This well-known cultivated herbaceous vine trails for great distances. (Photograph 329.) The citron, or preserving melon, is var. *citroides*.

*Celastrus scandens* (Celastraceae). American bittersweet, also called false bittersweet, or waxwork. (Photograph 333.) This climbing, twining shrub to 25 feet, native from Quebec to North Carolina and westward to New Mexico, has inconspicuous flowers at the tips of branches followed by ½-inch orange-yellow capsules which, when opened, disclose the crimson coloring of the pulp surrounding the seeds. Fruiting branches are much used for dried winter arrangements. Also commonly cultivated in the United States is the Asiatic *C. orbiculatus*, a vigorous climber to 40 feet, of similar appearance. (Photograph 332.) Numerous other Asiatic species of *Celastrus* are useful as wall or trellis cover because their bright-colored fruits are usually persistent through the winter. (For another vine called bittersweet, see *Solanum dulcamara*, farther on in this section.)

*Cotoneaster* (Rosaceae). This genus of ornamental shrubs contains many that are cultivated for their decorative fruits; a few of these are vines. *C. dammeri* (Photograph 335) is a prostrate shrub from China with trailing branches that root as they go in the vine manner. Small solitary flowers are followed by bright red fruits.

*Cucumis melo* (Cucurbitaceae), muskmelon; *C. sativus*, cucumber. These familiar garden fruits, as well as most of those below, scarcely need description. An ornamental relative is *C. dipsaceus*, whose 2-inch fruits are hard and dry and densely covered with long hairs. (Photograph 334.)

*Cucurbita pepo* (Cucurbitaceae), field pumpkin; *C. pepo* var. *melopepo*, Squashes and pumpkins; *C. pepo* var. *ovifera*, gourds. These are the yellow-flowered gourds cultivated in American gardens. The white-flowered gourds are *Lagenaria leucantha* (q.v.) Also see *Trichosanthes*. (Photograph 338.)

*Dioscorea* (Dioscoreaceae). The true yams (not the sweet-potatoes, *Ipomoea batatas*) comprise 600 species cultivated in the tropics of both worlds for their edible tubers. (Photograph 339.) One species, *D. bulbifera*, the air-potato, grows its tubers on the vine instead of underground.

*Gaultheria procumbens* (Ericaceae) teaberry; boxberry, checkerberry, win-

361

**328. ACTINIDIA KOLOMIKTA**    **329. CITRULLUS VULGARIS**

**330. BLASTANIA GARCINI**    **331. BLASTANIA GARCINI (FRUITS)**

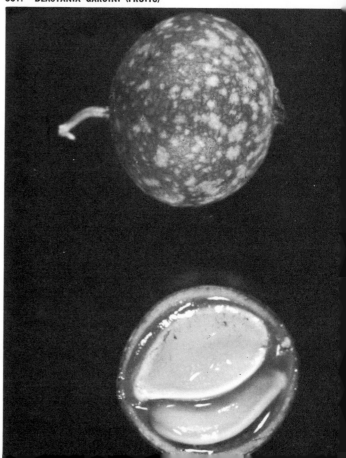

tergreen. All parts of the teaberry have a pleasant oil-of-wintergreen odor and taste. Formerly it was one of the sources of this oil, which long has been used medicinally and in flavoring candy and chewing gum. In the past this plant was also used in preparing a tea, hence the common name. Teaberry is native from Canada to Georgia, Alabama, and Minnesota. It is a creeping evergreen with erect stems not more than 6 inches tall and with alternate, usually obovate leaves to 2 inches long. (Photograph 336.) The solitary white flowers are produced toward the tips of ascending branches. The fruit is bright red, about ¼ inch across, and persists through the winter. The creeping snowberry (*G. hispidula*), which is native from North Carolina to Idaho, is occasionally cultivated as a groundcover. It also has the odor and taste of wintergreen. Leaves are ovate, about 1/3 inch long. The solitary nodding white flowers arise from the axils of the leaves. Their bell-shaped corollas are 4-cleft. The fruit, which is juicy and snow-white, is pleasantly acid.—S. Mc. D.

*Holboellia* (Lardizabalaceae). In India and China, 5 species of evergreen climbing shrubs cultivated for their edible fruits, one kind also for its fragrant white flowers. (*See also Sargentodoxa* and *Sinofranchetia* under "Inconspicuous Flowers.")

*Humulus japonicus* (Moraceae). Hops. Tall twining herb usually grown as an annual for an ornamental screen; also known as *H. scandens*. The related species *H. lupulus* is used in brewing.

*Ipomoea batatas* (Convolvulaceae). Sweet-potato. It is the tuberous root of this morning-glory relative, rather than the fruit, for which this plant is cultivated.

*Lagenaria siceraria* (Cucurbitaceae) is the bottle gourd, an annual creeper, of which the woody outer shell makes a flask or a dish. The shape and size vary considerably. (Photograph 338.)

*Luffa cylindrica* (Cucurbitaceae). Sponge gourd. Tropical vine from Old World, widely cultivated. Flowers showy, yellow or white. Fruits fibrous inside, this part dried for use as sponges. (Photograph 340.)

*Lycium.* (Solanaceae). Matrimony-vine or box-thorn. This includes a number of species suitable for cold climates where they are valued as groundcovers, especially on banks. They produce a brilliant display of orange-red berries in fall and winter. They are useful for erosion control but their great invasiveness can become a problem. The two species most used in the northern United States and Canada are *L. halimifolium* and the Chinese matrimony-vine. *L. chinense,* which is even showier and more rampant. The latter species has a thornless variety. *L. chilense,* from Chile, has grayish foliage and is a shrub with procumbent branches. It has been useful in seashore plantings in southern California, but forms the attractive orange-red berries only in favored areas.—V. T. S.

*Melothria pendula* (Cucurbitaceae). A slender, herbaceous perennial, either climbing or trailing, bearing very small greenish flowers and blackish berries. Native from Virginia to Oklahoma and southward. (Photograph 341.)

*Momordica charantia* (Cucurbitaceae). balsam-pear. Firminger (37) calls this a jungle creeper with ivy-like leaves and "an exceedingly bright orange-yellow (1-inch) flower; well worth a place in the garden." It is an herbaceous

332. CELASTRUS ORBICULATUS VAR. HERMAPHRODITUS  333. CELASTRUS SCANDENS

334. CUCUMIS DIPSACEUS  335. COTONEASTER DAMMERI

336. GAULTHERIA PROCUMBENS

337. GOURDS

338. LAGENARIA SICERARIA

339. DIOSCOREA BULBIFERA

trailer on which the 6-inch fruits are more conspicuous than the flowers, for they split three ways to disclose the bright red arils and white seeds which are prized by American Chinese as edible. Common as a weed in Florida gardens is var. *abbreviata* with bright orange fruits 2 inches long. (Photograph 342.) The balsam-apple (*M. balsamina*) with 2 to 3-inch orange fruit and 1-inch yellow flowers with black center, is a smaller, neater vine, as is *M. involucrata* with yellow fruits that turn red; both of these are occasionally grown in gardens of the southern states.

*Pernettya mucronata* (Ericaceae). A beautiful scandent shrub from Chile with red to purple (occasionally white) berries that remain on the branches over winter. (Photograph 343.)

*Piper nigrum* (Piperaceae). Black pepper. This is one of 2,000 species of *Piper* found in all parts of the world, most of them woody climbers. Dried berries of this species yield black pepper. Various other species are cultivated in collections of economic plants. (Photograph 344.) Pepper is cultivated chiefly in Malaya.

*Pisum sativum* (Leguminosae). The common garden pea, of which there are many varieties.

*Pyracantha* (Rosaceae). Firethorn. About 6 species of thorny evergreen shrubs with long flexuous branches, often trained as a vine. The fruits, orange or red, are small but showy. (Photograph 345.)

*Salacia reticulata* (Celastraceae). A giant climber from India, related to American bittersweet (*Celastrus scandens*), but with edible fruit.

*Salpichroa rhomboidea* (Solanaceae). Lily-of-the-valley-vine. This climber from Argentina and Paraguay has somewhat woody perennial greenish stems and is a rapid grower under heat and in alkaline soil. It has small white flowers and edible yellowish or white fruits which are sold in the native markets. This vine is best cut to the ground each winter and may be expected to grow to 5 feet or more. It is quite resistant to drought and is considered somewhat weedy.—V. T. S.

*Sechium edule* (Cucurbitaceae). Chayote. Hairy perennial vine from tropical America, cultivated for its delicious squashlike fruit. (Photograph 346.)

*Solanum dulcamara* (Solanaceae). Nightshade or European bittersweet. (American bittersweet is the woody vine *Celastrus scandens*.) Purple-flowered perennial climber to 6 feet bearing drooping clusters of ornamental red berries which are poisonous.

*Tetrapathaea tetrandra* (Passifloraceae). New Zealand passion-fruit, kohia (Maori). The only passionflower native to New Zealand and found nowhere else. It is a slender liane that climbs by tendrils in the axils of the leaves. The green flowers, ½ to 1 inch across, are scented but otherwise insignificant. Male and female flowers are on separate plants. The fruit is handsome, bright orange and about 1½ inches across. (Photograph 347.) According to Colenso, one of the early explorers in New Zealand, the dried wood of the passion-fruit vine formed an excellent slow-match by which the Maoris used to carry a spark from village to village.—D. E.

*Tetrastigma harmandii* (Vitaceae). This high-climbing vine from the Philippines bears edible round fruits similar to those of the Scuppernong grape.

340. LUFFA CYLINDRICA    341. MELOTHRIA PENDULA

342. MOMORDICA CHARANTIA VAR. ABBREVIATA    343. PERNETTYA MUCRONATA

344. PIPER (MALAYA)    345. PYRACANTHA COCCINEA

346. SECHIUM EDULE     347. TETRAPATHAEA TETRANDRA

*Trichosanthes* (Cucurbitaceae). Close to 50 species in tropical Asia and adjacent areas, bearing fringed flowers and abundant red or orange fruits the size of duck eggs. Several are suited for greenhouse culture.

*Vaccinium macrocarpum* (Ericaceae). Cranberry. Now a part of American Thanksgiving tradition, the cranberry is grown by the thousands of acres in the northeastern United States and on the Pacific Coast. It is a prostrate, slenderly creeping, evergreen shrub, often rooting at the nodes, native in bogs from Canada to North Carolina and Minnesota. The leaves are alternate, oblong-elliptical, and about ½ inch long. The flowers are pale pink and borne laterally. The corolla is 4-parted with reflexed lobes. The acid-flavored berry at maturity is red and 1/3 to 1 inch long. A related species, *V. oxycoccus.,* the small cranberry, is also occasionally cultivated and may be distinguished by the terminal inflorescences and generally smaller features throughout. The mountain cranberry (*V. vitis-idaea*) bears acid or slightly bitter fruits that are sometimes used as a substitute for the large cranberry. The plant is occasionally cultivated in northern areas as a ground-cover. It is a low evergreen shrub with creeping slender stems and erect branches. The pink to reddish flowers are about ¼ inch long, campanulate, and borne in terminal, often nodding clusters. The globose fruit is red and about 1/3 inch in diameter.

[Editor's Note: These plants are no kin to the so-called cranberry-bush (*Viburnum trilobum*).]

Blueberries also belong to the genus *Vaccinium*. The creeping blueberry is *V. crassifolium,* a prostrate plant which will form a carpet 6 feet across. It grows in sandy pine woods from southeastern Virginia to Georgia. The berry, which is nearly black, is sweet and juicy. *V. lamarckii* is one of the names for another one of the blueberries (Photograph 348), the species in which have become somewhat confused through the freedom with which they hybridize. This one is stoloniferous.—S. McD.

*Vitis* (Vitaceae). Grape. The 60 or 70 species of grapes are all climbing plants, cultivated in most warm countries for their attractive foliage as well as for the fruit. *V. vinifera* is the common grape. The fox grape (*V. labrusca*) and the Muscadine grape (*V. rotundifolia*) are North American species. Scuppernong is a variety of Muscadine.

Mustang grape, also known as bird grape or everlasting grape (*V. munsoniana*) (Photograph 350), is a very slender, evergreen vine that runs on the ground or over low bushes, flowering more or less continuously. It is a Florida native from Jacksonville to the Keys.

*V. voineriana* (Photograph 349) from southeast Asia is a climbing shrub with tendrils not coiled when they first appear but later spiraled. All parts of the plant are coated with reddish-brown hairs. The evergreen leaves are leathery, the veins on the underside prominent and fuzzy. The upper surface is bright green and smooth. Flower clusters on old wood are light green dotted with red. Fruits (grapes) are large, of acid flavor. Because of its lush foliage, this is valued as a conservatory plant for cool climates. It is often planted in Florida on a trellis.

348. VACCINIUM LAMARCKII 349. VITIS VOINERIANA

350. VITIS MUNSONIANA 351. VANCOUVERIA HEXANDRA

A few species of *Vitis* are used as ornamental groundcovers, notably *V. coignetiate,* with large leaves that turn scarlet in autumn.

*Zschokkea lactescens* (Apocynaceae). Thorny, scandent Brazilian shrub, one of 8 species cultivated as a source of chicle.

## 6—HORIZONTAL VINES THAT COVER THE EARTH WITH GREEN

The word "groundcover" is loosely applied to indicate that the plants can be used to produce a low turf that normally requires no mowing. Many such plants are vines that grow horizontally in exactly the same way that ivy grows vertically on the chimney, rooting at the nodes as it goes. The ground vines do the same thing. Sometimes they are mat-forming and can be very dense. Our language acknowledges this in the use of such names as "trailing-arbutus" which admittedly is a vine because of the application of the modifier "trailing." In the case of this particular plant, its flowers are pretty enough to win it a place in the body of this book, along with at least one variety of heather. *Pachysandra* is a typical horizontal vine with insignificant flowers.

*Asarum europaeum* (Aristolochiaceae). European wild-ginger, asarabacca. This plant, rarely a foot high, has creeping stems that are sympodial, each annual joint bearing several scale leaves below, then two green leaves and a terminal flower above. Common as a groundcover in England. (Photograph 352.)

*Baccharis pilularis* (Compositae). Groundsel-bush. This slow-growing, nearly prostrate form among 400 kinds of *Baccharis* is native to the west coast of the United States and has been found useful in covering banks along highways, especially near the ocean because of the high resistance of its foliage to salt spray. (Photograph 353.)

*Bacopa* (Scrophulariaceae). The species called coastal water hyssop in Florida is a creeping, mat-forming succulent herb with ½-inch leaves. It is frequently found on sandy shores within reach of ocean tides as far north as Virginia and west to Texas. It was formerly called *Bramia.*

*Batis maritima* (Batidaceae). Beachwort. This spreading prostrate shrub with creeping stems is usually found in salt marshes or mangrove mud. The striking pale green foliage crunches underfoot. This plant is found from New Guinea and Queensland to Hawaii, the West Indies and the Atlantic coast of South America.

*Dichondra carolinensis* (Convolvulaceae). This is a creeping herb of southeastern United States. It seldom exceeds 1 inch in height but produces bright green kidney-shaped or round leaves ½ to 1 inch across. It is sometimes used as a groundcover. It tolerates some trampling but not as much as lawn grasses.

*Dryas octopetala* (Rosaceae). This evergreen, creeping, subshrub comes from high altitudes near the North Pole. It is a groundcover with 1-inch leaves green above and white-fuzzy beneath, the stems bearing 1-inch white flowers. *D. drummondii,* similarly used, has smaller yellowish flowers.

*Ernodea littoralis* (Rubiaceae). This Florida native is a creeping, vinelike shrub of coastal sand dunes, completely covering acres of sand with its wiry stems and myriad fleshy leaves. Flowers are white. (Photograph 354.)

371

352. ASARUM EUROPAEUM    353. BACCHARIS PILULARIS

354. ERNODEA LITTORALIS    355. MAIANTHEMUM BIFOLIUM

*Maianthemum* (Liliaceae). This small genus of low perennial herbs with creeping stems is the only member of the lily family with its flower parts in 2's and 4's instead of 3's and 6's. *M. canadense,* known as Canada Mayflower, grows 2 to 9 inches high, has 1 to 3-inch leaves, and small white flowers in clusters of 12 to 30; rather dense. A similar, slightly larger species is *M. bifolium.* They are mat-making, hardy plants for cool, shady, moist places. (Photograph 355.)

*Metastelma bahamense* (Asclepiadaceae). Bahama milkweed. This slender West Indian vine found also on south Florida sand dunes has small whitish flowers. It often spreads copious growth over other plants.

*Nepeta hederacea* (Labiatae). Ground-ivy; gill-over-the-ground. This miniature perennial with creeping, leafy stems makes a dense mat with little blue flowers, often common as a groundcover. Also known as *Glechoma hederacea.* Several other species are similarly used but some have a tendency to become weedy.

*Pachysandra terminalis* (Buxaceae). This Japanese prostrate evergreen herb, rarely 8 inches high, makes a dense mass several feet across. It is a common groundcover, especially in seaside gardens. (Photograph 356.)

*Philoxerus vermicularis* (Amaranthaceae). This Florida native is a prostrate herb of coastal sand dunes and damp places. Its creeping 6-foot branches are clothed with tiny succulent leaves and silvery-white flower spikes 1 inch high. (Photograph 359.)

*Pilea nummularifolia* (Urticaeceae). Sometimes grown in hanging baskets, this creeping, rooting perennial covers mounds in tropical and subtropical regions, according to Bailey (5). The round hairy leaves are ¾ inch across and the flowers are minute. Its common name is Creeping Charley.

*Salicornia perennis* (Chenopodiaceae). Samphire, woody glasswort. This Florida native is a woody perennial, trailing its succulent stems over the beach. Flowers and leaves are insignificant. The popular name of glasswort originated from the crunching sound the plants make underfoot. *S. bigelovii* is similar, with thicker green stems. (Photograph 358.)

*Sesuvium portulacastrum* (Aizoaceae). Sea-purslane. The 6-foot stems that this Florida perennial succulent herb develop sprawl on the coastal beaches. Narrow leaves, freely produced, lie flat on the sand. The plant makes a good sand binder. (Photograph 357.)

*Vancouveria hexandra* (Berberidaceae). Three species of this genus are perennial herbs native to western North America. They are graceful, hardy, creeping woodland plants with slender rhizomes, suited to cool shady places in peaty soil. This species grows 4 to 16 inches high, bears white flowers ½ inch long in many-flowered clusters. (Photograph 351.)

*Veronica buxifolia* var. *prostrata* (Scrophulariaceae). Only one of the 300 different kinds of the popular speedwell plants grow flat on the ground, rooting as it grows. The tiny flowers on 1-inch spikes are almost lost in the thick, glossy-green foliage.

Editor's Note: For other attractive groundcover plants, see *Gaultheria procumbens* under "Fruits" (Part V) and *Juniperus* under "Plants with Inconspicuous Flowers" (Part IV).

356. PACHYSANDRA TERMINALIS     357. SESUVIUM PORTULACASTRUM

358. SALICORNIA BIGELOVII     359. PHILOXERUS VERMICULARIS

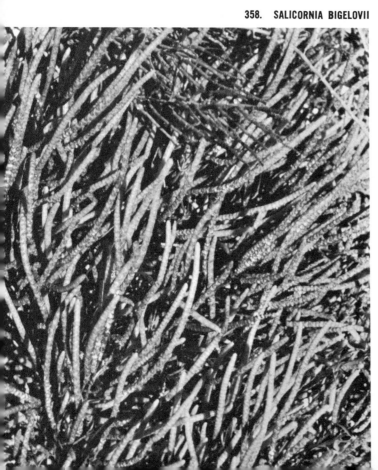

### 7—VINING AND SCRAMBLING FERNS

Not many of these are found in cultivation, and of course ferns have no flowers and therefore should not be in this book at all. However, in the jungles they are an important part of the plant community and some are briefly described here.

Most genera of ferns have erect rhizomes and neither form vines nor scramble. The few genera which do form vines or scramble over other plants are only occasionally cultivated, probably because of their rather weedy habit.

*Lygodium,* a pantropical genus with some temperate extensions, has greatly elongated leaves with a twining axis, which bears widely spaced, usually more or less palmately compound leaflets. (Photograph 362.) The fertile portions of the leaflets are marginal and spikelike. The natural habitat of most species is second-growth scrub or recently disturbed areas, and most remain dwarfed and sterile in the shade, but produce larger, fertile leaves in full sun. The Hartford fern or climbing fern, *L. palmatum,* is the one native species, found at the margins of highly acid swamps and bogs from Massachusetts to the Carolinas. It is difficult to cultivate.

*L. japonicum* is an easily cultivated plant, which has escaped in disturbed areas from North Carolina southward. *L. microphyllum* (*L. scandens*) is a recent escape from cultivation in Florida.

*Gleichenia* (Photograph 361) and *Dicranopteris* are two related genera characterized by their repeatedly forked leaves with evenly lobed leaflets. Both genera are sun plants whose fronds scramble over other vegetation. They are common on roadside banks in their native New World and Old World tropics. *Dicranopteris flexuosa* is an escape in Alabama and Florida. It and a few other species are cultivated occasionally.

*Drymoglossum heterophyllum* is a low creeping fern that grows on trees and has tongue-shaped fronds. The barren fronds are up to 2 inches long, ½ inch wide. The fertile fronds are up to 4 inches long and ¼ inch wide. (Photograph 360.) This is one of 6 Malayan species often cultivated in glasshouses. Another attractive Malayan genus is *Teratophyllum.* (Photograph 363.)

Several other genera of ferns in cultivation have long-creeping, climbing rootstocks which adhere to tree trunks in nature and which may or may not be rooted in the ground. These plants do not form vines or scramble. *Davallia, Oleandra, Salpichlaena, Stenochlaena,* and some species of *Polypodium* are examples.

### 8—CLIMBING PALMS

The climbing palms are by far the most gigantic of all vines. Many of them have beautiful and spectacular flowers, but they are jungle dwellers in the tropics. They are not known at all in the Temperate Zones and are not amenable to garden usage. The principal genera and the nature of these enormous plants can only be summarized here.

Probably the most important omissions belong in the 375 species of *Calamus* scattered throughout the tropics but chiefly in Asia and Africa, and

**360. DRYMOGLOSSUM HETEROPHYLLUM**    **361. GLEICHENIA (MALAYA)**

**362. LYGODIUM (MALAYA)**    **363. TERATOPHYLLUM**

the 65 species of *Desmoncus* in tropical America. Most of them are leaf climbers with thin reedy stems. Sometimes there are hooks on the back of the midrib of each leaf. Sometimes at the tip of each leaf the leaflets that should be there are replaced by stout hooks pointing backward. Willis (118) says that the leaf shoots almost vertically out of the bud and the hooks take hold on the surrounding vegetation when the wind blows. The stems of both *Calamus* and *Desmoncus* grow to immense lengths, often 500 to 600 feet and the palms are troublesome in tropical forests because the hooks catch viciously, particularly when the climbers have lost their grip on foliage above and have fallen back in heaps to the ground.

There is a third way in which some of the palms climb. On *Calamus deeratus* (Photograph 364), the flagellant spines are not of a foliage nature and are not connected with the leaves. They are on a separate lateral branch, and at the base of each one is a single reduced leaf. Of course the effect is the same, as the plants whip around in the forest and catch on any neighboring plant and use it as a basis of climbing. Other differences and exceptions in the climbing methods are discussed in detail by Corner (126), who also describes fully how the stems of *Calamus* are stripped to become the rattan used in furniture. The stems are also used in a thousand other ways, not only in places where the palms grow but all over the world. Rattans are never cultivated: enough still grow in the forest to provide all the rattan the world can use.

Here are other important climbing palms:

*Ancystrophyllum.* These 6 species of huge climbing palms in tropical Africa have flagellant spines at the tips of the leaves.

*Daemonorops.* Of the 100 species of this group of Indomalaysian palms, many are climbers. (Photograph 366).

In the genus *Desmoncus,* the stems are reedy. The leaflets at the end of the leaf axis are shortened and transformed into tough, reflexed hooks, set in regular pairs on either side of the leaf-axis. (Photograph 365.) While this arrangement may seem less effective than that of *Calamus,* it may be more appropriate for climbing in the broken and open canopy of the American forests.

*Korthalsia grandis.* This is one of 35 species of palms in this genus in Indomalaysia, most of them climbers. (Photograph 367.)

## 9—CLIMBING AROIDS      ⚘ DAN H. NICOLSON ⚘

Willis (118) says that 92 per cent of the 2,000 kinds of aroids are strictly tropical. Many, like calla-lilies, are terrestrial plants, but a considerable number, including the edible ceriman, are tropical climbers, sometimes huge. A number of the climbing forms produce longer and longer aerial roots as they grow upwards. The original roots at the base thus become of less and less importance and they often die away, together with the lower end of the stem, so that the plant thus becomes epiphytic. Again, the same plants may originate from seeds dropped on a lofty branch by a bird. The seeds germinate and as the plants grow they drop roots which grow downward steadily to the soil even if it be 150 feet below, and the climber becomes terrestrial.

**364. CALAMUS DEERATUS**   **365. DESMONCUS**

**366. DAEMONOROPS**   **367. KORTHALSIA GRANDIS**

Many climbing aroids are cultivated in warm-country gardens, as pot plants in glasshouses, and in other suitable locations. A few of these are described and illustrated.

The Jack-in-the-pulpit or aroid family (Araceae) is instantly recognizable by its inflorescence, a sticklike "jack" (spadix) with a leaflike "pulpit" (spathe). Its members often contain an irritating sap which "burns" when put in the mouth or on the hands. Some of the climbers contain needle-like cells (sclereids) up to ¼ inch long.

The climbing species include more than half the family and all are tropical. The cultivated species are grown for their foliage rather than for their inflorescences. As house plants they normally have a juvenile foliage quite different from adult, and they rarely flower. In the wild they range from humble ground creepers like *Amydrium humile* to enormous, high-climbing giants like *Scindapsus altissimus,* with leaves up to 4 feet in length. The long aerial roots of some species are used for temporary ropes by natives.

In Central and South America the commonest genera are *Philodendron* (250 species), *Monstera* (30 species), *Syngonium* (20 species) (Photograph 370), and *Anthurium* (500 species). Most species of *Philodendron* can be recognized by the petioles arising from the side of the stem instead of clasping the stem as all other aroids do. All species of *Syngonium* have milky sap.

The cultivated species of *Monstera* commonly have perforated leaves. (Photograph 369.) The ceriman (*M. deliciosa*), occasionally grown in Florida, bears edible fruit the size of an ear of sweet corn (Photograph 368), but unlike most fruits, it does not ripen all over at the same time. The tip ripens first, shown by the falling away of the fleshy outer part of the flowers. This stylar part is full of needle-like cells (trichoscereids) which look and feel like glass slivers. When the outer portion goes the needles go with it, leaving the fragrant, edible interior. The taste is like pineapples and bananas. The texture is like that of cherimoya (*Anona*). A week elapses before the base of the inflorescence is ripe enough to eat, by which time the tip is long gone.

In Africa the chief genera are *Culcasia* (15 species), *Rhektophyllum* (1 species, *R. mirabile*), and *Afrorhaphidophora* (2 species). *Rhektophyllum* often has variegated leaves, which are irregularly cut and perforated.

In southeast Asia the commonest genera are *Rhaphidophora* (70 species), *Pothos* (50 species), *Scindapsus* (30 species), and *Epipremnum* (8 species), (Photograph 371).

The aroid climbers are a common element in tropical rain forests. They are poorly known because their large size and fleshiness make them hard to press and dry. Collectors often prefer to pass them by.

### 10—MISTLETOES AND OTHER PARASITES ⚜ JOB KUIJT ⚜

Because almost none of these is ever cultivated in the garden they are largely excluded from this book, despite the fact that many of them have spectacular flowers. Parasites, such as our common mistletoe (*Phoradendron* species) are rarely spoken of in polite garden circles. These plants get their start in a tree when some bird deposits a seed in a crotch; another sponger is thus born to

368. MONSTERA DELICIOSA (FRUIT)  369. MONSTERA DELICIOSA VAR. BORSIGINIANA

370. SYNGONIUM PODOPHYLLUM  371. EPIPREMNUM AUREUM

bury its roots in the tree's tissues and live off its host. Some of these are parasitic climbers. *Psittacanthus* (Color Plate 122), for example, can smother the top of the host tree in a season with quantities of beautiful flowers, and an unsuspecting passerby thinks he has seen a new kind of flowering tree. Fifty kinds of *Psittacanthus* vines are clobbering treetops in the American tropics, and they are only one among many genera of climbing parasites.

The mistletoe habit (parasitism on tree branches) has developed independently in several families of the order Santalales. One family, the Myzodendraceae, consists of plants parasitic mostly on the Antarctic beech tree (*Nothofagus*) at the southern tip of South America. It has perhaps half a dozen species, all with very minute flowers and peculiar, feathery fruits. In the sandalwood family (Santalaceae), the very inconspicuous plants in the genus *Phacellaria* of southeast Asia are sometimes parasitic on the branches of trees.

There remain the mistletoes in the normal sense of the word. There are more than a thousand species, very few of which are found outside the tropics. The Christmas mistletoes, however—*Viscum album* of Europe and *Phoradendron flavescens* (Photograph 372) and related species of North America—reach at least part way into temperate regions. These and most other mistletoes have inconspicuous flowers, followed by small berries, either white or colored, that are eaten by birds, the main dispersal agents. Being parasites, many mistletoes are economically important pests in forests and orchards.

Among the mistletoes there are several which are not limited to a single point of attack on the tree. *Phyrygilanthus eugenioides* of Argentina is a liana-like species which reaches from the forest floor to the crown of the tree, sometimes parasitizing the tree in both places. *Gaiadendron* is a small tree with white or brilliant golden-yellow flowers, found at high elevations in the northern Andes and Central America. In undisturbed forests it is perched on the branches of large trees, where it parasitizes its fellow-epiphytes, but apparently not the tree. In disturbed places this mistletoe occurs in terrestrial stations. Finally, there are many species in the paleotropics which "walk" along the branches of the host, attacking the tree in new places as they go. In tropical, continental America, *Struthanthus* behaves similarly, and may cover trees with a clinging blanket of green, leafy branches.

In the Olacaceae there are several liana-like or scandent species, all with inconspicuous flowers, but only certain ones of them parasitic.

Editor's note: The above summary of parasitic plants was abstracted from Kuijt (128).

Neal (84) says that Hawaiian mistletoes appear to be leafless and to consist only of cylindrical or flat stems with numerous joints and branches. A wide-stemmed species, *Korthalsella latissima* (Photograph 375), is partly parasitic on the host tree, attached by roots that penetrate deeply enough to tap the food supply flowing under the bark, sometimes seriously injuring the host.

Editor's Note: For *Psittacanthus* see Index. For other parasitic plants see Part II of this chapter, on Weeds.

372. PHORADENDRON FLAVESCENS 373. CUSCUTA AMERICANA

374. CASSYTHA FILIFORMIS 375. KORTHALSELLA LATISSIMA

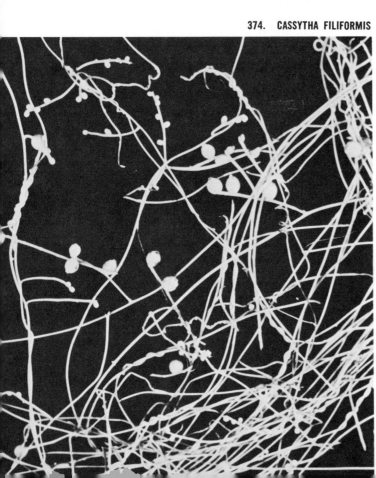

The parasitic plants that are commonly known as dodder belong to two or more genera. The yellow, hairlike plants of *Cuscuta* (Photograph 373) have been known since antiquity. Belonging to Cuscutaceae, the genus is nearly worldwide in distribution and attacks a great variety of hosts, including trees and shrubs. Dodders are noxious weeds in many areas, and sometimes important pests of crops. Willis (118) says there are 107 species of *Cuscuta*.

"Many have extended their boundaries through being carried about with their host plants. The stem twines and is sensitive to contact like a tendril so that it clasps the support tightly; it rarely makes more than three turns about the same branch of the host. At the points in close contact suckers are developed which penetrate the tissues of the host, growing into organic union with them and drawing off all the food materials required by the parasite, which has no green tissue of its own. The seeds of *Cuscuta* germinate later than those of the host plant; a very short anchorage root is formed and the stem nutates [changes its position through an automatic, more or less rhythmical movement] in search of a host; as soon as it has clasped one the root dies away."

A quite unrelated genus, *Cassytha* of the Lauraceae, has assumed an almost identical parasitic habit and is sometimes called bush-dodder or laurel-dodder.

The most common species, *C. filiformis* (Photograph 374), is nearly pantropical; other species are restricted to Australia. *Cassytha* often covers shrubs with an unsightly mass of brownish branches, and is a menace in Puerto Rico and other places.

## 11—GNETUM—A FLOWERLESS VINE ⚜ ROBERT J. RODIN ⚜

Among the strangest of all climbers are those that belong to the genus *Gnetum,* found only in eastern Asia. One member of the genus is a tree; it and the species that are vines are frequently cultivated for their edible fruit.

One hardly expects to find pine cones on a magnolia tree, yet that may be one of the easiest ways to visualize the appearance of this rather strange plant, *Gnetum.* (Color Plate 168.) One species is a tree, very much like a magnolia in appearance, but the remaining approximately 30 species are all woody vines.

This rare plant is not grown in cultivation in the temperate parts of the world and is found only in a few tropical greenhouses in botanical gardens in the United States. It is a native of the rain forests in the tropics, where it thrives, often climbing high into the tops of forest trees. There are 6 species in the American tropics from Brazil to Panama, 2 species in Central Africa, especially the Congo and Cameroons, and the remainder are in the tropical islands of the Pacific Ocean and southeast Asia, with 3 species as far west in Asia as India.

This plant is a gymnosperm as are the pines, because it has naked seeds not enclosed in an ovary, as in the angiosperms or flowering plants. Male and female cones are borne on separate plants.

Female cones of *Gnetum* do not closely resemble the cones of pines and other conifers because they do not have seeds which are flattened and covered by cone scales. Also the seeds get larger in most species, oval and up to 2 inches long. They are the only living plants to have 3 separate seed coats: the outer being quite fleshy and fibrous, the middle one filled with fibers and stone cells, and the innermost a thin membrane. The roasted seeds are eaten in Brazil, Africa, Indonesia, and Malaysia. The young leaves and inflorescences are also reportedly used as food. The fibers from the bark are said to be used for making rope and fish nets on some islands in the Pacific Ocean.

It has proved difficult to obtain a satisfactory supply of seeds, even for experimental studies. Seeds often prove to be sterile, since, unlike most other plants, even when the pistillate flowers have not been pollinated and hence no embryo could form, seeds will form. Germination of seeds often takes a year or longer, and they must be kept in moist soil in a warm greenhouse, preferably in a sand-peat mixture. The plants themselves must be kept in warmhouses, and do best in cultivation if kept in glasshouses with high humidity.

*Where the Gnetaceae stand in relation to other plants*

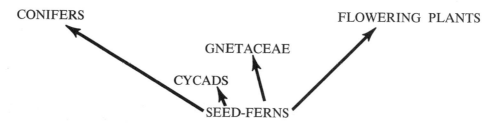

Several features make this a very specialized plant, including the presence of special vessels, cells in the xylem, which conduct water, usually only found in angiosperms. Other angiospermous characteristics are the presence of an embryo sac in the female ovule, stamen-like pollen sacs in the male cones, and broad leaves with a net-venation pattern like many dicotyledons, and not found in any other gymnosperm. It is assumed that in the process of evolution the gnetums have developed characteristics similar to those of the angiosperms, and that they are not the intermediate types from which angiosperms were derived.

A book by Professor P. Maheshwari and Dr. Vimla Vasil, entitled *Gnetum,* published in 1961, is the most complete account of the distribution and comparative morphology of the genus.

## 12—CLIMBING BAMBOOS

Bamboos really are grasses, but are distinct in many of their habits. Some of them grow erect to 100 feet or more, and some of them are climbers—a far cry from the old fishing pole.

The bamboos are giants of the grass world. They are usually thought of separately because of their distinctive and characteristic manner of growth and appearance. Some 77 genera have been described but the taxonomic literature on them is so exceedingly confused and contradictory that the entire group is now in process of revision by Dr. F. A. McClure of the Smithsonian Institution, Washington, D.C., for the new edition of Engler & Prantl's *Die Natürlichen Pflanzenfamilien.*

The difficulty in getting bamboos described correctly is that individual plants may live anywhere from 20 to 120 years. Man does not live long enough to keep records of particular plants over such an extended period. Too many of the records on the ages of individual bamboo plants are based strictly on hearsay. One factor that helps to support the oral records is that many species are known to be monocarps. This means that in their lifetime they flower and fruit only once, and then die. In this respect they are like annuals in the garden except that bamboos live so many years without flowering that when they do flower, there may be only hazy historical support for a statement that this bamboo was planted in such a location at such and such a time.

Eight genera of bamboo include climbing forms. In the Old World these are *Dinochloa, Melocalamus,* and *Merostachys.* In the New World the genera which have climbing forms are *Arthrostylidium, Athroostachys, Chusquea, Electrostachys,* and *Guadua.* So far as is known by bamboo experts, all of these are monocarps, but whether they live 20, 50, or 120 years, nobody knows with any surety. Their life spans as recorded in the literature, are incomplete and inconsistent.

Bamboos that climb utilize three methods. *Schizostachyum hainanense* and some species of *Dinochloa* clamber, supporting the upper part of each culm by resting it on the branches of overhanging trees; the branch complement at each culm node provides a bracket to prevent backsliding. Some species of *Dinochloa* support themselves by circumnutation during the elongation of the young culms (129, Fig. 19-E). Scandent species of *Chusquea* and *Arthrostylidium* have retrorse hooks on the surface of the upper internodes of the clums that serve to prevent backsliding (130).

Both these genera are native to Puerto Rico. *A. angustifolium* has linear leaf-blades crowded on the dense pseudo-whorls of short branches at the far-apart nodes of the slender culms; the appearance is that of great pompons strung along the stems at distant intervals. In dense forests, without undergrowth, these lianas may become of practical importance to travelers. For instance, in the forest of Quindiu on the western slopes of the Cordillera, *Aulonemia queko* is almost the only resource for any animal which has to be taken through. It serves as fodder, and, to get it, the haulms, which hang from the trees like cords, are dragged down with a strong pull, so that they bring their leaves with them. An account by Chase (168) of the climbing bamboos of Puerto Rico may be quoted:

"The three species of *Arthrostylidium* have much the same habit, climbing high, repeatedly branching, and in their greatest development swinging

376. CLUSIA ROSEA      377. CLUSIA GRANDIFLORA

378. PHILODENDRON PINNATIFIDUM      379. EPIPHYTIC ORCHID (MALAY)

down in great curtains from the trees overhanging trails or streamlets. They love the glints of sunlight along the trails or water courses and are very rarely found in deep shade."

In *A. angustifolium* the culms hang straight 20 or 30 feet from trees 40 or 50 feet high, or festoon themselves over lower growth. In *A. multispicatum* we meet with another peculiarity—the development of prickles. The slender naked growing ends of the culms and branches are beset with very short, sharp-pointed retrorse prickles. These ends, 5 to 12 feet or more long, swing in the breeze like whip lashes until they strike a place to take hold. Only after attaching themselves to some support do the leaves and branches develop from the clusters of short, sharp, radiating, scale-covered branch buds. The grappling branches form an inextricably tangled mass that draws blood at every foot of one's progress through it.

These climbing bamboos from Puerto Rico are interesting but they are pests and should never be planted anywhere.

One Burma species of bamboo is unique. *Melocalamus bambusoides* bears luscious edible fruit. Troup (134) says the smooth green fruit is large, fleshy, and pear-shaped, 3 to 5 inches long and 2 to 3 inches broad, with a stalk inserted at the thick end and the apex terminating in a curved beak. The fruits are filled with starch, and they are readily devoured by cattle, elephants, bison, rhinoceros, deer, pigs and other animals; 8 or 10 ripening fruits may be found hanging in clusters around each node down the 70-foot length of the culm.

## 13—GRASSES THAT CLIMB

Only the briefest consideration can be given to the very large number of grasses that climb. They are of no garden interest and are certainly never cultivated for their flowers. The rampant species are not worth mentioning except as potential pests.

Of the 10,000 kinds of grasses, a few, like Bermuda (*Cynodon dactylon*), grow by extending their rootstocks; some, like St. Augustine (*Stenotaphrum secudatum*), increase by extending their stems and rooting at the nodes like any other horizontal vine. In addition there are many grasses that climb vertically, gaining height by entwining with other plants. Richard Spruce in his *Notes of a Botanist on the Amazon and Andes* described rampant species of *Panicum* which occur in the red-bark forests, and "spread among adjacent branches to a height of 15 feet or more."

Agnes Arber (130) says that these climbers, however, are outclassed in their measurements by certain swamp and water grasses. She continues:

"The aquatic form of *Coix lacryma-jobi,* for instance, is said to reach a length of 100 feet. From a floating grass island on the upper Amazon, consisting exclusively of *Paspalum pyramiadale* Nees, Spruce succeeded in drawing up an entire stem, which measured 45 feet in length and possessed 78 nodes. Even in our cold climate, we can find a parallel for this elongation. There is a singular form of the reed, *Phragmites communis* TRINIUS var.

387

*repens* MEYER, which has been described from 'the slipped banks of wet and almost semifluid clay, skirting the southern shores' of the Isle of Wight. In this form the culms are said to depend like long and slender ropes on the steep sides of the landslips, or to trail in a straight or serpentine direction on the shingly beach, or smooth and level sand, without rooting at the joints, to the length of 20 to 40, or even 50 feet. These elongated axes are apparently always sterile, and their leaves are very much reduced. Occasionally a few rootlets arise from the joints, but in general the plant lies quite prostrate and entirely unconnected with the soil, so that it may be wound about any object like a cord.

"The barren shoots of various grasses, especially *Agrostis palustris* HUDSON and species of *Alopecurus,* may attain great lengths when they grow under swamp conditions."

These climbing grasses are of only casual interest to the dirt gardener.

## 14—CLIMBING EPIPHYTES

Many tropical plants begin life as epiphytes—air plants resting on high branches of "host plants," instead of making contact with the ground. Some terrestrial plants that start with their roots in the soil grow up into the branches of a nearby tree and then disconnect themselves from the earth, usually by the rotting away of the main stem, and they become epiphytes in this manner. It is a confused world that requires a special section here to explain the mechanism of the climbers in this group.

"Epiphyte" is the name given to plants which live on other plants, but derive no nourishment from them. This is in contrast to parasites, which live on other plants and do derive their nourishment from the host.

In the temperate zone, lichens, some mosses, and some ferns are good examples of epiphytes. These are not climbers. In the tropics a great many other plants are epiphytes, such as orchids (Photograph 379), bromeliads, aroids (described elsewhere in this chapter), and even some cacti and rhododendrons. Some of these are climbers. Typical examples are described herein.

Chittenden (22) says that many of the epiphytes:

"have roots of a peculiar structure enabling them to condense and absorb moisture from the atmosphere, or leaf structures preventing dangerous loss of water. Their peculiar powers and habit of growth have earned for several the name of air plant. They are naturally most abundant where the atmosphere is humid and the temperature uniformly high, as in luxuriant tropical forests."

In the tropics many plants begin life as terrestrials, then climb a host plant such as a tree; later their connection with the earth rots away and they become strictly epiphytic. Species of *Philodendron* (Photograph 378) and *Monstera* are good examples and are described in another part of this chapter. (Aroids— Part IX.)

380.   MYRMECODIA BECCARI        381.   HYDNOPHYTUM FORMICARIUM

382.   DISCHIDIA COLLYRIS        383.   DISCHIDIA RAFFLESIANA

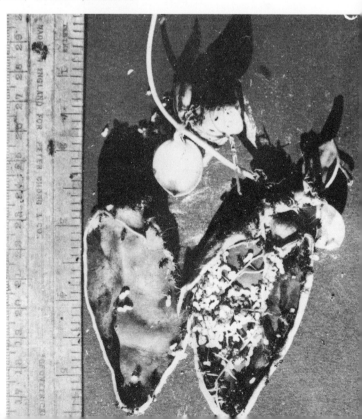

Contrariwise, some epiphytes begin life as air plants in the branch of a tree where the seed germinates. They begin to grow, then drop roots to the earth and later become terrestrial. This is particularly true of the fig species *Ficus parasitica,* in which the flowers are never seen because they are inside the fruit, but it is also a common manner of growth for many other shrubs and trees. A good example is *Clusia* of which there are 145 species in tropical America, Madagascar, and New Caledonia. Mostly they are climbing epiphytes, clasping the host, sometimes strangling it, then frequently dropping roots to the earth and becoming big trees. A few species of *Clusia* have beautiful flowers, for example *C. rosea* (Photograph 376), commonly called copey, scotch attorney, or autograph-tree. This is cultivated in seaside gardens in Florida, Hawaii, and Cuba as a tree because of its high resistance to winds and salt spray. It is never cultivated as an air plant.

A specimen of *C. grandiflora* has been cultivated as a tree in the Cambridge Botanical Garden, England, for more than 40 years, frequently being cut back to keep it within bounds. It is included here because, although never a climber in gardens, it is always a climber in nature. It has most spectacular white flowers 7 to 8 inches across, borne in 3's, at branch tips. (Photograph 377.) The end flower opens first; after it has finished blooming, the side flowers open. They are ephemeral, usually opening at night and falling off the next day.

A number of other species of *Clusia* are under cultivation at the Fairchild Tropical Garden in Miami, but as trees, not as climbers. (The Cambridge specimen is fully described in *Gardener's Chronicle* March 2, 1929.)

Historical records show that the dry, hard, tough, but flexible leaves of *Clusia* were used as playing cards by the sailors who accompanied Columbus to America 500 years ago.

Ordinarily epiphytes do not injure the host plant in any way, even when the plant is bulky and might be considered objectionable for other reasons. For example, *Myrmecodia.* (Photograph 380.) The basal part of these plants, sometimes armed with short spines, are very greatly enlarged and contain many tunnels where myriads of small black ants make their home. For the partnership which these ants form with the trees, in which each one protects the other, *see* Menninger: *Fantastic Trees.* It is doubtful if *Myrmecodia* does any climbing, although it spreads along the branch, and Willis (118) says it is doubtful whether the ants render any service to the plant.

Some of the epiphytic vines that are hosts to ants are described by Merrill (131):

> "Most peculiar are those leaf adaptations noted in *Hoya, Dischidia,* and *Conchophyllum,* all vines with abundant milky sap belonging in the milkweed family (*Asclepiadaceae*). Some of these hang free, as epiphytes or semi-epiphytes, but in *Conchophyllum* and in some species of *Hoya* the vines may be closely appressed to the tree trunks or branches, while the circular leaves, one row on each side of the slender stem, are convex with their margins very closely appressed to the bark. Under each leaf many roots are produced from the leaf axil, which often quite cover that part of

the bark protected by the leaf, serving to hold the plant in place and to absorb moisture and nourishment for the needs of the plant; each of these ready-made homes under each leaf is occupied by colonies of small ants."

*Dischidia* (Photograph 382) is described by Willis (118) thus:

". . . 80 species in Indomalaysia, Polynesia, and Australia. Epiphytic, climbing by adventitious roots, and with fleshy leaves covered by wax. The curious pitcher-plant, *D. rafflesiana,* besides the ordinary leaves, has pitcher-leaves. Each is a pitcher with incurved margin, about 4 inches deep. Into it grows an adventitious root, developed from the stem or petiole just beside it. The pitcher may hang with its mouth upwards or may stand horizontally or upside down. It usually contains a lot of debris, largely carried into it by nesting ants. Most contain some rain water, so that perhaps they act as humus collectors and water reservoirs. The inner surface is waxy, so that the water cannot be absorbed by the pitcher itself, but must be taken up by the roots. Developmental study shows the pitcher to be a leaf with its lower side invaginated. The existing species illustrate all stages. Many, e.g. *D. bengalensis,* have bi-convex leaves; others have the under-surface concave, e.g. *D. collyris,* and the roots are developed under and sheltered by the concave leaves. A further invagination would lead to *D. rafflesiana."* (Photograph 383.)

Chittenden (22) classifies *Myrmecodia* as a shrub in the coffee family. *Hydnophytum,* also of the coffee family, is a genus of about 30 species of "very curious, epiphytic, glabrous shrubs, with deformed, fleshy, tuberous, simple-lobed bases, which are excavated and inhabited by ants." Both may be shrubs but often they are vine-supported. (See illustration of *Hydnophytum,* Photograph 381.) Vine structure very definitely plays an important part in their existence.

––––––

The only vines completely ignored in this book are the seaweeds. This is strange because seaweeds are presumed to be the ancient ancestors from which all plant life has developed on the land.

# OTHER ACKNOWLEDGMENTS

In addition to the collaborators who have written parts of this book, at least fifty more persons have had a share in putting it together.

The first group includes those who provided inspiration. Chief among them I would name Dr. Richard A. Howard, Director of the Arnold Arboretum, who not only wrote parts of the manuscript himself but pinpointed other scholars who would help. He answered the author's endless questions, he identified photographs of tropical climbers (an almost impossible task), and he acted as a balance wheel when going was rough and the project seemed overwhelming.

E. J. H. Corner has been an inspiration to this writer since we sat together at David Fairchild's luncheon table a quarter of a century ago and talked for hours of the tropical plants we loved. Corner wanted to write a book about vines but never got time. I hope this study reflects his stimulus.

Dr. Leonard J. Brass of the Archbold Expeditions, American Museum of Natural History, New York, and J. S. Womersley, a botanist-forester in Lae, New Guinea, have worked together to make possible a presentation of the many beautiful vines in the South Pacific.

Harry Blossfeld of São Paulo, Brazil, for twenty years has responded wonderfully to my questions. If he did not have the answers, he found them. He is the author of a book about climbers in Brazil; consequently was a wonderful guide in that part of the world.

The second group of helpers has been the research librarians. Chief of these are Julia Morton of the Morton Collectanea, University of Miami, Coral Gables, Florida, and Peter Hyypio of the Bailey Hortorium, Cornell University, Ithaca, New York. Often sent on wild goose chases, they invariably came back with the information needed to make factual descriptions in this book.

Manuscript readers are a necessary advisory group for every author. These have included a composition expert, Mrs. L. T. Hawley of the University of Alabama; a botanist, Dorcas Brigham, who taught at Smith College, Northampton, Massachusetts, for 24 years; Mrs. Max Zeller, Mrs. George D. Wait, and Mrs. George Sollitt of Stuart, Florida, practical gardeners who know their vines; literary agent, Carol Woodward of Roxbury, Conn.; Mrs. Morton again, for she is also a botanist with special acquaintance with many tropical climbers; and my neighbors, Mary Blow and Louise Moyse of Cashiers, N.C. Special help with pictures was given by Mrs. Clyde Coutant and Mrs. Carl Turner of Stuart, Mrs. Margaret Clark of Cullowhee, N.C., Mrs. Mike Rodgers of Palm Beach and Mrs. Dora Hoffman of Miami. Many others have read this script helpfully and I am grateful to all of them.

I am indebted to hundreds of persons all over the world with whom I have made special contact to ask about this or that vine, to obtain pictures, to straighten out some misunderstanding, and in other ways to make this book as complete and as authoritative as possible. I induced a hundred plantsmen who have traveled far and seen a lot of vines to nominate the half dozen they thought were the most beautiful in the world; their opinions are reflected here. Many friends and secretaries have spent weary hours going over this manuscript. If the book sparkles, it is because of their interest and scholarship. I am indebted to the many who have helped make this book a reality.

Edwin A. Menninger

# PHOTOGRAPHIC CREDITS

The artistry and skill of the fourscore persons who supplied the photographs which enrich and enliven the pages of this book add enormously to its value, its usefulness, and its interest, especially to the layman who loves vines but knows nothing of their technical names and relationships. Because all the pictures are adjacent to the descriptions of the plants and are referred to by number in the text, the flower lover who consults this reference volume will find what he needs all in one place.

The author acknowledges his debt to those who took the pictures and expresses his gratitude to them for help that means so much. Here are the names of the photographers and the numbers of the photographs they took.

Allen, Paul, Golfo Dulce, Honduras; 305
Anderson, R. H., Botanical Gardens, Sydney; 87, 223
Anton-Smith, J., Chilanga, Malawi; color plates 4, 12, 72
Arnold Arboretum, Jamaica Plain, Mass.; 85, 127, 131, 168, 169, 170, 171, 225, 228, 235, 236, 239, 258, 328, 333
Ayres, Dr. Samuel, Jr., Los Angeles, Calif.; 92; color plates 78, 79
Baker, R. J., Honolulu; 106, 138, 165, 196, 208, 286, 315
Barry, David, Jr., Los Angeles, Calif.; color plates 135, 141, 145
Berrie, Dr. G. K., Limbe, Malawi; color plate 180
Bernice P. Bishop Museum, Honolulu; 107, 185, 245, 285, 375
Bogor Botanic Garden, Indonesia; 364; color plates 64, 103
Bose, Dr. T. K., Royal Agri-Horticultural Society, Calcutta; 34, 37, 79, 299, 314; color plate 92
Botanical Garden, Algiers; 134
Brigham, Dorcas, Mt. Dora, Fla.; color plates 38, 153
Brisbane Botanic Garden, Australia; color plate 59
Burkill, L. M., Botanic Garden, Singapore; 174, 175, 178, 366, 367, 381, 382, 383; color plates 20, 23, 94, 178, 196
Cambridge Botanical Garden, Cambridge, England; 377
Cavender, Florence, Medellín, Columbia; 340; color plates 15, 74, 96, 152, 161, 163
Cornell, Ralph D., Hollywood, Calif.; color plates 9, 10, 11, 21, 39, 118, 176
Corner, E. J. H., Cambridge, England; 290
Craighead, Dr. F. C., Homestead, Fla.; 153, 293, 300, 303, 358
Curtis's Botanical Magazine; 262, 263, 380
Cutak, Ladislaus, Missouri Botanic Garden, St. Louis; 63, 64, 65, 67, 68, 69, 71, 72, 73, 75, 76, 77, 98; color plate 46
Cypress Gardens, Winter Haven, Fla.; color plates 130, 131
Dale, Mrs. F. A., Asheville, N. C.; color plates 169, 174
Danley, Cole, Jr., Lake Placid, Fla.; 155
Delange, Yves, Montpellier, France; 97, 113, 117

Downward, J. E., Woodford Green, Essex, England; 6, 52, 86, 91, 105, 115, 116, 123, 135, 148, 152, 156, 183, 193, 216, 230, 231, 232, 234, 265, 273, 276, 278

Duran, Ramon, Rio de Janeiro; 3, 198, 256; color plate 144

Elliott, Douglas, New Plymouth, New Zealand; 4, 47, 58, 59, 61, 89, 100, 109, 120, 126, 132, 149, 159, 160, 163, 166, 188, 190, 191, 214, 215, 217, 218, 219, 229, 247, 262, 277, 347; color plates 93, 129

Fairchild, Dr. David; 143

Farnham, George, Harbor City, Calif.; 36, 82, 93, 96, 130, 192, 274, 298; color plates 2, 42, 81, 164

Finnis, Valerie, Wheatley, Oxford, England; color plate 15

Fitch, Charles Marden, Mamaroneck, N. Y.; color plates 84, 120, 188

Federal Agricultural Experiment Station, Mayaguez, Puerto Rico; 206

Florida Agricultural Experiment Station, Gainesville; 41, 43, 54, 74, 139, 140, 141, 195, 197, 199, 200, 201, 267, 272, 301, 308

Floristico, Album, Rio de Janeiro; 1

*The Gleaner,* Kingston, Jamaica; 270

Godbey, Robert J., Kendall, Fla.; 288; color plates 48, 56, 71, 148, 192

Golby, Eric, Reasoner's Tropical Nurseries, Bradenton, Fla.; 178; color plates 27, 47, 49, 61, 63, 112, 114, 143, 147

Greiff, Victor, Neponsit, N. Y.; 16, 259; color plates 7, 29, 43, 80, 104, 116

Guy, G. L., National Museum, Bulawayo, Rhodesia; color plates 40, 50

Halgrim, Robert E., Thomas A. Edison Estate, Ft. Myers, Fla.; 207

Hallé, Dr. Francis, Brazzaville, Congo; 42, 44, 45, 186, 233, 248, 249, 250, 251, 291, 311, 324, 325, 326, 327; color plates 5, 54, 62, 99, 182

Hallicy, Edwin, Stuart, Fla.; 187, 213

Hardin, Dr. James, North Carolina State University, Raleigh; color plate 127

Hargraves, Bob, Kailua, Hawaii; 50; color plates 89, 186

Holttum, Dr. R. E., Royal Botanic Gardens, Kew, England; color plates 134, 136, 137, 139, 140

Ho Sai-Huen, Kepong, Selangor, Malaya; 2, 90, 209, 212, 344, 360, 361, 362, 363, 371, 379

Jacksonville Journal, Jacksonville, Fla.; 177

Jolly, Mrs. A. L., c/o Caroni, Ltd., Coava, Trinidad; color plate 191

Langlois, M. A., Nassau, Bahamas; 365

Longwood Gardens, Kennett Square, Pa., 5, 7, 60, 88, 173, 203, 221, 304; color plate 45

Lord, Ernest E., Melbourne, Australia; 345; color plates 90, 91, 163, 165, 166, 167

Lothian, T. R. N., Adelaide Botanic Garden, Australia; 316, 322; color plates 100, 113, 117

Maheshwari, Dr. J. K., National Botanic Gardens, Lucknow, India; 99, 112, 312, 330, 331; color plates 69, 82

March, Dr. Sylvester G., U. S. National Arboretum, Washington, D. C.; color plates 170, 172, 173, 175

Mason, R. A., *Better Homes & Gardens,* Des Moines, Iowa; color plate 111

Mathias, Dr. Mildred, UCLA, Los Angeles; color plates 31, 51, 132

McKee Jungle Gardens, Vero Beach, Fla.; 205

Moran, Dr. Reid, Balboa Park, San Diego; 353; color plate 13

Morton, Mrs. Julia, Morton Collectanea, University of Miami, Coral Gables; 18, 30, 31, 39, 94, 95, 101, 102, 103, 104, 108, 145, 146, 154, 156, 158, 164, 180, 181, 220, 244, 287, 292, 296, 297, 302, 306, 310, 329, 334, 341, 342, 346, 349, 350, 354, 357, 359, 373, 374; color plates 30, 36, 95, 150, 193

National Botanic Gardens, Pretoria, South Africa; 32; color plates 26, 115, 142

Nixon, F. A., Hong Kong; color plate 194

Nogueira-Neto, Paulo, São Paulo, Brazil; color plate 122

Peart, Paul J., Monterey Park, Calif.; 12, 13, 83, 118, 122, 237

Pike, A. N., Trumpington, Cambridge, England; 175, 182, 268, 332

Quartey, L. M., Aburi, Ghana; 338

Quinn, J. Graham, Institute for Agricultural Research, Zaria, Nigeria; color plates 55, 57, 76, 85, 128

Reeves, H. T., Hawthorn, Victoria; 161, 162

Ricou, Earl Dyer, Stuart, Fla.; 112, 376

Rodin, Dr. Robt. J., California Polytechnic, San Luis Obispo; color plate 168

Root, Paul, Miami; 14, 70, 110, 224, 323, 368, 369; color plates 37, 52, 53, 110, 160

City of San Francisco, Park Dept.; 55

Sargent, Dr. Ralph, Highlands, N.C.; color plates 75, 181, 187

Scanlon, Edward H., *Trees,* Olmsted Falls, Ohio; 8, 9, 10, 11

Scowen, Kenneth, Headley Grove, Surrey; 49

Sharon, Ken, Boynton Beach, Fla; 194; color plates 3, 6, 18, 19, 22, 24, 25, 28, 33, 35, 41, 65, 66, 73, 77, 87, 97, 119, 125, 138, 149, 154, 155, 189, 195

Smith, Dr. A. C., University of Hawaii, Honolulu; color plate 121

Smith, Harry, Westcliff-on-Sea, England; 17, 40, 56, 80, 81, 84, 98, 114, 119, 121, 124, 129, 142, 184, 189, 202, 210, 222, 226, 227, 242, 243, 253, 254, 257, 261, 264, 319, 320, 335, 336, 343, 348, 351, 352, 355, 356; color plates 44, 83

Strang, Dr. Harold Edgard, Rio de Janeiro; color plates 8, 68, 101, 102, 108, 133, 156, 159

Strybing Arboretum, San Francisco; 38, 46, 53, 211, 255

Tillett, Dr. Stephen S., Univ. de la Region Centro-Occidentale, Baraquisimeto, Venezuela; color plates 60, 98, 151, 157, 158, 190

U.S.D.A., Washington, D.C.; 150, 151, 167, 238, 294, 295, 307, 313, 337, 372

Vaid, K. M., Dehra Dun, India; 35, 137, 204, 240, 241; color plates 16, 70, 86, 106, 107, 185

Van Steenis, C. G. G. J., Groningen, Holland; 289

Weissich, Paul, Foster Botanical Garden, Honolulu; 51

Whitman, Wm. F., Bal Harbour, Miami Beach; 15

Womersley, J. S., Lae, New Guinea; color plates 88, 105, 109, 179

Wright, Rob, P. R. O., Suva, Fiji; color plate 124

Wurdack, Dr. John J., Smithsonian Institution, Washington, D.C.; color plate 123

# DRAWINGS AND DIAGRAMS CREDITS

How Vines Climb by Eva Melady, Hackensack, New Jersey

Climbing Palms by Francis Hallé, Ecole des Sciences, Brazzaville, Congo

Gnetaceae Relationship by E.J.H. Corner, Cambridge University, Cambridge, England

*Marcgravia* and *Passiflora* by Edwin Taft Hallicy, Southeastern Printing Company, Stuart, Florida

*Dioscorea* from Massal & Barrau: *Food Plants of the South Sea Islands*

# PRINCIPAL PUBLICATIONS REFERRED TO IN THE TEXT

1. Arnold-Forster, W.: *Shrubs for the Milder Counties.* Country Life, Ltd., London, 1948.
2. Arnott, S.: *The Book of Climbing Plants and Wall Shrubs.* John Lane, London, 1903.
3. Bailey, Liberty Hyde and Bailey, Ethel Zoe: *Hortus Second.* Macmillan, New York, 1941.
4. Bailey, Liberty Hyde: *The Standard Cyclopedia of Horticulture.* 3 vols. Macmillan, New York. "New ed." (Repr.), 1939.
5. ———: *Manual of Cultivated Plants.* Macmillan, New York, 1949.
6. Bean, W. J.: *Wall Shrubs and Hardy Climbers.* Putnam, New York, 1945.
7. Bertrand, A.: *Succulent Plants Other Than Cacti.* Philosophical Library, New York, 1959.
8. Blossfeld, Harry: *Trepadeiras* (Vines). Part 13 of *Floriculture Brasileira,* 2d ed. Chacaras e Quintais, Sao Paulo, Brazil, 1964.
9. Bor, N. L. and Raizada, M. B.: *Some Beautiful Indian Climbers and Shrubs.* Bombay Natural History Society, Bombay, 1954.
10. Brilmayer, Bernice: *All About Vines and Hanging Plants.* Doubleday, Garden City, N. Y., 1962.
11. Brimer, John Burton: "You Can Train Plants to Do Tricks." *Horticulture,* Boston, April 1959.
12. Britton, N. L. and Rose, J. M.: *The Cactaceae.* Dover Publications, New York, 1963.
13. Britton, N. L. and Wilson, Percy: *Botany of Puerto Rico and the Virgin Islands.* New York Academy of Science, New York. (Scientific Survey of Porto Rico and the Virgin Islands, Vols. 5, 6. 1923-1930.)
14. Brooklyn Botanic Garden: *Greenhouse Handbook for the Amateur.* Vol. XIX:2 of *Plants & Gardens,* 1963.
15. ——— *Handbook on Vines.* Vol. X:1, 1954.
16. ——— *Trained & Succulent Plants.* Vol. XVII:2, 1961.
17. Brown, N. E. as *Tecoma brycei* N. E. Br. in *Gard. Chron.* Series III, xxxix, 344, 1906.
18. Brown, William Henry: *Useful Plants of the Philippines.* 3 vols. Philippine Dept. of Agriculture and Commerce, Manila. Repr. 1951-1958.
19. Bruggeman, L.: *Tropical Plants and Their Cultivation.* Viking Press, New York, 1962.
20. Burbidge, F. W.: *Gardens of the Sun.* John Murray, London, 1880.
21. Burkill, Isaac Henry: *A Dictionary of the Economic Products of the Malay Peninsula,* 2 vols. Crown Agents, London, 1935.
22. Chittenden, Frederick James: *The Royal Horticultural Society Dictionary of Gardening.* 4 vols., Clarendon Press, Oxford, 1951; first supplement, 1956; second supplement, 1969.
23. Codd, Leslie Edward W.: *Trees and Shrubs of the Kruger National Park.* Union of South Africa Dept. of Agriculture, Pretoria, 1951.
24. Crockett, James Underwood: *Greenhouse Gardening as a Hobby.* Doubleday, Garden City, N. Y., 1961.
25. Curto, Frank: "Vines" in *Horticulture,* Boston, Dec. 1964.
26. Dalzell, N. Z. and Gibson, A., *The Bombay Flora,* 1861.
27. Dalziel, John McEwen: *Useful Plants of West Tropical Africa.* Crown Agents, London. New ed., 1948.
28. Daubenmire, R. F.: *Plants and Environment.* 2d ed., John Wiley & Sons, New York, 1959.
29. Degener, Otto: *Flora Hawaiiensis.* Author, Honolulu, 1932 to date.
30. Dickey, R. D., West, Erdman, and Mowry, Harold: *Ornamental Vines for Florida.* Univ. of Florida, Agricultural Extension Service, Gainesville. Bulletin 172A. 1963.
31. Dyer, R. A., Chief, Botanical Search Institute, Pretoria, South Africa.
32. Eliovson, Sima: *Flowering Trees, Shrubs and Climbers for South Africa.* 4th ed. Howard Timmins, Cape Town, 1962.
33. Fairchild, David G.: *Exploring for Plants.* Macmillan, New York, 1930.
34. ——— *Garden Islands of the Great East.* Charles Scribner's Sons, New York, 1943.
35. ——— *The World Grows Round My Door.* Charles Scribner's Sons, New York, 1947.
36. ——— *The World Was My Garden.* Charles Scribner's Sons, New York, 1947.
37. Firminger: *Manual of Gardening for India.* 8th ed. Thacker, Spink & Co., Calcutta, 1958.
38. Fisk, Jim: *Success with Clematis.* Melson, London, 1962.
39. Fitzgerald, H. Purefoy: *A Concise Handbook of Climbers, Twiners and Wall Shrubs.* Methuen, London, 1906.
40. Foley, Daniel J.: *Ground Covers for Easier Gardening.* Chilton Co., Philadelphia, 1961.
41. Freeman, William George and Williams, Robert Orchard: *The Useful and Ornamental Plants of Trinidad and Tobago* (Dept. of Agriculture), Port-of-Spain. 2d ed., 1951.
42. Fritsch, F. E. and Salisbury, E. J.: *Plant Form and Function.* G. Bell & Sons, Ltd., London, 1941.
43. Garden Section, Woman's Club of Havana: *Flowering Plants from Cuban Gardens.* Criterion Books, New York, 1962.
44. Genders, Roy: *Covering a Wall.* Robert Hale, London, 1957.
45. Ginns, R.: *Cacti and Other Succulents.* Royal Horticultural Society, London, n.d.
46. Gough, Kathleen: *A Garden Book for Malaya.* H. F. & G. Witherby, London, 1928.
47. Grabham, Michael C.: *Plants Seen in Madeira.* Lewis, London, 1934.
48. Haage, Walther: *Cacti and Succulents.* E. P. Dutton, New York, 1963.
49. Hall, H.: *"Podranea brycei"* in *Gardener's Chronicle,* Series III, 125:170. May 14, 1949.
50. Hallé, Francis, botanist with I.R.S.T.O.M., Abidjan, Ivory Coast.
51. Harris, Thistle Yolette: *Australian Plants for the Garden.* Angus & Robertson, London and Sydney, 1953.
52. Higgins, Vera: *Succulents in Cultivation.* St. Martin's Press, New York, 1960.
53. Hodge, Walter H.: "Training Vines under Conservatory Conditions." *Plants & Gardens* (Brooklyn Botanic Garden), Summer 1961.
54. Holttum, Richard Eric: *Gardening in the Lowlands of Malaya.* Straits Times Press, Singapore, 1953.
55. ——— *Plant Life in Malaya.* Longmans, Green & Co., London, 1954.
56. Hottes, Alfred Carl: *Climbers and Ground Covers.* A. T. de la Mare Co., New York, 1947.
57. Howard, Frances: *Landscaping with Vines.* Macmillan, New York, 1959.
58. Hoyt, Roland Stewart: *Check Lists for the Ornamental Plants of Subtropical Regions.* Livingston Press, Los Angeles, 1958.
59. Hume, Edward P.: *Some Ornamental Vines for the Tropics.* Circular No. 31, Federal Experiment Station, Puerto Rico. USDA, 1949.
60. Hundley, H. G. and Ko Ko, U Chit: *List of Trees, Shrubs, Herbs and Principal Climbers, etc.* (Burma). Government Printer, Rangoon, 1961.
61. Hutchinson, John: *A Botanist in Southern Africa.* P. R. Gawthorn, Ltd., London, 1946.
62. ——— *The Families of Flowering Plants,* 2 vols. Clarendon Press, Oxford. Ed. 2, 1959.
63. Hutchinson, John and Dalziel, John McEwen: *Flora of West Tropical Africa.* 2 vols. in 4 parts. Crown Agents, London, 1927-1936. New ed., rev. by R. W. J. Keay, 1958.
64. Huttleston, Donald G. in *American Horticultural Magazine,* Oct. 1957.
65. Irvine, F. R.: *Woody Plants of Ghana.* Oxford University Press, London, 1961.
66. Jacobsen, Hermann: *A Handbook on Succulent Plants.* Blandford Press, London, 1960.
67. Jex-Blake, A. J. (Editor): *Gardening in East Africa.* 4th ed., Longmans, Green & Co., London, 1957.
68. Jones, Katherine D.: "Thirty Important Vines for California" in *American Horticultural Magazine,* Jan. 1936.
69. ——— "Thirty More Climbers for California" in *American Horticultural Magazine,* Jan. 1937.
70. Jussieu, A. L. de: *Ann. Sci. Nat. Ser.* 2:13.278. 1840.
71. Kuck, Loraine E. and Tongg, Richard C.: *The Modern Tropical Garden.* Tongg Publishing Co., Honolulu, 1955.
72. Kurian, K. C.: *"Bauhinia phoenicea,* a Climber of Rare Beauty from Malabar" in *Indian Horticulture,* July-Sept. 1963.

73. Lawson, Jean: "Vines: The Plants that Pay Off Best." *House Beautiful,* May 1957.

74. Leuthardt, Henry P.: "Espalier Trees in the Landscape." *Trees Magazine* 26:2:6-11 Jan.-Feb. 1966. Olmsted Falls, Ohio.

75. Lindley, John and Moore, Thomas: *Treasury of Botany.* 2 vols. Longmans, Green & Co., London. 2d ed., 1884.

76. Lord, Ernest E.: *Shrubs and Trees for Australian Gardens.* 4th ed. Lothian, Melbourne, 1964.

77. Macbride, J. Francis: *Flora of Peru.* Field Museum of Natural History, Botanical Series, vol. 13, Chicago, 1936 to date.

78. Macmillan, Hugh Fraser: *Tropical Planting and Gardening* with Special Reference to Ceylon. Macmillan & Co., Ltd., London, 5th ed., 1948.

79. Marsden, C.: *Grow Cacti.* 2d ed. Cleaver-Hume Press, London, 1958.

80. McCollum, William C.: *Vines and How to Grow Them.* William Heinemann, London, 1912.

81. McDonald, Elvin: *The Flowering Greenhouse Day by Day.* D. Van Nostrand Co., Princeton, N. J., 1966.

82. Miquel: *Linnaea* xviii (1844) 254; now correctly *C. latifolia* K. Shum. in Engl. & Prantl, *Naturlichen Pflanzenfamilien,* iv, 3b, 223, 1894.

83. Moore, Harold E. Jr.: *African Violets, Gloxinias, and Their Relatives.* Macmillan, New York, 1957.

84. Neal, Marie C.: *In Gardens of Hawaii.* Bernice P. Bishop Museum, Honolulu. Publication No. 50. Revised edition 1965.

85. Nehrling, Henry: *My Garden in Florida.* 2 vols. American Eagle, Estero, Fla. 1935.

86. Nielsen, Margaret Steentoft: *Introduction to the Flowering Plants of West Africa.* University of London Press, London, 1965.

87. Oakman, Harry, Park Supt., Canberra City, Australia.

88. Pal, B. P.: *Beautiful Climbers of India.* Indian Council of Agricultural Research, New Delhi, 1960.

89. Parham, J. W.: *Plants of the Fiji Islands.* Government Press, Suva, Fiji, 1964.

90. Pearce, S. A.: *Climbing and Trailing Plants.* Collingridge, London, 1957.

91. Peattie, Donald Culross: *Natural History of Western Trees.* Houghton-Mifflin Co., Boston, 1953.

92. Perkins, Harold O.: *Espaliers and Vines for the Home Gardener.* D. Van Nostrand Co., Princeton, N. J., 1964.

93. Peters, Ruth Marie: "Plants that Climb and Hang," in *Greenhouse Handbook* of Brooklyn Botanic Garden, vol. xix: 2 of *Plants & Gardens,* 1963.

94. Pike, Albert V.: "Seasonal Work with Greenhouse Climbers" in *Gardener's Chronicle,* Jan. 16, 1965.

95. Pulle, August Adriaan (Ed.): *Flora of Suriname* (Netherlands Guiana) Coloniaal Instituut te Amsterdam, Amsterdam, 1932-1951.

96. Riley, Herbert Parkes: *Families of Flowering Plants of Southern Africa.* University of Kentucky Press, Lexington, Ky., 1963.

97. Roxburgh, W.: *Flora Indica.* Thacker, Spink & Co., Bombay, 1874.

98. Schimper, A. F. W.: "Die Epiphytische Vegetation Amerikas." *Botanische Mittheilunger aus den Tropen* II. Jena, 1888.

99. Schulz, Peggie: *Gloxinias and How to Grow Them.* M. Barrows & Co., New York, 1965.

100. Smiley, Nixon: *Subtropical Gardening in Florida.* University of Miami Press, Coral Gables, 1951.

101. Spencer, Edwin Rollin: *Just Weeds.* 2d ed. Charles Scribner's Sons, New York, 1957.

102. Sprague, T. A., in Dyer: *Flora of Tropical Africa* IV, II 515 (1906) as *Tecoma brycei.*

103. Standley, Paul C.: *Flora of the Lancetilla Valley,* Honduras. Field Museum of Natural History, Botanical Series, vol. 10, pp. 1-418, Chicago, 1931.

104. ——— *Trees and Shrubs of Mexico.* Smithsonian Institution, Washington, D. C. 1924.

105. Standley, Paul Carpenter and Steyermark, Julian Alfred: *Flora of Guatemala.* Fieldiana, vol. 24. Chicago Natural History Museum, Chicago, 1946 to date.

106. Steiner, Mona Lisa: *Philippine Ornamental Plants.* 2nd ed. Philippine Education Co., Manila, 1960.

107. Story, R.: "Some Plants Used by the Bushmen in Obtaining Food and Water" in *Botanical Survey of South Africa,* Memoir No. 30.

108. Thomas, Arthur: *Gardening in Hot Countries.* Faber & Faber, London, 1965.

109. Thorne, Thomas: *Fuchsias for All Purposes.* W. H. & L. Collingridge, Ltd., London, 1959.

110. Tree Society of Southern Africa: *Trees and Shrubs of the Witwatersrand.* Witwatersrand University Press, Johannesburg, 1964.

111. Trimen, Henry: *A Handbook of the Flora of Ceylon.* Six parts. Dulan & Co., London, 1893-1930.

112. Van Steenis, C. G. G. J. (ed.): *Flora Malesiana.* Noordhof-Kolff N. V., Djakarta, 1948-1958; N. V. Erven P. Noordhoff, Groningen, 1959-.

113. Vines, Robert A.: *Trees, Shrubs and Woody Vines of the Southwest.* University of Texas Press, Austin, 1960.

114. Wallace, Alfred Russel: *The Malay Archipelago.* Macmillan, London, 1890.

115. Warren, John T.: "Greenhouse Climbers" in *Gardener's Chronicle,* Oct. 3, 1964.

116. Watson, William: *Climbing Plants.* T. C. & E. C. Jack, London, n.d.

117. Whitehead, Stanley B.: *Garden Clematis.* J. Gifford, London, 1959.

118. Willis, John Christopher: *Dictionary of the Flowering Plants and Ferns.* Cambridge University Press. 7th ed., rev. 1966.

119. Wilson, Stanley J.: *Fuchsias.* St. Martin's Press, New York, 1965.

120. Wyman, Donald: *Ground Cover Plants.* Macmillan, New York, 1056.

## MISCELLANEOUS REFERENCES

121. Green, Peter S.: Studies in the genus *Jasminum* I. *Notes Roy. Bot. Gard.* Edin. 23:355-84. 1961.

122. Green, Peter S.: Studies in the genus *Jasminum* II. *Jour. Arnold Arb.* 43:109-131. 1962.

123. Green, Peter S.: Studies in the genus *Jasminum* III. The species in cultivation in North America. *Baileya* 13:4:137-172. 1965.

124. Kobuski, Clarence E.: Synopsis of the Chinese species of *Jasminum. Jour. Arnold Arb.* 13:145-179. 1932.

125. Wyman, Donald: "Registration List of Cultivar Names in *Forsythia*" in *Arnoldia* 21:39-42, 1961.

126. Corner, E. J. H.: *A Natural History of Palms.* University of California Press, Berkeley. 1966.

127. Smith, A. C.: The American Species of Thibaudieae. *Contrib. U.S. National Herbarium* 28: 311-547.

128. Kuijt, Job: *The Biology of Parasitic Flowering Plants.* University of California Press, 1969.

129. McClure, F. A.: *The Bamboos, A Fresh Perspective.* Harvard University Press, Cambridge, Mass., 1965.

130. Arber, Agnes: *The Gramineae: Cereal, Bamboo and Grass.* Stechert-Hafner, New York, 1965.

131. Merrill, E. D.: *Plant Life of the Pacific World.* Macmillan, New York, 1945.

132. Howard, R. A.: "Notes On The Cultivated Woody Species of Clitoria." *Baileya* 15:1, Jan.-Mar. 1967.

133. July-Sept., 1963.

134. Troup, Robert Scott: *The Silviculture of Indian Trees.* Clarendon Press, Oxford, England, 1918.

135. *Royal Horticultural Society Proceedings* 35, p. lix.

136. *Revue Horticole* 1909, p. 247.

137. *Revue Horticole* 1915, p. 376.

138. *Proc. Roy. Hort. Soc.* Volume 5, p. 90.

139. *Ill. Hort.* Vol. 13, t. 466, 1866.

140. *Flora of Peru,* Field Museum of Natural History, Botanical Series 13 (part 3, number 3): p. 910, 1950.

141. Standley, Paul and Steyermark, Julian A.: *Flora of Guatemala,* Fieldiana: Botany 24 (part 6): 21-22, 1949.

142. *Epixiphium wislizeni* (Engelm.) Munz [Syn.: *Maurandya wislizeni* Engelm.; *Asarina wislizeni* (Engelm.) Pennell].

400

143. *Lophospermum erubescens* Don [Sny.: *Maurandya erubescens* (Don) Gray; *M. erubescens* var. *typica* Munz; *Asarina erubescens* (Don) Pennell].

144. *Maurandella antirrhiniflora* (HBK) Rothm. [Syn.: *Maurandia antirrhiniflora* HBK; *Antirrhinum maurandioides* Gray; *Asarina antirrhiniflora* (HBK) Pennell].

145. *Neogaerrhinum filipes* (Gray) Rothm. [Syn.: *Antirrhinum filipes* Gray; *Antirrhinum cooperi* Gray; *Asarina filipes* (Gray) Pennell].

146. *N. kelloggii* (Greene) Thieret [Syn.: *Maurandya stricta* Hook. & Arn.; *Antirrhinum strictum* (Hook. & Arn.) Gray; *Antirrhinum kelloggii* Greene; *Antirrhinum hookerianum* Pennell; *Asarina stricta* (Hook. & Arn.) Pennell].

147. *Rhodochiton atrosanguineum* (Zucc.) Rothm. [Syn.: *Lophospermum atrosanguineum* Zucc.; *Rhodochiton volubile* Zucc. apud Otto & Dietr.].

148. *Bot. Mag.* plate 451.

149. *Bot. Mag.* plate 8099.

150. *Contr. U.S. Nat. Herb.* 37:82-84.

151. *Bot. Mag.* plate 4553 as *O. vagans*.

152. *Bot. Mag.* plate 5629.

153. Wilson, Helen Van Pelt: *Climbing Roses.*

154. Stevens, G. A.: *Climbing Roses.*

155. Shepherd, Roy E.: *History of the Rose.*

156. Thomson, Richard: *Old Roses for Modern Gardens.*

157. Thomas, Graham Stuart: *The Old Shrub Roses.*

158. Thomas, Graham Stuart: *Shrub Roses of Today.*

159. Steen, Nancy: *The Charm of Old Roses.*

160. de Wit, H. C. D.: "A Revision of Malaysian Bauhinieae." *Reinwardtia* 3:381-541. (1956).

161. Story, R.: "Some Plants Used By The Bushmen In Obtaining Food And Water" in *Botanical Survey of South Africa*, Memoir No. 30, Department of Agric., Div. of Botany, Pretoria, 1958.

162. Codd, L. E.: *Wild Flowers of the Transvaal.* Cape Town 1952.

163. Exell, A. W., et al. *Flora Zambesiaca*, vol. 2, part 1, pp. 110-111, 1963.

164. Hutchinson, J. and Dalziel, J. M.: *Flora of West Tropical Africa.* 2nd ed. revised by R. W. J. Keay, vol. 1, part 2, pp. 350-352, 1958.

165. *Ibid.* 1(2):353.

166. Standley, P. C. *Flora of Costa Rica.* Field Museum of Natural History, Botanical Series, 13(2):588, 1937.

167. Ridley, Henry N.: *Flora of the Malay Peninsula.* 5 vols. Lovell Reeve & Co., Ltd., London, 1922-1925.

168. Chase, Agnes: "Notes on the Climbing Bamboos of Porto Rico." *Botanical Gazette* 58:279, 1914.

169. Part I—Ceanothus for Gardens, Parks and Roadsides by Maunsell Van Rensselaer. Part II—A Systematic Study of the Genus *Ceanothus* by Howard E. McMinn. Santa Barbara Botanic Garden, Santa Barbara, California.

170. Nicholson, G.: *The Illustrated Dictionary of Gardening.* 4 vols., London, 1884-1887.

171. Lawrence, G. H. M.: Identification of the Cultivated Passion Flowers. *Baileya* vol. 8, Number 4, pp. 121-132; Dec. 1960.

172. Uribe, Lorenzo: *Passifloraceas y Begoniaceas de la* ........................ Flora de la Real Expedición Botánica del Nuevo Reino de Granada, Tomo XXVII, Ediciones Cultura Hispánica; Sucs. de Rivadeneyra, printers, Madrid, 1955. Full Folio.

# INDEX

403

405

406